A

# TREATISE

OF

## Mathematical Inſtruments

Alſo from Flower-de-Luce Books
*The Practical Surveyor*, the 1725 firſt Edition, by Samuel Wyld

A

# TREATISE

OF SUCH

## Mathematical Inftruments,

As are ufually put into a

# PORTABLE CASE.

A Reprint of the THIRD EDITION.

By JOHN ROBERTSON,
Librarian to the Royal Society.

With NOTES
By DAVID MANTHEY.

Flower-de-Luce Books
The Invisible College Press
Arlington, Virginia

A Treatife of Mathematical Inftruments

by John Robertfon

Original Third Edition publifhed in London, England, 1775

Flower-de-Luce Edition
Editing and Notes by David Manthey
Copyright © 2002 by David Manthey


ISBN: 1-931468-11-7


First Printing

Flower-de-Luce Books
    Published by
The Invisible College Press, LLC
P.O.Box 209
Woodbridge, Virginia 22194-0209
http://www.invisipress.com

Please send questions and comments to
editor@invisipress.com

This reprint is dedicated to my parents,
William and Catherine,
for giving me a love of mathematics and of books.

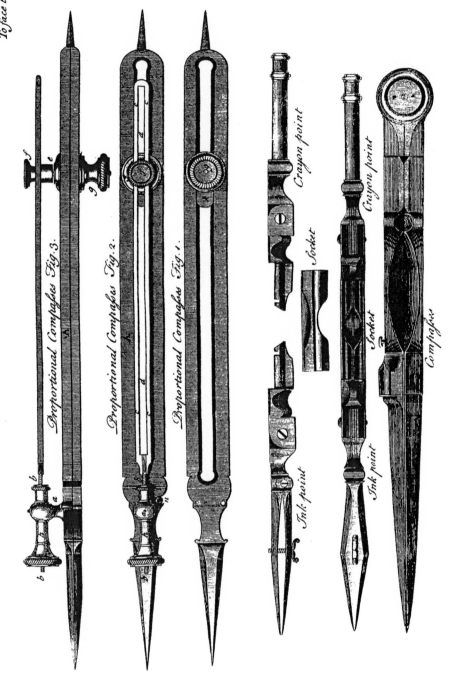

Proportional Compasses Fig. 3.

Proportional Compasses Fig. 2.

Proportional Compasses Fig. 1.

Crayon point

Socket

Ink point

Crayon point

Socket

Ink point

Compasses

Plane Scale

Protractor & Parallel Ruler

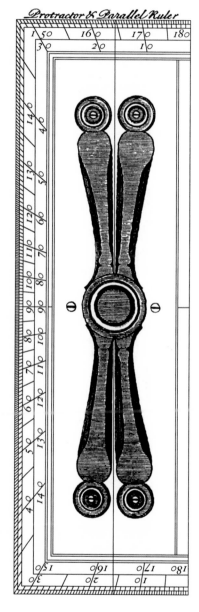

Bows

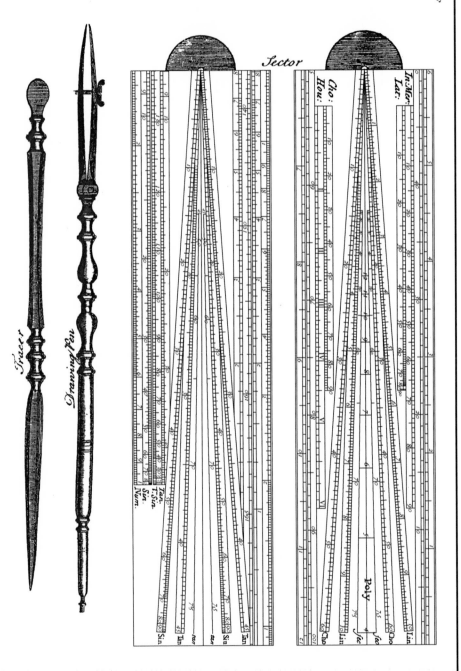

Sector

Tracer

Drawing Pen

A

# TREATISE

OF SUCH

## Mathematical Inſtruments,

As are uſually put into a

# PORTABLE CASE.

Shewing ſome of their Uſes in

| ARITHMETIC, | ARCHITECTURE, |
| GEOMETRY, | SURVEYING, |
| TRIGONOMETRY, | GEOGRAPHY, |
| SPHERICS, | PERSPECTIVE, &c. |

WITH

# AN APPENDIX;

CONTAINING

The DESCRIPTION and USE of the

# GUNNERS CALLIPERS.

AND

The Deſcription of, and Precepts for the Delineation of,

# SHIP-GUNS and SEA MORTARS.

To this Treatiſe, is prefixed

A Brief Account of Authors, who have wrote on the
PROPORTIONAL COMPASSES and SECTOR.

The THIRD EDITION, with many ADDITIONS.

By JOHN ROBERTSON,
LIBRARIAN to the ROYAL SOCIETY.

LONDON:
Printed for J. NOURSE, Bookſeller to His MAJESTY, in the STRAND.

M.DCC.LXXV.

# Sir JAMES BURROW,

SIR,

IT might be neceſſary to apologize for addreſſing a work of this kind to a Gentleman whoſe time is devoted to affairs of more general importance, were it not well known that many of the moſt eminent Lawyers have, on public occaſions, ſhewn their intimate acquaintance with the Mathematical Sciences. The very uſeful work, that has for many years paſt chiefly engaged your attention, may indeed have prevented you lately from beſtowing much of your time in contemplating writings of a different kind; yet the Mathematical principles which were once familiar to you, joined to the diſcernment which you are known to poſſeſs, make you a competent judge of the utility of Elementary and Practical Treatiſes on ſuch ſubjects.

However, I have particular motives. It was through your friendly communication, that the Second Edition of this work was diveſted of many typographical errors which were in the firſt; and alſo furniſhed with ſome uſeful Obſervations: Therefore, with great propriety, I think, the preſent Publication claims the favour of being addreſſed to yourſelf; who are not only a friend to the Author, but lived in the moſt ſtrict friendſhip with the late Martin Folkes, Preſident, and Peter Davall, Secretary, of the Royal Society, to whom the two former Editions were Dedicated.

Theſe,

Thefe, I hope, will be fufficient to plead an excufe for this addrefs, from him who is, with great refpect,

SIR,

Your moft obedient Servant,

J. ROBERTSON.

# TO THE

# READER.

IT is needlefs to enumerate the many purpofes to which *mathematical inftruments* ferve; their ufe feems quite neceffary to perfons employed in moft of the active ftations of life.

The *Architect*, whether *civil*, *military*, or *naval*, never offers to effect any undertaking, before he has firft made ufe of his *rule* and *compaffes*, and fixed upon a fcheme or drawing; which unavoidably requires thofe *inftruments*, and others equally neceffary.

The *Engineer*, cannot well attempt to put in execution and defign, whether for *defence*, *offence*, *ornament*, *pleafure*, &c. without firft laying before his view, the plan of the whole; which is not to be conveniently performed, but by *rulers*, *compaffes*, &c.

There are indeed, very few good *Artificers*, who have not, in fome meafure, occafion for the ufe of one or more *mathematical inftruments*; and whenever there is required, an accurate drawing or reprefentation of a thing to be executed; that collection of inftruments, ufually put into *portable cafes*, is then abfolutely neceffary: And of thefe, the moft common ones, or others applicable to like fervice, muft have been in ufe, ever fince mankind have had occafion to provide for the neceffary conveniences of life: But the *parallel ruler*, the *proportional compaffes*, and the *fector*, are not of any great antiquity.

However, by means of the opportunity, which the author had of confulting moft, if not all, of the principal pieces, that have been wrote on this fubject *; he thinks it will fufficiently

appear

* In the collection of the late *William Jones*, Esq;

appear from what follows, who were the inventors of thefe latter inftruments; and when they were firft known and made ufe of.

I. *Gafpar Mordente*, in his book *on the compaffes*, printed in folio at *Antwerp*, 1584; gives the conftruction and ufe of an inftrument, invented by his brother *Fabricius Mordente*, in 1554; and by him prefented to the emperor *Maximilian* II. in 1572: *Fabricius* prefented it afterwards, with fome improvements to *Rodolphus* II. the fon of *Maximilian*: In 1578, *Gafpar* ftudied to apply the inftrument to various ufes, by the command of the then governor of the *Netherlands*. The inftrument confifts of two flat legs, moveable around a joint like a common pair of compaffes; but the ends or points are turned down at right angles to the legs, fo as to meet in one point when the legs are clofed. In each leg there is a groove, with a flider fitted to it, carrying a perpendicular point; fo that thefe alfo appear like one point when the legs are clofed, and the fliders are oppofite. This compafs is jointly ufed with a rod, containing a fcale of equal parts; whereof 30 are equal to the length of each leg. As the operations with the compafs, depend on the properties of fimilar triangles, therefore its principles are the fame with thofe of the fector: And moft, or all of the problems that are performed by the line of lines only, can with almoft the fame eafe, be performed by thefe; the tranfition from the inftrument to the fector is very natural and eafy.

The ufe of this inftrument, is exemplified in problems concerning lines, fuperficies, folids, and meafuring inacceffible diftances.

The author, p. 22, fays, he invented an inftrument there defcribed; which is our parallel ruler with parallel bars: The parallel ruler with crofs bars, is a more modern contrivance.

II. *Daniel Speckle*, in the year 1589, publifhed in folio, his *military architecture*, at *Strasburg*; where he was architect. In his fecond chapter, he takes notice of compaffes then in ufe of a curious invention, whofe center could be moved forward or backwards; fo that by the figures and divifions mark'd thereon, a right line could be readily and correctly divided into any

number

number of equal parts, not exceeding 20. This inftrument has fince been called the *proportional compafs.*

In the fame chapter he mentions another compafs with an immovable center, and broad legs, whereon were drawn lines proceeding from the center, and divided into equal parts; whereby a right line could be divided into equal parts not exceeding 20; becaufe the divifions on the lines ftill kept the fame proportion, to whatever diftance the legs were opened. Such an inftrument has fince been called a *fector.*

III. Dr. *Thomas Hood*, printed at *London, Anno* 1598, a quarto book, entitled, *The making and ufe of a Geometrical Inftrument, called a Sector.* This inftrument confifts of two flat legs, moveable about a joint; on thefe are fectoral lines, of equal parts, of polygons, and of fuperficies; that is, lines fo difpofed, as to make all the operations that depend on fimilar triangles quite eafy, and that without the laying down of any figure. To the legs is fitted a circular arc, an index moveable on a joint, and fights, whereby it is made fit to take angles.

IV. *Chriftopher Clavius*, in his *practical geometry*, printed in quarto at *Rome, Anno* 1604, in page 4, fhews the conftruction and ufe of an inftrument, which he calls the *inftrument of parts*; it confifts of two flat rulers moveable on a joint; on one fide of thefe legs, are the fectoral lines of equal parts; on the other fide, are thofe of the chords: After fhewing fome of their ufes, he concludes with faying, he is fenfible of many others to which it may be applied, but leaves them for the exercife of the reader to difcover.

V. *Levinus Hulfius*, in his book of *mechanical inftruments*, printed in quarto at *Frankfort, Anno* 1605; gives, in the third part, the defcription and ufe of an inftrument, which *Juftus Burgius* called the *proportional compafs. Hulfius* fays, the ufe of it had not been publifhed before, although the inftrument had been long known.

VI. *Anno* 1605, *Philip Horfcher*, M. D. publifhed at *Mentz*, a quarto book, containing the ufe and conftruction of the *proportional compafs.* This author does not pretend to be the inventor; but that feeing fuch an inftrument, he thought he could,

could, from *Euclid*, fhew its conftruction and the grounds of its operations.

VII. *Anno* 1606, *Galilæus* publifhed in *Italian*, a treatife of the ufe of an inftrument, which he calls, *The geometrical and military compafs.* On this inftrument are defcribed fectoral lines of equal parts, furfaces, folids, metals, infcribed polygons, polygons of given areas, and fegments of circles. In the preface to an edition of this book, printed at *Padua, Anno* 1640, by *Paola Frambotti; Galilæus* fays, that on account of the opportunity he had of teaching mathematics at *Padua*, he thought it proper to feek out a method of fhortening thofe ftudies. In another part of the preface he fays, that he fhould not have publifhed this tract, but in vindication of his own reputation; for he was informed that a perfon had by fome means or other, got one of his inftruments and pretended to be the inventor, although himfelf had taught it ever fince the year 1597.

VIII. *Anno* 1607, *Baldeffar Capra*, publifhed a treatife of the conftruction and ufe of the *compafs* of *proportion*, (or fector.) He claims the invention of this inftrument; and hence arofe a difpute between *Galilæus* and *Capra*; fome particulars of which have been mentioned by feveral, and particularly by *Thomas Salusbury*, Efq; in his life of *Galilæus*, publifhed at the end of the fecond volume of his *mathematical collections and tranflations*, at *London*, in fol. *Anno* 1664.

It appears from thefe accounts, that one *Simon Marius* a German, who was in *Padua* about the year 1607, tranflated into Latin, the book publifhed the year before by *Galilæus*, and caufed his difciple *Capra* to print it as his own: *Marius* dreading a profecution, retired, and left *Capra* in the lurch, who was proceeded againft. At that time *Galilæus* publifhed an apology, intitled, "*The defence of* Galilæus Galilæi, *a* Florentine *gentleman, reader in the univerfity of* Padua, *againft the calumnies and impoftures of* Baldeffar Capra *a* Milanefe, *divulged againft him as well in his confideratione aftronomica upon the new ftar of* 1604, *as (and more notorioufly) in lately publifhing for his invention the conftruction and ufes of the geometrical and military compafs, under the title of Ufes & Fabrica circini cujufdam proportionus, &c.*"

*Galilæus*

*Galilæus* begins with an addrefs to the reader, wherein he concludes, that a perfon robbed of his inventions, fuffers the greateft lofs that can be fuftained; becaufe it defpoileth him of "*honour, fame, and deferved glory.*" He proceeds, and fays, "*into this ultimate of miferies and unhappinefs of condition,* Baldeffar Capra, *a* Milanefe, *with unheard-of fraud, and unparallel'd impudence hath endeavored to reduce me, by lately publifhing, and committing to the prefs my geometrical and military compafs, as his proper invention, and as a production of his own wit, (for fo he calls it in the work itfelf) when it was I alone, that ten years fince (viz. Anno* 1597*) thought of, found and compleated the fame, fo as that no one elfe hath any fhare in it; and I alone from that time forward imparted, difcovered and prefented it unto many great princes, and other noble lords; and in fine, only that I a year fince caufed the operations thereof to be printed, and confecrated to the glorious name of the moft ferene prince of* Tufcany, *my lord. Of which faid inftrument, the above-named* Capra, *hath not only made himfelf the author, but reports me for its fhamelefs ufurper, (thefe are his very words) and confequently bound to blufh within my felf with extream confufion, as unworthy to appear in fight of learned and ingenuous men.*" *Galilæus* then proceeds, among other things, to produce the atteftations of four confiderable perfons, fhewing that ten years before that time, he had taught the ufe of the inftrument, and that *Capra* who had for four years paft feen them making at the workman's houfe, had never challenged the invention as his own.

*Galilæus* after this, fays that he went to *Venice*, and laid the affair before the lords reformers of the univerfity of *Padua*, on the 8th of *April* 1607; at the fame time fhewing them his own book, publifhed *June* the 10th 1606; and that of *Capra*'s publifhed *March* the 7th 1607. The lords thereupon cited *Capra* to appear before them on the 18th of *April*; the next day the caufe was heard and the parties difmiffed: But on the 4th of *May* following, their lordfhips pronounced fentence, and fent it to *Padua* to be put in execution; the amount of their fentence was, that having fully confidered the affair, it appeared to them that *Galilæus* had been abufed, and that all the remaining copies

of

of *Capra*'s book fhould be "*brought before their lordſhips to be ſuppreſſed in ſuch faſhion as they ſhall think fit, reſerving to themſelves to proceed againſt the printer and bookſeller, for the tranſgreſſions they may have committed againſt the laws of printing; ordering the ſame to be made known accordingly.*

*The ſame day all the copies of the ſaid book were ſent to* Venice *unto the lords reformers; there being found* 440 *with the bookſeller, and* 13 *with the author, he having diſtributed* 30 *of them into ſundry parts of Europe,* &c."

IX. *Anno* 1610, *John Remmelin*, M. D. publiſhed at *Frankfort*, a quarto edition of two tracts of *John Faulhaber*; one of theſe contains the uſe of the *ſector*, on which are lines of equal parts, ſuperficies, ſolids, metals, chords, &c. He ſays, that *G. Brendel*, a painter, uſed this inſtrument in perſpective painting.

X. *D. Henrion*, in his *mathematical memoirs*, *Anno* 1612, gave a ſhort tract of the uſe of the compaſs of *proportion* (or *ſector*.) In 1616 he printed a book of the uſe of the ſector; and a fifth edition, in the year 1637, the preface to which, ſeems to be wrote in the year 1626; wherein he ſays, that about the year 1608, he had ſeen in the hands of *M. Alleaume*, engineer to the king of *France*, one of theſe ſectors; whereupon he wrote ſome uſes of it, which he publiſhed in his memoirs, as above. He alſo declares, that before his firſt publication, he had not ſeen any book on the uſe of the ſector, and therefore calls what he publiſhes his own. He charges Mr. *Gunter* with having uſed many of his propoſitions. This author printed at *Paris* 1626, an octavo book of logarithms, at the end of which is a tract call'd logocanon, or the proportional ruler; which is a deſcription and uſe of an inſtrument, he calls a lattice, (perhaps from the chequer-like appearance of the lines drawn thereon) which operates the problems performed by the *French* ſectors very accurately.

XI. *Anno* 1615, *Stephen Michael Spackers*, publiſhed in quarto at *Ulm*, a treatiſe of the *proportional rule and compaſs of G. Galgemeyer*, reviſed by *G. Brendel*, a painter at *Laugingen*. On theſe proportional compaſſes, are lines of equal parts, of polygons, ſuperficies, ſolids, ratio of the diameter to the circumference;

circumference; reduction of planes, and reduction of folids. The ufe and conftruction of thefe lines, are fhewn by a great variety of examples.

XII. *Benjamin Bramer*, in his book of *the defcription of the proportional ruler and parallelogram*, printed in quarto at *Marpurg*, *Anno* 1617; fays, his ruler is applicable to the fame ufes as *Juftus Burgius's* inftrument. *Bramer's* inftrument confifts of a ruler, on which are lines of equal parts, of fuperficies, of folids, of regular folids, of circles, of chords, and of equal polygons; at the beginning of each fcale, is a pinhole, whereby he can apply the edge of another ruler, and fo conftitute a fector for each fcale.

XIII. *Anno* 1623, *Adriano Metio Alcmariano*, printed at *Amfterdam* a quarto book, fhewing the ufe of an inftrument called the *rule of proportion*. In his dedication, he fays, that whilft he was reviewing fome things related to practical geometry, he met with *Galileo's* book of the ufe of the fector, which gave him opportunity to improve on it, and occafioned the publifhing of this book.

XIV. Mr. *Edmund Gunter*, profeffor of aftronomy in *Grefham* college, printed at *London*, *Anno* 1624, a quarto book, called *the defcription and ufe of the fector*; on which are fectoral lines, 1ft. of equal parts; 2d. fuperficies; 3d. folids; 4th. fines and chords; 5th. tangents; 6th. rhumbs; 7th fecants: Alfo lateral lines of, 8th. quadratures; 9th. fegments; 10th. infcribed bodies; 11th. equated bodies; 12th. metals: On the edges are a line of inches and a line of tangents.

Mr. *Gunter* does not fay any thing concerning the invention, and has no preface; but at the end of the tract, in a conclufion to the reader, he fays, that the fector was thus contrived, moft part of the book written, and many copies difperfed, more than fixteen years before, *&c.* this article being written *May* 1, 1623, brings the time he fpeaks of to about the year 1607, which was before the time *Henrion* fays he firft faw the fector.

The fcale of logarithm numbers, fines, and tangents, were firft publifhed in 1624, in *Gunter's* defcription of the crofs ftaff.

XV.

XV. *Mutio Oddi* of *Urbino* printed at *Milan*, *An.* 1633, a quarto book, called *the conftruction and ufe of the compaffo polimetro*, (or fector.) The lines on this inftrument, were fuch as were common at that time: He fays in the dedication to his friend *Peter Linder* of *Nurenburg*, he firft taught the ufe of it.

In the preface, he fays, that about the year 1568, *Commandine*, who then taught at *Urbino*, did contrive a pair of compaffes with a moveable center, to divide right lines into equal parts; which was done at the requeft of a gentleman, name *Bartholomew Euftachio*, who wifhed to avoid the trouble of the common methods, or of being obliged to have many compaffes for fuch divifions of right lines.

He farther fays, that about that time, *Guidibaldo*, marquefs of *Monte*, who lived at *Urbino* for the fake of *Commandine*'s company, being frequently at the houfe of *Simone Boraccio*, who made *Commandine*'s proportional compaffes, did contrive, and caufe to be made, an inftrument with flat legs, (like the fector) which performed the operations of the compafs more eafily. *Oddi* fays alfo, that great numbers were made, and in a few years, had many ufeful and curious additions, with treatifes written on its ufe in diverfe languages, and called by different names; which occafioned the doubt of who was the true author, every one having found means to fupport his caufe: But *Oddi* fays, he not intending to decide the difpute, leaves it to the time to difcover; and feems contented to have pointed out, probably, the inventor; his chief intention being that of making the ufe public, and the conftruction eafy to workmen.

The following authors have alfo wrote on the fector, and fectoral lines.

XVI. *Anno* 1634, *P. Petit*, printed in 8vo. at *Paris*, a treatife on the fector. He thinks *Galilæus* was the inventor.

XVII. *An.* 1635, *Matthias Berneggerus* printed at *Strasburg*, a 4to. edition of *Galilæus*'s book on the fector, which confifts of two parts: To this is added a third part, fhewing the conftruction of *Galilæus*'s lines, and fome additional ufes and tables.

XVIII. *An.* 1639, *Nicholas Foreft Duchefne* printed at *Paris*,

in

in 12mo. a book of the fector. He feems to be little more than a copier of *Henrion*.

XIX. *An.* 1645, *Bettinus* in his *Apiaria univerfa*, &c. *apiar.* 3d. p. 95, and *apiar.* 12, p. 4. In his *Ærarium philo. math.* 4to. *an.* 1648, vol. I. p. 262. In his *Recreationum math. appiariæ*, &c. 12mo. *an.* 1658, p. 75, applied the fector to mufic.

XX. *John Chatfield* printed at *London*, in 12mo. his *trigonal fector, anno* 1650.

XXI. *An.* 1656, *Nicholas Goldman* printed at *Leyden*, in folio, his *treaftife on the fector*. He fays that *Galilæus* was the firft who publifhed the defcription of the fector, an invention ufeful in all parts of the mathematics, and other affairs of life.

XXII. *John Collins* printed at *London*, in 4to. his book of *the fector on a quadrant, an.* 1659.

XXIII. *Pietro Ruggiero*, in his *military architecture*, in 4to. printed at *Milan, an.* 1661, p. 230, applies the fector to the practice of fortification.

XXIV. *An.* 1662, *Gafpar Schottus* printed at *Strasburg* his *mathefis cæfarea*, in 4to. in which he gives a defcription and ufe of the fector: In the preface he mentions *Galilæo* as the inventor of the fector.

XXV. *J. Templar* printed in 12mo. at *London, an.* 1667, a book called *the femicircle on a fector*. He fays, the applying of Mr. *Forfter*'s line of verfed fines to the fector, was firft publifhed *an.* 1660, by *John Brown*, mathematical inftrument maker in *London*.

XXVI. *Daniel Schwenter* in his *practical geometry*, revifed and augmented by *George Andrew Bocklern*, printed in 4to. at *Nuremburg, an.* 1667, treats on the defcription and ufe of the fector.

XXVII. *John Caramuel* printed at *Campania, an.* 1670, his *mathefis nova*, in 2 vols. folio. In the ad. vol. p. 1158, he treats on the fector, relates the conteft between *Galilæus* and *Capra*, and thinks the fame might have been objected againft others, as well as againft *Capra*: He alfo fays, that *Clavius* had fuch an inftrument before that of *Galilæus* appeared; and *Clavius* having taught for a long time at *Rome*, had many fcholars, fome of whom might have carried his inftruments to feveral countries. *Caramuel* mentions a ftory of a *Hollander* fhewing to *Galilæus* an inftrument of this fort, that he brought from his country, and of which *Galilæus* took a copy.

XXVIII. *John Brown*, in his book on *the triangular quadrant*, printed in 8vo, at *London*, *an.* 1671, treats on the fector.

XXIX. And fo does *John Chriftopher Rohlhans*, in his *math. and optical curiofities*, printed in 4to. at *Leipfic*, *an.* 1677, p. 216.

XXX. *An.* 1683, *Staniflawa Solskiego* printed at *Kracow*, his *geometria et architectura Polski*, in folio. p. 69, treats on fome fectoral lines.

XXXI. *Henrick Jafper Nuis*, printed at *Tezwolle*, in 4to. his *Rectangulum catholicum geometrico aftronomicum*, *an.* 1686, treats alfo on the fector.

XXXII. *De Chales*, in his *curfus mathem.* printed at *Leyden*, in 2 vols. fol. *an.* 1690. Vol. 2d. p. 58, relates the conteft between *Galilæus* and *Capra*, and afcribes the invention of the proportional compafs to Dr. *Horfcher*, or *Juftus Burgius*.

XXXIII. *An.* 1691, an edition in 8vo. of Mr. *Ozanam's* treatife of the fector, was printed at the *Hague*.

XXXIV. *P. Hofte* printed at *Paris* his courfe of mathematics, in 3 vols. 8vo. *an.* 1692. In vol. 2d. p. 27. he gives a tract on the fector.

XXXV. *Thomas Allingham* gave a *fhort treatife on the fector*, in 4to. *London*, 1698.

XXXVI. *J. Good*, publifhed a *treatife on the fector* in 12mo. *London*, 1713.

XXXVII. *Chriftian Wolfius*, in his *math. lexicon* 8vo. printed at *Leipfic*, *an.* 1716, under the word *circinus proportionum*, relates, that *Levinus Hulfius*, in his treatife on the proportional compaffes, printed at *Frankfort* the 10th of *May* 1603, fays, that he firft faw the faid inftrument at *Ratisbon*, on the day of the imperial dyet: That he had fold them far and near before 1603; and that it had been inaccurately copied in feveral places: *Wolfius* fays farther, that *Juftus Burgius* was certainly the inventor, but ufed to let his inventions lye unpublifhed.

He

He then relates the conteſt between *Galilæus* and *Capra*, and ends with ſhewing the difference between the inſtruments of *Burgius* and *Galilæus*.

XXXVIII. *M. Bion*, in his collection of mathematical inſtruments, tranſlated by *Edmund Stone*, fol. *London*, 1723, treats of the ſector.

XXXIX. And ſo does Mr. *Belidor*, in his *new courſe of math.* in 4to. p. 364. *Paris*, 1725.

XL. Alſo *Roger Rea*, in his *ſector and plane ſcale compared*, 8vo. *London*, 1727, 2d. edition.

XLI. And *Vincent Toſco*, in his *compendium of the math.* in 9 vols. 8vo. *Madrid*, 1727, vol. I. p. 359.

XLII. *Jacob Leupold*, in his *theatrum arithmetico-geome-tricum*, in fol. *Leipſic*, 1727, p. 86, gives a detail of the inventors of the proportional compaſſes and ſector, which goes on to p. 121, and then he gives a liſt of the authors who have wrote on proportional inſtruments, *viz. Bramer*, 1617; *Capra*, 1607; *Caſati*, 1664; *Conette*, 1626; *Dechales*, 1690; *Dolz*, 1618; *Faulhaber*, 1610; *Galgemeyer*, 1615; *Brendell*, 1611; *Galilæus*, 1612; *Goldman*, 1656; *Horſcher*, 1605; *Horen*, 1605; *Hulſius*, 1604; *Clavius*, 1615; *Lockmann*, 1626; *Metius*, 1623; *Patridge* —; *de Saxonica*, 1619; *Scheffelts*, 1697; *Steymann*, 1624; *Uttenhoffers*, 1626.

XLIII. *Samuel Cunn*, publiſhed his *new treatiſe on the ſector*, 8vo. *London*, 1729.

XLIV. *William Webſter*, in his appendix to a tranſlation of *P. Hoſt*'s mathematics, 8vo. 2 vols. *London*, 1730, treats of the ſector.

There may be ſeveral other authors who have wrote on the conſtruction and uſe of the ſector, or on ſome of the ſectoral lines; but thoſe above, are all that have come to hand; and indeed there are many more than are wanted to determine this enquiry; which may be collected chiefly, from *Mordente*, *Speckle*, *Hood*, *Clavius*, *Hulſius*, *Galilæus*, *Oddi*, *Salusbury*, *Caramuel*, *Dechales*, *Wolfius*, and *Leupold*; the others ſerving only to inform the reader what works are extant on this ſubject. From the whole he may obſerve, that there are few countries in

*Europe,*

*Europe*, but have one or more treatises on the proportional compasses and sector, in their own language; and this is sufficient to shew, that these instruments have been in universal esteem.

As the publication of *Mordente*'s book was in 1584, it is not improbable, as *Caramuel* relates, that a *Hollander* (or one from the neighbourhood of *Antwerp*) might shew one of *Mordente*'s instruments to *Galilæus*: Neither is it improbable that *Galilæus* had seen both *Mordente*'s and *Speckle*'s books, the former having been published thirteen years, and the latter eight years, before *Galilæus*, by his own accounts, thought of his instrument.

As *Mutio Oddi* was a native of *Urbino*, and from what he says in his dedication, it is not improbable but he was acquainted with one or more of the persons he mentions in his preface, or at least with some of their acquaintance, from whom he might gather the particulars he relates; to which, if any credit may be given, *Commandine* was the inventor of the proportional compasses, and *Guidobaldo* of the sector: And in the intercourse between *Italy* and *Germany*, some of *Simone Borrachio*'s work might get into the hands of many ingenious Germans, and give *Justus Burgius*, to whom the proportional compass is usually ascribed, opportunity of getting an early copy; and also put into *Speckle*'s way, the instrument he mentions to have seen: His description pretty nearly agreeing with what *Oddi* says was contrived by *Guidobaldo*.

But while we are searching among foreigners for the inventor of the sector, what are we to think of our countryman Dr. *Hood*? who in 1598 published his account of an instrument which he really calls a sector: And though we should allow that *Hood* as well as *Galilæus* might have seen *Mordente*'s and *Speckle*'s books; and both of them might have seen some of *Borrachio*'s work, yet it is not very probable that *Hood* could have got the form of his instrument from *Galilæus* the year after he thought of it; and as *Hood* published eight years before *Galilæus*, *Hood* certainly has an equal right with *Galilæus*, if not a greater, to the honour of the invention of the sector.

After all it may be said, that it is not impossible for the same
thing

thing to be difcovered by different perfons who have no connexion with one another; examples of a like coincidence of thoughts being known on other fubjeᴄts. Perhaps, *Hood, Galilæus*, and fome others, who have already been mentioned, did no more than add one or more lines to an Inftrument then known; and wrote Treatifes under their name from their own skill in the Mathematical Sciences: So that a diftinᴄtion is to be made between the Inventor of the Inftrument, and of the original Authors who wrote on their ufe, even though improved by fome additional lines.

To the fecond impreffion of this work was added an Appendix on the gunners callipers, as promifed in the firft, befide feveral improvements in different parts of the Treatife: this third publication has alfo many additions, as well in the body of the book, as in the Appendix; therefore, it is conceived that by thefe augmentations the book is now rendered more generally ufeful.

What is done in the foregoing effay, and in the following work, is fubmitted to the reader's judgement; the author intending no more than to have the honour of invention afcribed to whom it is due; and alfo to give fome affiftance to beginners in the mathematical ftudies.

( xviii )

# THE

# CONTENTS.

*To*

# APPENDIX.

# THE

## DESCRIPTION *and* USE

### OF A

# CASE,

### OR

## PORTABLE COLLECTION,

#### Of the moſt Neceſſary

## Mathematical Inſtruments.

### SECT. I.

CASES of *Mathematical Inſtruments* are of various ſorts and ſizes; and frequently conſiſt of ſuch articles only as ſuit the fancy or occaſion of the perſons who buy them: See the plate fronting the title page:

The ſmalleſt collection put into a caſe, commonly conſiſts of,

I. A flat ruler or plane ſcale, having ſcales of equal parts on it.

II. A *pair of compaſſes*, one of whoſe points may be taken off, and its place ſupplied, either with

A *crayon* for lead or chalks; or

A *drawing pen* for ink.

With

With thefe inftruments only, a tolerable fhift may be made to draw moft mathematical figures.

But in fets, called *complete pocket-cafes*, befide the inftruments above, are the following:

III. A fmaller pair of *compaffes*.

IV. A pair of *bows*.

V. A *black-lead pencil*, with a *cap* and *feeder*.

VI. A *drawing-pen* with a *protracting-pin*.

VII. A *protractor*.

VIII. A *parallel ruler*.

IX. A *fector*.

In fome cafes, the plane fcale, protractor, and parallel-ruler, are included in one inftrument.

The common, and moft efteemed fize of thefe inftruments, is fix inches, reckoned by the length of the fcale; though they are often made of other fizes, and particularly of four inches and a half, to fuit the pocket.

Some artifts have contrived a very commodious flat cafe, or box, where the infide of the lid, or top, contains the rulers and fcales: The compaffes, drawing-pen, *&c.* lie in the partitions of an open box, that drops into the bottom part of the cafe, but not quite to the bottom; leaving room under it for *black lead pencils, hair pencils, Indian ink, colour cells,* &c. and befide the inftruments already enumerated, in boxes or cafes of this fort are put

X. A *tracing-point*.

XI. A pair of *proportional compaffes*.

XII. A *gunner's callipers*.

The cafe of inftruments called the *magazine*, is indeed the moft complete collection; for this contains whatever can be of ufe in the practice of *drawing, defigning,* &c. but as many of thefe inftruments are fcarcely ever ufed but in the ftudies or chambers of thofe who have occafion for them; therefore the defcription and ufe of the more common inftruments put into pocket cafes, will be here particularly treated on.

SECT.

## SECT. II.

## *Of the* COMPASSES *and* BOWS.

COMPASSES are ufually made of filver or brafs, and thofe are reckoned the beft, part of whofe joint is fteel; and where the *pin* or *axle* on which the joint turns, is a fteel fcrew; for the oppofition of the metals makes them wear more equable: and by means of the fcrew axle, with the help of a *turn-fcrew*, (which fhould have a place in the cafe) the compaffes can be made to move in the joint, ftiffer or eafier, at pleafure. If this motion is not uniformly fmooth, it renders the inftrument lefs accurate in ufe. Their points fhould be of fteel, and pretty well hardened, elfe in taking meafures off the fcales, they will bend, or be foon blunted. They alfo fhould be well polifhed, whereby they will be preferved free from ruft a long time.

To one leg of the fmaller compaffes, it is common to fix in the fhank a fpring, which by means of a fcrew, moves the point; fo that when the compafs is opened nearly to a required diftance, by the help of the fcrew the points may be fet exactly to that diftance; which cannot be done fo well by the motion in the joint.

### *To ufe the fpring point.*

Hold the compaffes in the left hand with the fcrew turned towards the right; turn the fcrew towards you, or flacken it, and the fpring point will be brought nearer to the other point: On the contrary, by turning the fcrew from you, or tightening it, the fpring point will be fet farther from the other point.

The ufe of thefe leffer compaffes, is to transfer the meafures of diftances from one place to another; or to defcribe obfcure arcs.

Of the large fized compaffes, thofe are efteemed the beft, whofe moveable points are locked in by a fpring and catch fixed in the fhank; for if this fpring be well effected, the point is
thereby

thereby kept tight and fteady; the contrary of which frequently happens, when the point is kept by a fcrew in the fhank.

The ufe of thefe compaffes is to defcribe arcs or circumferences of circles with given radius's: and it is eafy to conceive, that thefe arcs or circumferences can be defcribed, either obfcurely by the fteel point; in ink, by the ink-point; in black-lead or chalks, by the crayon; and with dots, by the dotting-wheel; for either of them may be fixed in the fhank in the place of the fteel point.

As the dotting-wheel has not hitherto been effected, fo as to defcribe dotted lines or arcs, with any tolerable degree of accuracy, it feems therefore to be ufelefs: and, indeed, dotted lines of any kind are much better made by the drawing-pen.

The drawing-pen point, and crayon, have generally (in the beft fort of cafes) a focket fitted to them: fo that they occupy but one of the holes, or partitions, in the cafe. See the plate fronting the title page.

The ink, and crayon points, have a joint in them, juft under the part which locks into the fhank of the compaffes; becaufe the part below the joint fhould ftand perpendicular to the plane on which the lines are defcribed, when the compafs is opened.

If inftead of the large compafs being made with fhifting points, there were two pair put into the cafe; to one of which the ink point was fixed, and to the other the crayon point; this would fave the trouble of changing the points in the compafs at every time they were ufed; and would increafe the expence, or bulk of the cafe, but a trifle.

The crayon point, fuch as has been in common ufe, will admit only fo fhort a piece of black lead pencil, as to be foon worn out, and thereby occafion much trouble: to avoid this, the artificers have for fome years paft, contrived this point fo, as that a whole pencil may be applied to it; which is done by a focket open at both ends, with a fpring fo as to hold firmly a pencil of different fizes. This focket by a fhort arm annexed, holds the pencil in a parallel pofition to the fhank of the compaffes; and may be ufed either as a fhifting point, or fixed

to

to a part of compaffes; neither way will much increafe the price or fize of the cafe.

Another contrivance has been lately made to defcribe arcs or circles, with a radius of about double the length which the compaffes themfelves could defcribe: this is effected by the addition of a ftrait piece, one end of which receives the crayon or ink point, and the other end flips into the fhank of the compaffes; fo that one leg, by this apparatus, becomes about double the length of the other leg. A hole is left in the cafe to hold this additional piece.

Moft perfons, at firft, handle a pair of compaffes but auk-wardly, whether in the taking of diftances between the points, or in defcribing of circles. Long practice indeed brings on eafy habits in the ufe of things, however a caution or two may be ferviceable to beginners.

### *To open and work the compaffes.*

With the thumb and middle finger of the right hand, pinch the compaffes in the hollow part of the fhank, and it will open a little way; then the third finger being applied to the infide of the neareft leg, and the nail of the middle finger acting againft the fartheft, will open the compaffes far enough to introduce the fingers between the legs: then the hither one being held by the thumb and third finger, the farther leg may be moved forwards and backwards very eafily by the fore and middle fingers, the fore finger preffing on the outfide to fhut, and the middle one acting on the infide to open, the compaffes to any defired extent. In this manner, the compaffes are manageable with one hand, which is convenient when the other hand is holding a ruler, or other inftrument.

### *To take a diftance between the points of the compaffes.*

Hold the compaffes upright, fet one point on one end of the diftance to be taken, there let it reft; and (as before fhewn)
extend

extend the other point to the other end.

Always take care to avoid working the compaffes with both hands at once; and never ufe them otherwife than nearly upright.

### *To defcribe circles or arcs with the compaffes.*

Set one foot of the compaffes on the point defigned for the center, hold the head between the thumb and middle finger, and let the fore finger reft on the head, but not to prefs it: then by rolling the head between the finger and the thumb, and at the fame time touching the paper with the other point, a circle or arc may be defcribed with great eafe, either in lead or ink.

In defcribing of arcs it fhould be obferved, that the paper be not preffed at the center, or under the foot, with more weight than that of the compaffes; for thereby the great holes and blots may be avoided, which too frequently deface figures when they are made by thofe who are aukward or carelefs in the ufe of their inftruments.

## *Of the* Bows.

The bows are a fmall fort of compafs, that commonly fhut into a hoop, which ferves as a handle to them. Their ufe is to defcribe arcs, or the circumference of circles, whofe radius's are very fmall, and could not be done near fo well by larger compaffes. See the plate fronting the title page.

## Sect. III.

## *Of the Black-lead Pencil, Feeder, and Tracing Point.*

THE *Black-lead Pencil* is ufeful to defcribe the firft draught of a drawing, before it is marked with ink; becaufe any falfe ftrokes, or fuperfluous lines, may be rubb'd out with a

handkerchief

handkerchief or a piece of bread.

The *Feeder* is a thin flat piece of metal, and is fometimes fixed to a cap that flips on the top of the pencil, and ferves either to put ink between the blades of the drawing-pen, or to pafs between the points, when the ink by drying, does not flow freely.

The *Tracing Point* is a pointed piece of fteel; and commonly has the feeder fixed to the other end of the handle. Its ufe, is to mark out the outlines of a drawing or print when an exact copy thereof is wanted, which may be done as follows:

On a piece of paper, large enough to cover the thing to be copied, let there be ftrewn the fcrapings of *red chalk*, or of *black chalk*, or of *black lead*; rub thefe on the paper, fo that it be uniformly covered; and wipe off, with a piece of muflin, as much as will come away with gentle rubbing. Lay the coloured fide of this paper, next to the vellum, paper, &c. on which the drawing is to be made: on the clean fide of the coloured paper, lay the drawing, &c. to be copied. Secure all the corners with weights, or pins, that the papers may not flip: trace the lines of the thing to be copied, with the *tracing point*; and the lines fo traced will from the coloured paper be imprefs'd on the clean paper.

And thus, with care, may a drawing or print, be copied without much being damaged.

The colored paper will ferve a great many times.

There is not perhaps, a more ufeful inftrument in being, for ready fervice in making sketches or finifhed plans; whether of architecture, fortification, machines, landskips, ornaments, &c. than a black-lead pencil; and therefore it may be proper to give a few hints concerning this excellent mineral.

Black-lead is produced in many countries, but the beft yet difcovered is found in the north of England: it is dug out of the ground in lumps, and fawed into fcantlings proper for ufe: the kinds moft proper to ufe on paper muft be of an uniform texture, which is difcoverable by paring a piece to a point with a penknife; for if it cuts fmooth and free from hard flinty particles, and will bear a fine point, it may be pronounced good.

There

There are three forts of good black-lead; the foft, the midling, and the hard: the foft is fitteft for taking of rough sketches, the midling for drawing of landskips and ornaments, and the hard for drawing of lines in mathematical figures, fortification, architecture, &c. The indifferent kinds, or thofe which in cutting are found flinty, are ufeful enough to carpenters or fuch artificers who draw lines on wood, &c.

The beft way of fitting black-lead for ufe, is firft to faw it into long flips about the fize of a crow-quill, and then fix it in a cafe of foft wood, generally cedar, of about the fize of a goofe-quill, or larger; and this cafe or wood is cut away with the lead as it is ufed.

## Sect. IV.

### *Of the Drawing-Pen, and Protracting-Pin.*

THE *Drawing-pen* is an inftrument ufed only for drawing of ftraight lines; and confifts of two blades, with fteel points, fixed to a handle: the blades by being a little bent, caufe the fteel points to come nearly together; but by means of a fcrew paffing through both of them, they are brought clofer at pleafure, as the line to be drawn fhould be ftronger or finer.

In ufing this inftrument, put the ink between the blades with a common *pen*, or with the *feeder*; and (by the fcrew) bring them to a proper diftance for drawing the intended line: hold the *pen* a little inclined, but fo that both blades touch the paper, and preffing them lightly againft the edge of the ruler; a line may be drawn very fmooth, and of equal breadth, which could not be done fo well with a common *pen*.

Before the *drawing-pen* is put into the cafe, the ink fhould be wiped from between the blades; otherwife they will foon ruft and fpoil, efpecially with common ink: and that they may be cleaned eafily, one of the blades fhould move on a joint.

The directions given about this *drawing-pen*, will ferve for the *drawing-pen* point, ufed with the compaffes. But it muft be

observed,

obferved, that when any arc or circle is defcribed of more than an inch radius, then the ink point fhould be bent in the joint, fo that the blades of the pen ftanding perpendicular, both of them may touch the paper, otherwife the arc defcribed will not be fmooth.

The *Protracting-pin* is a piece of pointed fteel (like the point of a needle) fixed into one end of a part of the handle of the *drawing-pen*; into the other part, the piece with the *pin* in it, generally fcrews. Its ufe is to point out the interfections of lines; and to mark off the divifions of the protractor, as here-after directed.

Sometimes on the top of the *drawing-pen* is a focket, into which a piece of black-lead pencil may be put.

## S E C T.  V.

### *Of the* P A R A L L E L - R U L E R.

THIS inftrument confifts of two flat *Rulers*, connected together by metal bars, moving eafily round the rivets which faften their ends.

*In the firft fort*, are two bars fo placed that both have the fame inclination to each *Ruler*, to which they are fixed; whereby the edges of the rulers will be *Parallel* at every diftance, to which the bars will fuffer them to receed.

*A fecond fort* of *Parallel-Rulers* have their bars to crofs each other, and turn on a joint at their interfection; one end of each bar moving on a center, and the other end fliding in a groove as the *Rulers* receed.

*Third fort* confifts of two equal flat rulers, a middle piece, and four equal metal bars.

One end of each of two of the bars, is rivetted on the middle line of one ruler; and of the other two bars, the ends are alike fixed to the other ruler; the rivetts on each ruler being directly oppofite: the other ends of the bars, are taken together two and two, and rivetted on the middle line of the middle piece; fo that

that each adjacent two bars ſtand in the form of $\wedge$ when the rulers are cloſe; and this obliquity gives the liberty of the rulers being moved aſunder.

This kind of parallel-ruler firſt appeared in the London ſhops about the year 1760.

*Fourth ſort*, called the rolling Parallel-Ruler. This is a ſingle flat ruler, which by the means of two rollers fixed to it, is moved in a direction parallel to itſelf.

The centers of the rollers lie in the middle line of the ruler, near its ends; their circumferences project a little below the under ſide of the ruler, ſo as juſt to keep it free from the paper along which the rollers move; and being indented, contribute to prevent their ſliding on the paper.

A ſcale of equal parts being fitted to the edge of the Ruler, fits the inſtrument for the practical ſolution of ſome problems.

This Ruler was contrived a few years ſince by a Dutch gentleman, A. George Eckhard, F. R. S. who thought it worth the expence of a patent, which he has transferred to Meſſrs. Dollonds, opticians.

The *Parallel Ruler* is very uſeful in delineating civil and military architecture, where there are many *Parallel* lines to be drawn; and alſo in the ſolution of ſeveral geometrical *Problems*; ſome of which are the following.

## PROBLEM I.

*A right line* A B *being given, to draw a line parallel thereto, that ſhall paſs through a given point* C (Fig. 1. Pl. IV.)

CONSTRUCTION. Apply one edge of the *parallel-ruler* to the given line AB; preſs one *ruler* tight againſt the paper, and move the other until its edge cuts the point C; there ſtay that *ruler*, and by its edge draw a line through C, then this line will be parallel to AB.

If the point C happens to be farther from the line AB, than the *rulers* will open to, ſtay that *ruler* neareſt to C, and bring the other cloſe to it, where let the latter reſt, and move forward the *ruler* neareſt to C, and ſo continue till one *ruler* is brought to the

point

point intended.

The rolling *parallel-ruler* performs this problem more readily.

The manner of ufing the *parallel-ruler* as here directed, is underftood to be the fame in the folution of the following PROBLEMS.

# PROBLEM II.

*A right line* A B *being given, to divided it into any propofed number of equal parts; fuppofe 5.* (Fig. 2.)

CONSTRUCTION. Draw the indefinite right line, BC, fo as to make with AB, any angle at pleafure; with any convenient opening of the compaffes, lay off on BC, the required number of equal parts, by turning the points of the compaffes over and over, fo many times, *viz.* 1, 2, 3, 4, 5; lay the edge of the *parallel-ruler* by the points 5 and A, and *parallel* thereto, through the points 4, 3, 2, 1, draw lines; then AB, by the inter-fection of thofe lines will be divided into 5 equal parts.

The number of equal parts being laid into BC, from a fcale of equal parts on the edge of the ruler; the divifions on AB may be obtained without the compaffes.

# PROBLEM III.

*A right line quadrangle, or polygon, being given, to make a right lined triangle of equal area.*

EXAM. I. *To make a triangle of equal area to the quadrilateral* ABDC. (Fig. 3.)

CONSTRUCTION. Prolong AB; draw CB; and through D, draw DE *parallel* to CD, cutting AE in E; then a line drawn from C to E forms the triangle ACE, of equal area to the quadrangle ABDC.

EXAM. II. *Given the pentagon* ABCDE; *requir'd to make a triangle*

*triangle of equal area.* (Fig. 4.)

CONSTRUCTION. Produce DC towards F; draw AC; through B and *parallel* to AC, draw BF cutting DC in F; and draw AF. Then the area of the trapezium AFDE will be equal to the area of the *pentagon* ABCDE.

*Again.* Produce ED towards G; draw AD; through F, draw FG *parallel* to AD, and draw AG. Then the area of the triangle AGE, will be equal to that of the trapezium AFDE; and confequently, to that of the pentagon ABCDE.

EXAM. III. *To make a triangle equal in area to the Hexagon,* ABCDEF. (Fig. 5.)

CONSTRUCTION. Draw FD, and *parallel* thereto, through E, draw EG meeting CD produced in G, and draw GF. Then the triangle FGD is equal to the triangle FED, and the given *Hexagon* is reduced to the *Pentagon* ABCGF equal in area.

*Again.* Draw AG; through F, draw FH *parallel* to AG, meeting CG produced in H; draw AH, and the *pentagon* is reduced to the trapezium ABCH.

*Laftly,* Draw AC, and *parallel* thereto, through H, draw HI, meeting BC produced in I, and draw AI. Then the trapezium is reduced to the triangle ABI, which is equal in area to the given *Hexagon* ABCDEF.

EXAM. IV. *Given the nine fided figure* ABCDEFGHI, *to make a triangle of equal area.* (Fig. 6.)

CONSTRUCTION. 1ft, Draw IB, and through A draw AK *parallel* to IB, meeting HI produced in K, and draw BK; fo the three fides HI, IA, AB, are reduced to the two fides HK, KB.

2d, Draw KC, and through B, draw BL, *parallel* to KC, meeting CD in L; draw KL; and the three fides DC, CB, BK, are reduced to the two fides DL, LK.

3d, Draw KG; through H, draw HM, *parallel* to KG, meeting GF in M, and draw KM; fo the three fides KH, HG, GF, are reduced to the fides KM, and MF.

4th, Draw KF; through M, draw MN, *parallel* to KE, meeting FE in N, and draw KN; fo the three fides KM, MF, FE, are reduced

to

to two fides KN, NE.

5th, Draw LN; and through K, draw KO, *parallel* to LN, meeting EF produced in O, and draw LO; fo the three fides EN, NK, KL, are reduced to the two fides EO, OL.

*Laftly,* Draw LE; and through D, draw DP *parallel* to LE, meeting OE produced in P, and draw LP; fo fhall the triangle OLP be equal in area to the given nine fided figure.

Proceeding in the fame manner; a figure of any number of fides may be reduced to a triangle of equal area.

## S E C T. VI.

## *Of the* P R O T R A C T O R.

THE *Protractor,* is an inftrument of a femicircular form; being terminated by a right line reprefenting the diameter of a circle, and a curve line of half the circumference of the fame circle. As at Fig. 7. Pl. IV. The point C, (the middle of AB) is the center of the femicircumference ADB, which femicircumference is divided into 180 equal parts called degrees; and for the convenience of reckoning both ways, is numbered from the left hand towards the right, and from the right hand towards the left, with 10, 20, 30, 40, &c. to 180, being the half of 360, the degrees in a whole circumference. The ufe of this inftrument is to *protract,* or lay down an angle of any number of degrees, and to find the number of degrees contained in any given angle.

But this inftrument is made much more commodious, by transferring the divifions on the femicircumference, to the edge of a *ruler,* whofe fide EF is *parallel* to AB; (fee Fig. 7.) which is done by laying a *ruler* on the center C, and the feveral divifions on the femicircumference ADB, and marking the interfections of that *ruler* on the line EF, which may eafily be conceived by obferving the lines drawn from the center C to the divifions 90, 60, 30; fo that a *ruler* with thefe divifions marked on 3 of its fides and numbered both ways, as in the *Protractor,* (the fourth

or

or blank fide reprefenting the diameter of the circle) is of the fame ufe as a *Protractor*, and is much better adapted to a pocket cafe.

That fide of the inftrument on which the divifions are marked, is called the graduated fide, or limb of the inftrument, which fhould be floped away to an edge, whereby the divifions on the limb will be much eafier pointed off.

# PROBLEM IV.

*A number of degrees being given; to protract, or lay down an angle whofe meafure fhall be equal thereto. And an angle being protracted, or laid down, to find what number of degrees meafures that angle.*

EXAM. I. *To draw a line from point* A, *that fhall make an angle with the line* AB *of 48 deg.* Fig. 8. Pl. V.

Apply the blank edge of the protractor to the line AB, fo that the middle or center thereof (which is always marked) may fall on the point A; then with the protracting-pin, make a mark on the paper againft the divifion on the limb of the inftrument numbered with the degrees given; (fuppofe 48.) counting from the right hand towards the left; a line drawn from A, through the faid mark, as AC, fhall with AB, form the angle required, *viz.* 48 degrees.

If the line had been to make an angle with AB, at the point B; then the center muft have been laid on B, and the divifions counted from the left hand towards the right.

EXAM. II. *To find the number of degrees which meafure the angle* ABC. Fig. 9.

Apply the blank edge of the protractor to the line AB fo that the center fhall fall on the point B; then will the line BC cut the limb of the inftrument in the number expreffing the degrees that meafure the given angle; which in this example is 125 degrees, counting from the left hand towards the right.

PROBLEM

# PROBLEM V.

*From any given point* A, *in a line* AB, *to draw a line perpendicular to* AB. Fig. 10.

Lay the protractor acrofs the line AB in fuch a manner that the center on the blank edge, and the divifion numbered with 90, on the limb, may both be cut by the given line; then keeping the ruler in this pofition, flide it along the line, till one of thefe points touch the given point A, draw the line CA, and it will be perpendicular to AB.

In the fame manner, a line may be drawn perpendicular to a given line from a given point out of that line.

To do this by the rolling parallel-ruler.

Lay the edge of the ruler to the line AB, fo that one of its divifions on the edge touches the point A; then the ruler rolled to fome diftance, make a point to touch the fame divifion; a right line drawn from this point to A, will be the perpendicular required.

*A* TABLE, *fhewing the Angles at the Centers and Circumferences of regular* Polygons *from three to twelve Sides inclufive.*

| Names. | Sides. | Angles at Center | Angles at Cir. |
|--------|--------|------------------|----------------|
| Trigon | 3 | 120° 00′ | 60° 00′ |
| Square | 4 | 90 00 | 90 00 |
| Pentagon | 5 | 72 00 | 108 00 |
| Hexagon | 6 | 60 00 | 120 00 |
| Heptagon | 7 | 51 25 $\frac{5}{7}$ | 128 34 $\frac{2}{7}$ |
| Octagon | 8 | 45 00 | 135 00 |
| Nonagon | 9 | 40 00 | 140 00 |
| Decagon | 10 | 36 00 | 144 00 |
| Endecagon | 11 | 32 43 $\frac{7}{11}$ | 147 16 $\frac{4}{11}$ |
| Dodecagon | 12 | 30 00 | 150 00 |

This

This table is conftructed, by dividing 360, the degrees in a circumference, by the number of fides in each polygon; and the quotients are the angles at the centers; the angle at the centre fubtracted from 180 degrees, leaves the angle at the circumference.

## PROBLEM VI.

*In a circle given to infcribe any regular Polygon, fuppofe an octagon.* Fig. 11.

CONSTRUCTION. Apply the blank edge of the *protractor* to AB the diameter of the *Circle*, fo that their centers fhall coincide; fet off a number of degrees from B to D equal to an angle at the center of that *polygon*, (viz. 45,) and through that mark draw a radius CD then fhall the diftance BD, or the chord of the arc exprefling thofe degrees, be the fide of the intended *polygon*; which chord taken between the compaffes, and applied to the circumference, will divide it into as many equal parts as the *polygon* has fides, *viz.* 8; and the feveral chords being drawn will form the *polygon* required.

It will rarely happen that this operation, though true in theory, will give the fide of the *polygon* exact; for when the chord of the arc prickt off from the protractor, is taken with the compaffes and applied to the circle, it at laft generally falls beyond, or fhort, of the point fet out from: for it muft be obferved that the point where two lines interfect one another is not to be readily determined in a practical manner; and a very fmall error, in the taking the length of the chord, being feveral times repeated becomes confiderable at laft. Here the compaffes with the fpring point will be found of great ufe.

## PROBLEM VII.

*Upon a given right line* AB, *to defcribe any regular polygon.* Fig. 12.

CONSTRUCTION. From the ends of the given line, draw the
lines

lines AD, BC; fo that the angles BAD, ABC, may each be equal to
the angle at the circumference in that polygon; make AD, BC,
each equal to AB; from the points D and C, draw lines that fhall
make with DA, CB, angles equal to the former; make thefe lines
each equal to AB; and fo continue, till a polygon is formed of as
many fides as required.

EXAM. I. *Upon the line* AB *to defcribe an hexagon.* Fig. 12.

Draw AD, BC, fo that the angles BAD, ABC, may be each 120
degrees; make AD, BC, each equal to AB: alfo, make the angles
ADF, BCE, each equal to 120 degrees, and make DF, CE, each
equal to AB; draw FE and 'tis done.

Or it may be done with the help of the parallel ruler, when
the polygon has an even number of fides. Thus,

Having formed the three fides AD, AB, BC, as before
directed; through D, draw DF parallel to BC; make DF equal to
AB; through F draw FE parallel to AB: make FE equal to AB and
join CE.

EXAM. II. *Upon the line* AB *to defcribe a pentagon.* Fig. 13.

Draw AC, BD, that each may make with AB, an angle of 108
degrees. Make AC, BD, each equal to AB; on the points C and D,
with the compaffes opened to the diftance AB, defcribe arcs to
crofs each other in E; draw EC, ED, and 'tis done.

In any regular polygon, having found all the fides but two,
as above directed; thofe may be found as the laft two in the
pentagon were.

But a regular polygon defcribed upon a given line AB may
be conftructed with more accuracy, thus. See Fig. 12, 13.

Make an angle BAP, and another ABP, each equal to half the
angle of the required polygon; on the point P, where the lines
AP, BP, cut one another, and with the radius PA, defcribe a
circle, in which if the given line AB be applied, the polygon
fought will be formed.

SECT.

# SECT. VII.

## *Of the Plain Scale.*

THE lines generally drawn on the plane fcale, are thefe
following:

|  |  | Marked |
|---|---|---|
| I. | Lines of equal parts. | E. P. |
| II. | ———— Chords. | Cho. |
| III. | ———— Rhumbs. | Ru. |
| IV. | ———— Sines. | Sin. |
| V. | ———— Tangents. | Tan. |
| VI. | ———— Secants. | Sec. |
| VII. | ———— Half Tangents. | S. T. |
| VIII. | ———— Longitude. | Lon. |
| IX. | ———— Latitude. | Lat. |
| X. | ———— Hours. | Ho. |
| XI. | ———— Inclinations. | In. Mer. |

## *Of the Lines of Equal Parts.*

LINES of equal parts are of two forts, *viz.* fimply divided,
and diagonally divided. Pl. V.

I. *Simply divided.* Draw 3 lines parallel to one another, at
unequal diftances, (Fig. 14.) and of any convenient length;
divide this length into what number of equal parts is thought
neceffary, allowing fome certain number of thefe parts to an
inch, fuch as 2, 2½, 3, 3½, 4, 4½, &c. which divifions diftinguifh
by lines drawn acrofs the three parallels. Divide the left hand
divifion into 10 equal parts, which diftinguifh by lines drawn
acrofs the lower parallels only; but, for diftinction fake, let the
5th divifion be fomewhat longer than the others: and it may
not be inconvenient to divide the fame left-hand divifion into
12 equal parts, which are laid down on the upper parallel line,
having the 3d, 6th, and 9th divifions diftinguifhed by longer

ftrokes

ſtrokes than the reſt, whereof that at the 6th make the longeſt.

There are, for the moſt part, ſeveral of theſe ſimply divided ſcales put on rulers, one above the other, with numbers on the left hand, ſhewing in each ſcale, how many equal parts an inch is divided into; ſuch as 20, 25, 30, 35, 40, 45, *&c.* and are ſeverally uſed, as the plan to be expreſſed ſhould be larger or ſmaller.

The uſe of theſe lines of equal parts, is to lay down any line expreſſed by a number of two places or denominations, whether decimally, or duodecimally divided; as leagues, miles, chains, poles, yards, feet, inches, *&c.* and their tenth parts, or twelfth parts: thus, if each of the diviſions be reckoned 1, as 1 league, mile, chain, *&c.* then each of the ſubdiviſions will expreſs $\frac{1}{10}$ part thereof; and if each of the large diviſions be called 10, then each ſmall one will be 1: and if the large diviſions be 100, then each ſmall one will be 10, *&c.*

Therefore, to lay off a line 8 $\frac{7}{10}$, 87, or 870 parts, let them be leagues, miles, chains, *&c.* ſet one point of the compaſſes on the 8th of the large diviſions, counting from the left hand towards the right, and open the compaſſes, till the other point falls on the 7th of the ſmall diviſions, counting from the right hand towards the left, then are the compaſſes opened to expreſs a line of 8 $\frac{7}{10}$, 87 or 870 leagues, miles, chains, *&c.* and bears ſuch proportion in the plan, as the line meaſured does to the thing repreſented.

But if the length of feet and inches was to be expreſſed, the ſame large diviſions may repreſent the feet, but the inches muſt be taken from the upper part of the firſt diviſion, which (as before noted) is divided into 12 equal parts.

Thus, if a line 7 feet 5 inches was to be laid down; ſet one point of the compaſſes on the 5th diviſion among the 12, counting from the right hand towards the left, and extend the other to 7, among the large diviſions, and that diſtance laid down in the plan, ſhall expreſs a line of 7 feet 5 inches: and the like is to be underſtood of any other dimenſions.

II. *Diagonally divided.* Draw eleven lines parallel to each other, and at equal diſtances; divide the upper of theſe lines

into

into fuch a number of equal parts as the fcale to be expreffed is intended to contain; and from each of thefe divifions draw perpendiculars through the eleven parallels, (Fig. 15) fubdivide the firft of thefe divifions into 10 equal parts, both in the upper and lower lines; then each of thefe fubdivifions may alfo be fubdivided into 10 equal parts, by drawing diagonal lines; *viz.* from the 10th below, to the 9th above; from the 9th below to the 8th above; from the 8th below to the 7th above, *&c.* till from the 1ft below to the oth above, fo that by thefe means one of the primary divifions on the fcale, will be divided into 100 equal parts.

There are generally two diagonal fcales laid on the fame plane or face of the ruler, one being commonly half the other. (Fig. 15.)

The ufe of the diagonal fcale is much the fame with the fimple fcale; all the difference is, that a plan may be laid down more accurately by it: becaufe in this, a line may be taken of three denominations; whereas from the former, only two could be taken.

Now from this conftruction it is plain, if each of the primary divifions reprefent 1, each of the firft fubdivifions will exprefs $\frac{1}{10}$ of 1; and each of the fecond fubdivifions, (which are taken on the diagonal lines, counting from the top downwards) will exprefs $\frac{1}{10}$ of the former fubdivifions, or a 100th of the primary divifions; and if each of the primary divifions exprefs 10, the each of the firft fubdivifions will exprefs 1, and each of the 2d, $\frac{1}{10}$; and if each of the primary divifions reprefent 100, then each of the firft fubdivifions will be 10; and each of the 2d will be 1, *&c.*

Therefore to lay down a line, whofe length is exprefs'd by 347, 34 $\frac{7}{10}$ or 3 $\frac{47}{100}$ whether leagues, miles, chain, *&c.*

On the diagonal line, joined to the 4th of the firft fubdivifions, count 7 downwards, reckoning the diftance of each parallel 1; there fet one point of the compaffes, and extend the other, till it falls on the interfection of the third primary divifion with the fame parallel in which the other foot refts, and the compaffes will then be opened to exprefs a line of 347, 34 $\frac{7}{10}$,

or

or 3 $\frac{47}{100}$, *&c.*

Thofe who have frequent occafion to ufe the fcales, will perhaps find, that a ruler with the 20 following fcales on it, *viz.* 10 on each face, will fuit more purpofes than any fet of fimply divided fcales hitherto made public, on one ruler.

One Side } The divifions { 10,11,12,13½,15,16½,18,20,22,25.
Other Side } to an inch { 28,32,36,40,45,50,60,70,85,100.

The left hand primary divifion, to be divided into 10 and 12 and 8 parts; for thefe fubdivifions are of great ufe in drawing the parts of a fortrefs, and of a piece of cannon.

It will here be convenient to fhew, how any plan exprefled by right lines and angles, may be delineated by the fcales of equal parts, and the protractor.

## PROBLEM VIII.

*Three adjacent things in any right lined triangle being given, to form the plan thereof.*

EXAM. *Suppofe a triangular field,* ABC, (Fig. 16.) the fide AB = 327 yards; AC = 208 yards; and the angle A = 44½ degrees.

CONSTRUCTION. Draw a line AB at pleafure; then from the diagonal fcale take 327 between the points of the compafles, and lay it from A to B; fet the center of the protractor to the point A, lay off 44½ degrees, and by that mark draw AC: take with the compafles from the fcale 208, lay it from A to C, and join CB; fo fhall the parts of the triangle ABC, in the plan, bear the fame proportion to each other, as the real parts in the field do.

The fide CB may be meafured on the fame fcale from which the fides AB, AC, were taken: and the angles at B and C may be meafured by applying the protractor to them as fhewn at problem IV.

*If two angles and the fide contained between them were given.*

Draw

Draw a line to exprefs the fide; (as before) at the ends of that line, point off the angles, as obferved in the field; lines drawn from the ends of the given line through thofe marks, fhall form a triangle fimilar to that of the field.

# PROBLEM IX.

*Five adjacent things, fides and angles, in a right lin'd quadri-lateral, being given, to lay down the plan thereof,* Fig. 17.

EXAM. *Given* ∠ * A = 70°; AB = 215 links; ∠ B = 115°; BC = 596 links; ∠ C = 114°.

CONSTRUCTION. Draw AD at pleafure; from A draw AB, fo as to make with AD and angle of 70°: make AB = 215 (taken from the fcales); from B, draw BC, to make with AB an angle of 115°: make BC = 596; from C, draw CD, to make with CB an angle of 114°; and by the interfection of CD with AD, a quadrilateral will be form'd fimilar to the figure in which fuch meafures could be taken as are expreffed in the example.

If 3 of the things were fides, the plan might be formed with equal eafe.

Following the fame method, a figure may be delineated; and in this manner, or fome other like to it, do fome furveyors make their plans of furveys.

*The*

---

* This mark or character ∠, signifies *the angle.*

A small ° put above figures, denotes them to be degrees. Thus 70° stands for seventy degrees.

This mark = signifies *equal to.*

By links is meant the $\frac{1}{100}$th part of a chain of four poles or of 66 feet long.

# The Conſtruction of the remaining Lines of the PLAIN SCALE.

## PREPARATION. Fig. 18. Pl. VI.

Deſcribe a circumference with any convenient radius, and draw the diameters AB, DE, at right angles to each other; continue BA, at pleaſure towards F; through D, draw DG parallel to BF; and draw the chords BD, BE, AD, AE. Circumſcribe the circle with the ſquare HMN, whoſe ſides HM, MN, ſhall be parallel to AB, ED.

## I. *To conſtruct the Line of Chords* *.

Divide the arc AD into 90 equal parts; mark the 10th diviſions with the figures 10, 20, 30, 40, 50, 60, 70, 80, 90; on D, as a center, with the compaſſes, transfer the ſeveral diviſions of the quadrantal arc, to the chord AD, which marked with the figures correſponding, will become a line of chords.

*Note*, In the conſtruction of this, and the following ſcales, only the primary diviſions are drawn; the intermediate ones are omitted, that the figure may not appear too much crowded.

## II. *The Line of Rhumbs* †.

Divide the arc BE into 8 equal parts; which mark with the figures 1, 2, 3, 4, 5, 6, 7, 8; and divide each of thoſe parts into quarters; on B, as a center, transfer the diviſions of the arc to the chord BE, which marked with the correſponding figures, will be a line of rhumbs.

III.

* The chord of an arc, is a right line drawn from one end of the arc to the other end.

† The rhumbs here, are the chords answering to the points of the mariners compass, which are 32 in the whole circle, or 8 in the quarter circle.

## III. *The Line of Sines* *.

Through each of the divisions of the arc AD, draw right lines parallel to the radius AC; and CD will be divided into the lines of sines which are to be numbered from C to D for the right sines; and from D to C for the versed sines. The versed sines may be continued to 180 degrees by laying the divisions of the radius CD, from C to E.

## IV. *The Line of Tangents* †.

A ruler on C, and the several divisions of the arc AD, will intersect the line DG, which will become a line of tangents, and is to be figured from D to G with 10, 20, 30, 40, &c.

## V. *The Line of Secants* ‡.

The distances from the center C to the divisions on the line of tangents being transferred to the line CF from the center C, will give the divisions of the line of secants; which must be numbered from A towards F, with 10, 20, 30, &c.

## VI. *The Line of Half-Tangents (or the Tangents of half the Arcs.)*

A ruler on E, and the several divisions of the arc AD, will
interfect

* The *sine of an arc*, is a right line drawn from one end of an arc perpendicular to a radius drawn to the other end.

And the *versed sine*, is the part of the radius lying between the arc and its right sine.

† The *tangent of an arc*, is a right line touching that arc at one end, and terminated by a secant drawn through the other end.

‡ The *secant of an arc*, is a right line drawn from the centre through one end of an arc, and limited by the tangent of that arc.

interfect the radius CA, in the divisions of the semi, or half tangents; mark these with the corresponding figures of the arc AD.

The semi-tangents on the plane scales are generally continued as far as the length of the ruler they are laid on will admit; the divisions beyond 90° are found by dividing the arc AE like the arc AD, then laying a ruler by E and these divisions of the arc AE, the divisions of the semi tangents above 90 degrees will be obtained on the line CA continued.

## VII. *The Line of Longitude.*

Divide AH, into 60 equal parts; through each of these divisions, parallels to the radius AC, will interfect the arc AE, in as many points; from E as a center, the divisions of the arc EA, being transferred to the chord EA, will give the divisions of the line of longitude.

The points thus found on the quadrantal arc, taken from A to E, belong to the sines of the equally increasing sexagenary parts of the radius: And those arcs reckoned from E, belong to the cosines of these sexagenary parts.

## VIII. *The Line of Latitude.*

A Ruler on A, and the several divisions of the sines on CD, will interfect the arc BD, in as many points; on B as a center, transfer the interfections of the arc BD, to the right line BD; number the divisions from B to D, with 10, 20, 30, &c. to 90; and ED will be a line of latitude.

## IX. *The Line of Hours.*

Bisect the quadrantal arcs BD, BE, in *a*, *b*; divide the quadrantal arc *ab* into 6 equal parts, (which gives 15 degrees for each hour;) and each of these into 4 others; (which will give the quarters.) A ruler on C, and the several divisions of the arc

*ab,*

*ab*, will interſect the line MN in the hour, &c. points, which are to be marked as in the figure.

## X. *The Line of Inclinations of Meridians.*

Biſect the arcs EA in *c*; divide the quadrantal arc *bc* into 90 equal parts; lay a ruler on C and the ſeveral diviſions of the arc *bc*, and the interſections of the line HM will be the diviſions of a line of inclinations of meridians.

## S E C T.  VIII.

## *The uſes of ſome of the Lines on the Plain Scale.*

### I. *Of the Line of Chords.* Pl. VI.

One of the uſes of the line of chords is *to lay down a propoſed angle, or to meaſure an angle already laid down.* Thus, to draw a line AC, that ſhall make with the line AB an angle containing a given number of degrees, (ſuppoſe 36.) Figure 19.

On A, as a centre, with a radius equal to the chord of 60 degrees, deſcribe the arc BC; on this arc, lay the chord of the given number of degrees from the interſection B, to C; draw AC, and the angle BAC will contain the given number of degrees.

*Note,* Degrees taken from the chords are always to be counted from the beginning of the ſcale.

*The degrees contained in an angle already laid down, may be meaſured thus.* Fig. 19.

On A as a centre, deſcribe an arc BC with the chord of 60 degrees; the diſtance BC, meaſured on the chords, will give the number of degrees contained in the angle BAC.

If the number of degrees are more than 90; they muſt be taken from, or meaſured by the chords, at twice; thus if 140 degrees were to be protracted, 70° may be taken from the chords, and thoſe degrees laid off twice upon the arc deſcribed

with

with a chord of 60 degrees.

## II. *Of the Line of Rhumbs.*

Their ufe is to delineate or meafure a fhip's courfe; which is the angle made by a fhip's way and the meridian.

Now having the points, and ¼ points of the compafs contained in any courfe; draw a line AB (fig. 19.) for the meridian; on A as a centre, with a chord of 60° defcribe an arc BC; take the number of points and ¼ points from the fcale of rhumbs, counting from o, and lay this diftance on the arc BC, from the interfection B to C; draw AC, and the angle BAC fhall reprefent the fhip's courfe.

## II. *The ufe of the Line of Longitude.*

If any two meridians be diftant one degree or 60 geographical miles, under the equator, their diftance will be lefs than 60 miles in any latitude between the equator and the pole.

Now let the line of longitude be put on the fcale clofe to the line of chords, but inverted, that is, let 60° in the fcale of longitude by againft o° in the chords, and o° longitude againft 90° chords. Then mark any degree of latitude counted on the chords and oppofite thereto, on the line of longitude, will be the miles contain'd in one degree of longitude, in that latitude.

Thus 57,95 miles, make 1 degree of longitude in the latitude of 15 degrees; 45,97 miles, in latitude 40 degrees; 36,94 miles, in latitude 52 degrees; 30 miles in latitude 60 degrees, &c.

But as the fractional parts are not very obvious on fcales, here follows a table fhewing the miles in one degree of longitude to every degree of latitude.

This table is computed, upon the fuppofition of the earth being fpherical, by the following proportion.

*A* TABLE

## *A* T A B L E, *ſhewing the Miles in one Degree of Longitude to every Degree of Latitude.*

| D. L. | Miles. | D. L. | Miles. | D. L. | Miles. |
|-------|--------|-------|--------|-------|--------|
| 1  | 59,99 | 31 | 51,43 | 61 | 29,09 |
| 2  | 59,96 | 32 | 50,88 | 62 | 28,17 |
| 3  | 59,92 | 33 | 50,32 | 63 | 27,24 |
| 4  | 59,85 | 34 | 49,74 | 64 | 26,30 |
| 5  | 59,77 | 35 | 49,15 | 65 | 25,36 |
| 6  | 59,67 | 36 | 48,54 | 66 | 24,41 |
| 7  | 59,56 | 37 | 47,92 | 67 | 23,44 |
| 8  | 59,42 | 38 | 47,28 | 68 | 22,48 |
| 9  | 59,26 | 39 | 46,63 | 69 | 21,50 |
| 10 | 59,09 | 40 | 45,97 | 70 | 20,52 |
| 11 | 58,89 | 41 | 45,28 | 71 | 19,53 |
| 12 | 58,69 | 42 | 44,59 | 72 | 18,54 |
| 13 | 58,46 | 43 | 43,88 | 73 | 17,54 |
| 14 | 58,22 | 44 | 43,16 | 74 | 16,54 |
| 15 | 57,95 | 45 | 42,43 | 75 | 15,53 |
| 16 | 57,67 | 46 | 41,68 | 76 | 14,52 |
| 17 | 57,38 | 47 | 40,92 | 77 | 13,50 |
| 18 | 57,06 | 48 | 40,15 | 78 | 12,48 |
| 19 | 56,73 | 49 | 39,36 | 79 | 11,45 |
| 20 | 56,38 | 50 | 38,57 | 80 | 10,42 |
| 21 | 56,02 | 51 | 37,76 | 81 | 9,38 |
| 22 | 55,63 | 52 | 36,94 | 82 | 8,35 |
| 23 | 55,23 | 53 | 36,11 | 83 | 7,32 |
| 24 | 54,81 | 54 | 35,27 | 84 | 6,28 |
| 25 | 54,38 | 55 | 34,41 | 85 | 5,23 |
| 26 | 53,93 | 56 | 33,55 | 86 | 4,18 |
| 27 | 53,46 | 57 | 32,68 | 87 | 3,14 |
| 28 | 52,96 | 58 | 31,79 | 88 | 2,09 |
| 29 | 52,47 | 59 | 30,90 | 89 | 1,05 |
| 30 | 51,96 | 60 | 30,00 | 90 | 0,00 |

As

As the radius is to the cofine of any latitude, fo is the miles of longitude under the equator to the miles of longitude in that latitude.

Every perfon who is defirous of acquiring mathematical knowledge, fhould have a table of the logarithms of numbers, fines, tangents, and fecants; moft of the treatifes of navigation, and fome other books, have thefe tables; but one of the moft ufeful and efteemed collection is, *Sherwin*'s mathematical tables.

The ufes of the fcales of fines, tangents, fecants, and half tangents, are to find the poles and centres of the feveral circles reprefented in the orthographical and ftereographical projection of the fphere; which are referved until the explanation and ufe of the lines of the fame name on the fector are fhewn.

The lines of latitudes, hours, and inclinations of meridians, are applicable to the practice of dialing; on which there are feveral treatifes extant, which may be confulted.

# SECT. IX.

## *Of the* SECTOR.

A Sector is a figure formed by two radiufes of a circle, and that part of the circumference comprehended between the two radiufes.

The inftrument called a fector, confifts of two flat rulers moveable round an axis or joint; and from the center of this joint feveral fcales are drawn on the faces of the rulers.

The two rulers are called legs, and reprefent the radii of a circle; and the middle of the joint expreffes the center.

The fcales generally put on fectors, may be diftinguifhed into fingle, and double.

The fingle fcales are fuch as are commonly put on plain fcales, and from whence dimenfions or diftances are taken, as have been already directed.

The

The double fcales are thofe which proceed from the center; each fcale is laid twice on the fame face of the inftrument, *viz.* once on each leg: From thefe fcales, dimenfions or diftances are to be taken, when the legs of the inftrument are in an angular pofition, as will be fhewn hereafter.

## *The Scales commonly put on the beft Sectors, are*

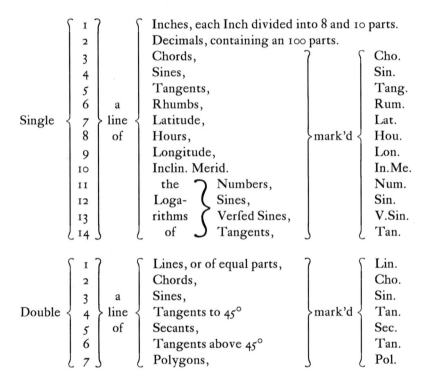

Single, a line of:
1, 2 — Inches, each Inch divided into 8 and 10 parts. Decimals, containing an 100 parts.
3 — Chords, — Cho.
4 — Sines, — Sin.
5 — Tangents, — Tang.
6 — Rhumbs, — Rum.
7 — Latitude, — Lat.
8 — Hours, — mark'd — Hou.
9 — Longitude, — Lon.
10 — Inclin. Merid. — In.Me.
11 — the — Numbers, — Num.
12 — Loga- — Sines, — Sin.
13 — rithms — Verfed Sines, — V.Sin.
14 — of — Tangents, — Tan.

Double, a line of:
1 — Lines, or of equal parts, — Lin.
2 — Chords, — Cho.
3 — Sines, — Sin.
4 — Tangents to 45° — mark'd — Tan.
5 — Secants, — Sec.
6 — Tangents above 45° — Tan.
7 — Polygons, — Pol.

The manner in which thefe fcales are difpofed of on the fector, is beft feen in the plate fronting the title page.

The fcales of lines, chords, fines, tangents, rhumbs, latitudes, hours, longitude, incl. merid. may be ufed, whether the inftrument is fhut or open, each of thefe fcales being contained on one of the legs only. The fcales of inches, decimals, log. numbers, log. fines, log. verfed fines and log. tangents, are to be ufed with the fector quite opened, part of each fcale lying on both legs.

The

The double fcales of lines, chords, fines, and lower tangents, or tangents under 45 degrees, are all of the fame radius or length; they begin at the center of the inftrument, and are terminated near the other extremity of each leg; *viz.* the lines at the divifion 10, the chords at 60, the fines at 90, and the tangents at 45; the remainder of the tangents, or thofe above 45°, are on other fcales beginning at ¼ of the length of the former, counted from the center, where they are marked with 45, and run to about 76 degrees.

The fecants alfo begin at the fame diftance from the center, where they are marked with 0, and are from thence continued to as many degrees as the length of the fector will allow, which is about 75°.

Each double fcale, one being on each leg and proceeding from the center, make an angle; and in an equal angular pofition are all the double fcales, whether of lines, or of chords, or of fines, or tangents to 45°.

And the angles made by the fcales of upper tangents, and of fecants, are alfo equal; and fometimes thefe angles are made equal to thofe made by the other double fcales.

The fcales of polygons are put near the inner edge of the legs, their beginning is not fo far removed from the center, as the 60 on the chords is: Where thefe fcales begin, they are mark'd with 4, and from thence are figured backwards, or towards the center, to 12.

From this difpofition of the double fcales, it is plain, that thofe angle which were equal to each other, while the legs of the fector were clofe, will ftill continue to be equal, although the fector be opened to any diftance it will admit of.

SECT.

## Sect. X.

## *Of the Construction of the Single Scales.*

### I. *The Scale of Inches.*

THIS scale, which is laid close to the edge of the sector, and sometimes on the edge, contains as many inches as the instrument will receive when opened: Each inch is usually divided into 8 equal parts, and also into 10 equal parts.

### II. *The Decimal Scale.*

This scale lies next to the scale of inches; it is of the same length of the sector when opened, and is divided into 10 equal parts, or primary divisions; and each of these into 10 other equal parts; so that the whole is divided into 100 equal parts. And when the sector is long enough, each of the subdivisions is divided into two, four, or five parts; and by this decimal scale, all the other scales, that are taken from tables, may be laid down.

The length of a sector is usually understood when it is shut, or the legs closed together. Thus a sector of six inches when shut, makes a ruler of twelve inches when opened, and a foot sector, is two feet long when quite opened.

### III. *The Scales of Chords, Rhumbs, Sines, Tangents, Hours, Latitudes, Longitudes, and Inclination of Meridians;*

Are such as have been already described in the account of the plane scale.

IV.

## IV. *The Scale of Logarithmic Numbers.*

This fcale, commonly called the artificial numbers, and by fome the *Gunter*'s fcale, or *Gunter*'s * line, is a fcale expreffing the logarithms of common numbers, taken in their natural order. To lay down the divifions in the beft manner, there is neceffary a good table of logarithms, (fuppofe *Sherwin*'s,) and a fcale of equal parts, accurately divided, and of fuch a length, that 20 of the primary divifions fhall make the whole length of the intended fcale of numbers, or logarithmic fcale.

### *The Conftruction.*

1. From the fcale of equal parts, take the firft 10 of the primary divifions, and lay this diftance down twice on the log fcale, making two equal intervals; marking the firft point 1, the fecond 1, (or rather 10) and the third 10, (or rather 100.)

2. From the fcale of equal parts, take the diftances expreffed by the logs. of the numbers, 2, 3, 4, 5, 6, 7, 8, 9, refpectively, (rejecting the indices:) lay thefe diftances on each interval of the log. fcale, between the marks 1 & 10, 10 & 100, reckoning each diftance from the beginning of its interval, *viz.* from 1, and from 10, and mark thefe diftances with the figures 2, 3, 4, 5, 6, 7, 8, 9, in order.

Thus the firft three figures of the logarithms of 2, 3, 4, 5, 6, 7, 8, 9, are, 301, 477, 602, 699, 778, 845, 903, 954; thefe are the numbers that are to be taken from the fcale of equal parts, and laid down in each interval, obferving that the extent for each is to be applied from the beginning of the interval in which it is laid.

3. The diftances expreffing the logs. of the numbers between 10 & 20, 20 & 30, 30 & 40, 40 & 50, 50 & 60, 60 & 70, 70 & 80,

---

* From Mr. *Edmund Gunter*, the Inventor: Astronomy-Professor in *Gresham College*, Anno 1624.

& 80, 80 & 90, 90 & 100, (rejecting the indices) are alſo to be taken from the ſcale of equal parts, and laid on the log. ſcale, in each of the primary intervals, between the marks 1 and 2, 2 & 3, 3 & 4, 4 & 5, 5 & 6, 6 & 7, 7 & 8, 8 & 9, 9 & 10, reſpectively; reckoning each diſtance from the beginning of its reſpective primary interval.

4. The laſt ſubdiviſions of the ſecond primary interval are to be divided into others, as many as the ſcale will admit of, which is done by laying down the logarithms of ſuch intermediate diviſions, as it ſhall be thought proper to introduce.

## V. *The Scale of Logarithmic Sines.*

1. From the ſcale of equal parts, take the diſtances ex- preſſed by the arithmetical complements * of the logarithmic ſines, (or the ſecants of the complements) of 80, 70, 60, 50, 40, 30, 20, 10, degrees reſpectively; rejecting the indices; and theſe diſtances lay on the ſcale of log. ſines, reckoning each from the mark intended to expreſs 90 degrees, which is ſet againſt, or under, the end of the ſecond interval of the line of numbers.

Thus, To the ſines of 80°, 70°, 60°, 50°, 40°, 30°, 20°, 10°, the three firſt figures of the arithmetical complements of their logarithms, are, 007, 026, 063, 115, 192, 301, 466, 760; theſe are the numbers to be taken from the ſcale of equal parts, uſed for laying down the logarithms of numbers, and every extent of the compaſſes is to be laid from the right hand towards the left, beginning at the point choſe for 90°, under the end of the line of numbers.

2. In the ſame manner, lay off the degrees under 10: and alſo, the degrees intermediate to thoſe of 10, 20, 30, &c.

3. Lay down as many of the multiples of 5 minutes, as may conveniently fall within the limits of thoſe degrees which will admit of ſuch ſubdiviſions of minutes.

VI.

* By the arithmetical complement of any sine, tangent, &c. is meant the remainder, when that sine, tangent, &c. is subtracted from radius, of 10,000000, &c.

## VI. *The Scale of Logarithmic Tangents.*

1. This scale, as far as 45 degrees, is constructed, in every particular, like that of the log. sines; using the arithmetical complements of the log. tangents.

2. The degrees above 45, are to be counted backwards on the scale: Thus 40 of the scale, represents both 40 degrees, and 50 degrees; 30 on the scale, represents both 30 degrees, and 60 degrees; and the like of the other marked degrees, and also of their intermediate ones.

## VII. *The Logarithmic versed Sines.*

1. From the scale of equal parts, take the arithmetical complements of the logarithm co-sines, (or the secants of the complements) of 5, 10, 15, 20, 25, 30, 35, 40, &c. degrees; (rejecting the indices,) and the double of these distances, respectively, laid on the scale intended for the log. versed sines, will give the divisions expressing 10, 20, 30, 40, 50, 60, 70, 80, &c. degrees; to as many as the length of the scale will take in.

2. Between every distance of 10 degrees, introduce as many degrees, $\frac{1}{2}$ degrees; $\frac{1}{3}$ degrees; $\frac{1}{4}$ degrees, &c. as the interval will admit.

The scale of the logarithms of numbers, sines, versed sines, and tangents, should have one common termination to one end of each scale; that is, the 10 on the numbers, the 90 on the sines, the 0 on the versed sines, and the 45 on the tangents, should be opposite to each other: The other end of each of the scales of sines, versed sines, and tangents, will run out beyond the beginning (mark'd 1) of the numbers; nearly opposite to which, will be the divisions representing 35 minutes on the sines and tangents, and 168 $\frac{1}{2}$ degrees, on the versed sines.

S E C T.

## S E C T.  XI.

### *Of the Conſtruction of the Double Scales.*

### I. *Of the Line of Lines.*

THIS is only a ſcale of equal parts, whoſe length is adapted to that of the legs of the ſector. Thus in the ſix inch ſector, the length is about $5\frac{3}{4}$ inches.

The length of this ſcale is divided into 10 primary diviſions; each of theſe into 10 equal ſecondary parts; and each ſecondary diviſion, into 4 equal parts.

Hence on any ſector, it will be eaſy to try if this line is accurately divided: Thus. Take between the compaſſes any number of equal parts from this line, and apply that diſtance to all the parts of the line; and if the ſame number of diviſions are contained between the points of the compaſſes in every application, the ſcale may be received as perfect.

### II. *Of the Line of Sines.*

1. Make the whole length of the ſcale, equal to that of the line on lines.

2. From the ſcale of the line of lines, take off ſeverally, the parts expreſſed by the numbers in the tables (ſuppoſe *Sherwin*'s) of the natural ſines, correſponding to the degrees, or to the degrees and minutes, intended to be laid on the ſcale.

3. Lay down theſe diſtances ſeverally on the ſcale, beginning from the center; and this will expreſs a ſcale of natural ſines.

EXAM. *To lay down* 35° 15′; *whoſe natural ſine found in the table is* 57714, *&c.*

Take this number as accurately as may be, from the line of lines, counting from the center; and this diſtance will read from

the

the beginning of the fines, at the center of the inftrument, to the divifion expreffing 35° 15′; and fo of the reft.

In fcales of this length, it is cuftomary to lay down divifions, expreffing every 15 minutes, from 0 degrees to 60 degrees; between 60 and 80 degrees, every half degree is expreffed; then every degree to 85; and the next is 90 degrees.

## III. *Of the Scale of Tangents.*

The length of this fcale is equal to that of the line of lines, and the feveral divifions thereon (to 45 degrees) are laid down from the table and line of lines, in the fame manner as has been defcribed in the fines; obferving to ufe the natural tangents in the tables.

## IV. *Of the Scale of upper Tangents.*

This fcale is to be laid down, by taking ¼ of fuch of the natural tabular tangents above 45 degrees, as are intended to be put on the fcale.

Although the pofition of this fcale on the fector refpects the center of the inftrument, yet its beginning, at 45 degrees, is diftant from the center, ¼ of the length or radius of the lower tangents.

## V. *Of the Scale of Secants.*

The diftance of the beginning of this fcale, from the center, and the manner of laying it down, is juft the fame as that of the upper tangents; only in this, the tabular fecants are to be ufed.

## VI. *Of the Scale of Chords.*

1. Make the length of this fcale, equal to that of the fines; and let the divifions to be laid down, exprefs every 15 minutes from 0 degrees to 60 degrees.

2. Take

2. Take the length of the fine of half the degrees and minutes, for every divifion to be laid down, (as before directed in the fcale of fines;) and twice this length, counted from the center, will give the divifions required.

Thus, twice the length of the fine 18° 15′, will give the chord of 36° 30′; and in the fame manner for the reft.

## VII. *Of the Scale of Polygons.*

This fcale ufually takes in the fides of the polygons from 6 to 12 inclufive: The divifions are laid down, by taking the lengths of the chords of the angles at the center of each polygon; and thefe diftances are laid from the center of the inftrument.

But it is beft to have the polygons of 4 and 5 fides alfo introduced; and then this line is conftructed from the fcale of chords, where the length of 90 degrees is equal to that of 60 degrees of the double fcale of chords on the fector.

In the place of fome of the double fcales here defcribed, there are found other fcales on the old fectors, and alfo on fome of the modern *French* ones, fuch as, fcales of fuperficies, of folids, or infcribed bodies, of metals, &c. But thefe feem to be juftly left out of fectors, as now conftructed, to make room for others of more general ufe: However, thefe fcales, and fome others, of ufe in gunnery, will be given in the Appendix, on the ufe of the gunners callipers.

## S ECT. XII.

## *Of the Ufes of the Double Scales.*

IN the following account of the ufes, as there will frequently occur the terms *lateral diftance*, and *tranfverfe diftance*; it will be proper to explain what is meant by thofe terms.

*Lateral diftance*, is a diftance taken by the compaffes on one
of

of the fcales only, beginning at the center of the fector.

*Tranfverfe diftance*, is the diftance taken between any two correfponding divifions of the fcales of the fame name, the legs of the fector being in an angular pofition: That is, one foot of the compaffes is fet on a divifion in a fcale on one leg of the fector, and the other foot is extended to the like divifion in the fcale of the fame name on the other leg of the fector.

It muft be obferved, that each of the fectoral fcales have three parallel lines, acrofs which the divifions of the fcale are marked: Now in taking tranfverfe diftances, the points of the compaffes muft always be fet on the infide line, or that line next the inner edge of the leg; for this line only in each fcale runs to the center.

## Some Ufes of the Line of Lines.

### PROBLEM X.

*To two given lines* AB = 2, BC = 6; *to find a third proportional.* Plate VI. Fig. 20.

OPERATION. 1. Take between the compaffes, the lateral diftance of the fecond term, (*viz.* 6.)

2. Set one point on the divifion expreffing the firft term (*viz.* 2.) on one leg, and open the legs of the fector till the other point will fall on the correfponding divifion on the other leg.

3. Keep the legs of the fector open in this pofition; take the tranfverfe diftance of the fecond term, (*viz.* 6.) and this diftance is the third term required.

4. This diftance meafured laterally, beginning from the center, will give (18) the number expreffing the meafure of the third term: For 2 : 6 :: 6 : 18.

Or, Take the diftance 2 laterally, and apply it tranfverfely to 6 and 6 (the fector being properly opened), then the tranfverfe diftance at 2 and 2 being taken with the compaffes and applied laterally from the center of the fector on the fcale

of

of lines, will give 0,66 $\frac{2}{3}$ = $\frac{2}{3}$, the third term when the proportion is decreasing: For 6 : 2 :: 2 : $\frac{2}{3}$.

*Note*, If the legs of the sector will not open so far as to let the lateral distance of the second term fall between the divisions expressing the first term; then take $\frac{1}{2}$, $\frac{1}{3}$, $\frac{1}{4}$, or any aliquot part of the second term, such as will conveniently fall within the opening of the sector, and make such part, the transverse distance of the first term; then if the transverse distance of the second term be multiplied by the denominator of the part taken of the second term, the product will give the third term.

# PROBLEM XI.

*To three given lines* AB = 3, BC = 7, CD = 10; *to find a fourth proportional.* Plate VI. Fig. 21.

OPERATION. Open the legs of the sector, until the transverse distance of the first term, (3) be equal to the lateral distance of the second term, (7) or to some part thereof; then will the transverse distance of the third term, (10) give the fourth term, (23 $\frac{1}{3}$) required; or such a submultiple thereof as was taken of the second term: For 3 : 7 :: 10 : 23 $\frac{1}{3}$.

Or, Set the lateral distance 7 transversely from 10 to 10 (opening the sector properly); then the transverse distance at 3 and 3 taken and applied laterally will give 2 $\frac{1}{10}$: For 10 : 7 :: 3 : 2 $\frac{1}{10}$.

Or thus,

*When the proportion is increasing.*

Open the sector till the length of the second term taken between the compasses, be a transverse distance to 10 and 10 on the lines; and in this position of the sector, mark the points where the length of the first term, between the compasses, falls transversely on the lines.

Open the sector till the extent of the third term is transverse to those marked points; then is the transverse distance between 10 and 10, the fourth term.

*When the proportion is decreasing.*

Open

Open the sector so that the first, or greatest, term be a transverse distance to 10 and 10 on the lines; and mark the transverse points which the extent of the third, or least, term gives.

Open the sector, so that 10 and 10 be a transverse distance to the extent of the second term; then will the transverse distance of the said marked points be the fourth term.

Thus in the first case. The 2d term 7, taken from any scale of equal parts, and applied transversely to 10 and 10; then the 1st term 3, taken from the same scale, will reach transversely to near 4,3; and the sector opened till the 3d term, 10 taken from the same scale and applied transversely to near 4,3, and 4,3, the fourth term will be thre transverse distance of 10 and 10, which applied to the same scale; will give 23 $\frac{1}{3}$.

And in the second case, the 1st term 10, taken from a scale, and, made a transverse to 10 and 10, on the lines; the least term 3, from the same scale, will be a transverse to 3 and 3; then the 2d term 7, from the same scale, being made a transverse to 10 and 10 on the lines; the transverse distance of 3 and 3 on the lines, being applied to the same scale, will give 2 $\frac{1}{10}$ for the fourth term.

From this problem is readily deduced, how to increase or diminish a given line, in any assigned proportion.

EXAM. *To diminish a line of 4 inches, in the proportion of 8 to 7.*

1. Open the sector until the transverse distance of 8 and 8, be equal to the lateral distance of 7.

2. Mark the point to where 4 inches will read, as a lateral distance taken from the center.

3. The transverse distance, taken at that point, will be the line required.

If the given line, suppose 12 inches, should be too long for the legs of the sector, take $\frac{1}{2}$, or $\frac{1}{3}$, or $\frac{1}{4}$, &c. part of the given line for the lateral distance; and the corresponding transverse distance, taken twice, or thrice, or four times, &c. will be the
line

line required.

# PROBLEM XII.

*To open the fector fo, that the two fcales of lines fhall make a right angle.*

OPERATION. Take the lateral diftance from the center to the divifion marked 5 between the points of the compaffes, and fet one foot on the divifion marked 4 on one of the fcales of lines, and open the legs of the fector till the other foot falls on the divifion marked 3 on the other fcale of lines, and then will thofe fcales ftand at right angles to one another.

For a triangle made with the lines 3, 4, 5, or any of their multiples, will be a right angle triangle.

# PROBLEM XIII.

*To two right lines given, to find a mean proportional. Suppofe the lines 40 and 90.*

OPERATION. 1ft. Set the two fcales of lines at right angles to one another.

2d. Find the half fum of the given lines $(= \dfrac{90 + 40}{2} =)$ 65;

alfo find the half difference of thofe lines $(= \dfrac{90 - 40}{2} =)$ 25.

3d. Take, with the compaffes, the lateral diftance of the half fum (65), and apply one foot to the half difference (25,) the other foot tranfverfely will reach to (60) the mean proportional required: For 40 : 60 :: 60 : 90.

# PROBLEM XIV.

*To divide a given line into any propofed number of equal parts: (fuppofe 9.)*

Make

Make the length of the given line, or some known part thereof, a transverse distance to 9 and 9: Then will the transverse distance of 1 and 1, be the $\frac{1}{9}$ part thereof; or such a submultiple of the $\frac{1}{9}$ part, as was taken of the given line.

Or the $\frac{1}{9}$ part, will be the difference between the given line, and the transverse distance of 8 and 8.

The latter of these methods is to be preferred when the part required falls near the center of the instrument.

*To this problem may be referred the method of making a scale of a given length, to contain a given number of equal parts.*

The practice of this is very useful to those who have occasion to take copies of surveys of lands; draughts of buildings, whether civil or military; and in every other case, where drawings are to be made to bear a given proportion to the things they represent.

EXAM. *Suppose the scale to the map of a survey is 6 inches long, and contains 140 poles; required to open the sector so, that a corresponding scale may be taken from the line of lines.*

SOLUTION. Make the transverse distance 7 and 7 (or 70 and 70, *viz.* $\frac{140}{2}$) equal to three inches ($= \frac{6}{2}$); and this position of the line of lines will produce the given scale.

*If it was required to make a scale of 140 poles, and to be only two inches long.*

SOLUTION. Make the transverse distance of 7 and 7 equal to one inch, and the scale is made.

EXAM. II. *To make a scale of 7 inches long contain 180 fathoms.*

SOLUTION. Make the transverse distance of 9 and 9 equal to
$3\frac{1}{2}$

3 ½ inches, and the ſcale is made.

EXAM. III.   *To make a ſcale which ſhall expreſs 286 yards, and be 18 inches long.*

SOLUTION.  Make the ⅓ of 18 inches (or 6 inches) a tranſverſe diſtance to the ⅓ of 286 (= 95 ⅓) and the ſcale is made.

Or, make the ¼ of 18 inches (= 4 ½ inches) a tranſverſe diſtance to ¼ of 286 (= 71 ½,) and the ſcale is made.

EXAM. IV.   *To divide a given line (ſuppoſe of 5 inches) into any aſſigned proportion (as of 4 to 5.)*

SOLUTION.  Take (5 inches) the length of the given line, between the compaſſes, and make this a tranſverſe diſtance to (9 and 9) the ſum of the propoſed parts; then the tranſverſe diſtance of the aſſigned numbers (4 and 5) will be the parts required.

# PROBLEM XV.

*The uſe of the line of lines in drawing the orders of Civil Architecture.*

In this place it is intended to give ſo much of Architecture as may enable a beginner to draw any one of the orders; but that the following precepts may be rightly underſtood, it will be proper to explain a few of the terms.

## DEFINITIONS.

1. ARCHITECTURE is the art of building well; and has for its object the Convenience, Strength, and Beauty of the building.

2. ORDER in Architecture, is generally underſtood as Ornament, and conſiſts of three grand parts, namely;

3. The ENTABLATURE, which repreſents, or is, the weight

to

to be fupported.

4. The COLUMN, that which fupports any weight.

5. The PEDESTAL, or foot, whereon the Column is fet for its better fecurity.

Each of thefe parts, confifts alfo of three parts.

6. The *Pedeftal* is compofed of a BASE, or a lower part, a DIE, and a CORNICE, or upper part.

7. The *Column* is made up of a BASE, a SHAFT, which is a middle part, and a CAPITAL, the upper part.

8. The *Entablature* confifts of an ARCHITRAVE, or lower part, a FREEZE, the middle part, and a CORNICE, the upper part.

So that an Order may be faid to confift of nine parts, each of which is made up of fmaller parts called Members; whereof fome are *Plane*, fome *Curved*, either convex or concave, or convexo-concave.

Plane members of different magnitude have different names.

9. A FILLET or *lift* is the leaft plane or flat member.

10. A PLINTH is that flat member at the bottom of the Pedeftal, or of the bafe of the Column.

11. A PLATEBAND, that at the top of the Pedeftal, or the upper member of the Architrave in the Entablature.

12. An ABACUS, that at the top of the capital.

13. The FACIÆ or faces are flat members in the Architrave.

14. The CORONA is a large flat member of the Cornice.

The Convex members are,

15. An ASTRAGAL of a fmall femicircular convexity.

16. A FUSAROLE when an Aftragal is cut into parts like beads.

17. A TORUS a large femicircular convexity.

18. An OVOLA nearly of a quadrantal convexity.

The concave members are,

19. A CAVETTO nearly of a quadrantal concavity.

20. A SCOTIE of a concavity nearly femicircular.

The Convexo-Concave members are, a Cymaife and a Cima.

21. A CYMAISE or *Ove*, that whofe convex part projects

moft;

moſt; and by workmen is uſually called an OGEE.

22. A CIMA, that whoſe concave part projects moſt.

23. SOFFIT is the under part of the Crown of an Arch, or of the Corona of an Entablature.

24. TRIGLYPHS (*i. e.* three channels) is an Ornament in the Freeze of the Doric Order.

25. METOPS (*i. e.* between three's) is the ſpace of the Freeze between two Triglyphs.

26. MODILIONS, or MUTULES, are the brackets or ends of beams ſupporting the Corona. In the Corinthian Order they are generally carved into a kind of Scrol.

27. DENTELS are an Ornament looking ſomewhat like a row of teeth; and are placed in the Cornice of the Entablature.

It is cuſtomary among Architects, to eſtimate the heights and projections of all the parts of every order, by the diameter of the column at the bottom of the ſhaft, which they call a module; and ſuppoſe it to conſiſt of 60 equal parts, which are called minutes.

## *Of the* TUSCAN ORDER.

This order, which ſome writers liken to a ſtrong robuſt labouring man, is the moſt ſimple and unadorned of any of the orders: The places moſt recommended to uſe it in, are country farm-houſes, ſtables, gateways to inns, and places where plainneſs and ſtrength are reckoned moſt neceſſary: Though there are inſtances where this order has been applied to buildings of a more public and elegant nature.

The general proportions aſſigned by *Palladio*.

1. Height of the column equal to ſeven diameters, or modules.

2. Height of the entablature equal to one fourth of the column, wanting half a minute.

3. Height of the pedeſtal equal to one module.

4. The capital and baſe, each half a module.

5. Breadth of the baſe on a level is $1\frac{1}{6}$ modules.

6. Breadth of the capital equal to one module.

7. Diminiſhing

7. Diminifhing of the column is $\frac{1}{4}$ module.

8. Projection of the beams fupporting the eaves is $1\frac{3}{4}$ modules.

9. In colonades, the diftance of the columns in the clear is 4 modules.

    10. In arches, and the columns fet on pedeftals,

        The diftance of the columns from middle to middle is $6\frac{5}{12}$ modules.

        Height of the arch is $7\frac{2}{3}$ modules.

        Breadth of the pilafter between the column and paffage is 26 minutes.

The ovolo under the corona, in the cornice of the entablature, is commonly continued within the corona, giving it a reverfe bending in the foffit, fomething like a cyma.

## *Of the* DORIC ORDER.

This order, fuppofed to be invented by *Dorus* a king of *Achaia*, may be likened to a well-limbed genteel man; and although of a bold afpect, yet not fo fturdy and rufticly clad as the Tufcan. Architects place this order indifferently in towns: But when they would decorate a country feat with it, the open champaign fituation feems beft for the reception of the Doric order; notwithftanding which, there are many fine buildings of this order in other fituations, where they have a very pleafing effect.

The following general proportions are given by *Palladio*.

1. Height of the column from $7\frac{1}{2}$ to 8, to $8\frac{2}{3}$ modules.

2. Height of the entablature is one fourth of the column.

3. Height of the pedeftal equal to $2\frac{1}{3}$ modules.

4. The Attic bafe is ufed with this order, it is half a module in height, and fo is the capital.

5. Breadth of the column's bafe is $1\frac{1}{6}$ module.

6. Breadth of the capital is 1 module $17\frac{1}{2}$ minutes.

7. Diminifhing of the column is 8 minutes.

8. In colonades, the diftance of the columns in the clear is $2\frac{3}{4}$ modules.

9. In

9. In arches, and the column fet on pedeftals,

Diftance of the columns from middle to middle is $7\frac{1}{2}$ modules.

Height of the arch to its foffit is $10\frac{1}{4}$ modules.

Breadth of the pilafters is 26 minutes.

In the Doric order, the architrave has two faces and a plinth; the upper face is ornamented with rows of fix *drips* or *bells*, covered with a plain cap: The freeze is divided into trigliphs and metops: The breadths of the drips, cap and trigliphs are each $\frac{1}{2}$ module: The trigliph confift of two channels, two half channels, and three voids; the breadths of the channels and voids are each $5$ minutes: The axis of the column continued, runs through the middle void, leaving the drips three on each fide: the metops, or diftances between the trigliphs, are equal to the height of the freeze, and are commonly ornamented with trophies, arms, rofes, &c.

Here follows a table for the particular conftruction of the ornaments with which the architrave and freeze are enriched.

| | Altitude. | Projection | Profile. |
|---|---|---|---|
| | Min. | Min. | Min. |
| Capital | $5$ | 16 | 3 |
| Freeze | 45 | — | — |
| Trigliphs | 40 | 15 | $\frac{1}{2} + 2\frac{1}{2}$ |
| Plinth | $4\frac{1}{2}$ | 16 | 3 |
| Cap | $1\frac{2}{3}$ | 15 | 2 |
| Drips | $3\frac{1}{3}$ | 15 | 2 |

The column figned altitude, gives the heights of the particular parts.

That figned projection, fhews the breadths of thofe parts on each fide of the middle line of the column continued.

And under the word profile, ftand the numbers fhewing

how

how far the feveral parts project beyond the planes or faces of the members on which they are made.

The foffit of the corona in the cornice of the entablature, is ufually ornamented with drips correfponding to the trigliphs, and rofes, arms, &c. over the metops.

The fhaft of the column is fometimes fluted; that is, cut into channels from top to bottom, the channels meeting one another in an edge, and are in number twenty.

## *Of the* IONIC ORDER.

This order, which is taller and flenderer than the Doric, does not appear with fuch mafculine ftrength; and is, by fome writers, compared to the figure of a grave matron. The *Ionions* who invented this order, applied it chiefly to decorate their temples: But when applied to the ornamenting a country palace, the rich and extended vale feems a proper fite: Workmen indeed ufe it indifferently in every place.

*Palladio* gives to the Ionic order the following general proportions.

1. Height of the column to be 9 modules.

2. The altitude of the entablature is equal to $\frac{1}{5}$ that of the column, and divided for the architrave, freeze, and cornice, in the proportion of 4, 3, 5.

3. The height of the pedeftal is equal to 2 modules 37 $\frac{1}{2}$ minutes; or (what he calls) $\frac{8}{27}$ of the column *.

4. Height of the bafe $\frac{1}{2}$ module; its breadth 1 module 22 $\frac{1}{2}$ minutes.

5. Height of the capital and volute is 31 $\frac{2}{3}$ minutes, and the breadth of its abaco is 1 module 3 $\frac{1}{3}$ minutes.

6. Diminution of the column is 7 $\frac{1}{4}$ minutes.

7. In colonades, the diftance of the columns in the clear is 2 $\frac{1}{4}$ modules.

8. In

---

* 9 Modules = 60 × 9 × 2 = 1080 half min.
  2 Mo. 37 $\frac{1}{2}$ m = 157 $\frac{1}{2}$ m = 315 half min.
  And 315 : 1080 :: 8 : 27 $\frac{3}{7}$.

8. In arches, and the columns set on pedestals,

Distance of the columns from middle to middle is $7\frac{7}{24}$
modules.

Height of the arch to its soffit is 11 modules.

Breadth of the pilasters is 26 ½ minutes, between the
column and the arch.

The distance of the modilions in the entablature is 22
minutes, and the breadth of each modilion is 10 minutes; the
axis of the column produced, always passes through the middle
of a modilion, which in this order is a plain block representing
the end of a beam. The three most elegant remains of the
ancient Ionic order, in *Rome*, have their cornice ornamented
with dentels instead of modilions; and it is the opinion of some,
eminent for their taste in Architecture, that in this order,
dentels would have a better effect than modilions; the height
of these dentels were usually twice their breadth, and their
distances half their breadth.

The freeze of this order is usually made swelling, and is
formed by the segment of a circle, whose chord is parallel to the
axis of the column, and the swelling projecting as far as the
plateband of the architrave.

The volutes of the capital are, now, commonly made to
project in the directions of the diagonals of the square cap, or
abaco, over the volutes; so that their drawing should be
expressed like the volutes in the Roman order: They are much
better drawn by an easy hand, than by any rules for describing
them with the compasses, observing the limits of their altitude
and projection: But the volutes in the ancient examples of this
order, and which are sometimes executed in modern buildings,
were curled in a plane parallel to the architrave. These volutes
are supposed to represent the plaited tresses, in which the
Grecian women used to dress their hair.

The shaft of the column is sometimes fluted, leaving a fillet
or list between each channel: In this order there are 24 flutes
and fillets.

*Of*

## *Of the* CORINTHIAN ORDER.

This order, the moſt elegant of all, is by ſome compared to a very fine woman clad in a wanton ſumptuous habit: It was invented at *Corinth*, and ſoon ſpread into other places to adorn their public buildings. A proper rural ſituation for this order, ſeems to be a ſpot commanding a rich and beautiful proſpect in a fine watered vale.

The general proportions aſſigned by *Palladio* are,

1. The height of the column to be $9\frac{1}{2}$ modules.

2. Height of the entablature equal to $\frac{1}{5}$ that of the column; the architrave, freeze and cornice to be in the proportion of 4, 3, 5; and the projection of the cornice to equal its height.

3. Height of the pedeſtal equal to $\frac{1}{4}$ of the column.

4. The height of the capital to be $1\frac{1}{6}$ module; of which the abaco is $\frac{1}{6}$ of a module; its horns projecting over the bottom of the column $\frac{1}{4}$ of a module.

5. The height of the baſe equal to $\frac{1}{2}$ module; and its greateſt breadth to be one module and a fifth.

6. The diminution of the column to be 8 minutes.

7. In colonades, the intercolumnation is 2 modules.

8. In arches, and the columns ſet on pedeſtals,

> The diſtance of the columns, from middle to middle, to be $6\frac{1}{2}$ modules.
>
> Height of the arch equal to $11\frac{1}{6}$ modules.
>
> Breadth of the pilaſter, between the column and ſides of the paſſage, to be 27 minutes.

In this order the ſhaft is frequently cut into 24 flutes, which are ſeparated from one another by as many fillets.

The capital is compoſed of three tiers of leaves, eight leaves in a tier, with the ſtalks or ſcrols, encircling the body of the capital, which repreſents a basket, whoſe bottom is juſt as broad as the diameter of the top of the column within the channels: The ornaments of this capital are beſt done by hand, without rule or compaſs, obſerving the proper altitudes and projections of the parts.

The

The architrave confifts of three facias, three fufaroles, an ogee, and a plateband; the firft, or lower facia, projeéts the fame as the top of the fhaft.

The freeze, which projeéts the fame as the top of the fhaft, has its lower part turned into a kind of cavetto, terminating with the extremity of the plateband of the architrave.

The breadth of the dentels are $3\frac{1}{3}$ minutes, and their diftance $1\frac{2}{3}$ minutes.

The breadths of the modilions are $11\frac{1}{3}$ minutes, and their diftance in the clear $23\frac{1}{4}$ minutes.

The middle of a dentel fhould be under the middle of a modilion, and the axis of the column paffes through the middles of both dentel and modilion.

## *Of the* COMPOSITE ORDER.

This order (the poor invention of the *Romans*, and therefore frequently called the Roman order), is ufually compofed of the Corinthian and Ionic; the Ionic capital being fet over the two lower rows of leaves in the Corinthian capital.

*Palladio* gives us the following general proportions.

1. The height of the column to be 10 modules.

2. The height of the entablature equal to $\frac{1}{5}$ of the column; the architrave, freeze and cornice, in the proportion of 4, 3, 5; the freeze fwelling like that of the Ionic.

3. Height of the pedeftal to be $\frac{1}{3}$ of the column.

4. Height of the capital equal to $1\frac{1}{6}$ module; of which the abaco is $\frac{1}{6}$ module, its horns projeéting from the center of the column 1 module.

5. Height of the bafe $31\frac{1}{2}$ minutes, and its greateft breadth to be $1\frac{1}{5}$ modules.

6. Diminution of the column equal to 8 minutes.

7. In colonades, the intercolumnation is $1\frac{1}{2}$ modules.

8. In arches, and the columns fet on pedeftals,

> The diftance of the columns from middle to middle is $7\frac{1}{4}$ modules.
>
> Height of the arch equal to $12\frac{1}{3}$ modules: In the clear, the

the height is to the ſpan as 5 to 2.

The breadth of the pilaſters between the column and arch is $\frac{7}{10}$ modules, or 42 minutes.

In this order the ſhaft, if fluted, is to have 24 channels and 24 fillets, one between each two flutes.

The volutes of the capital are angular, to have the ſame appearances on every ſide, and they are drawn like thoſe in the Ionic.

The modilions in this order are worked into two faces, with an ogee between them; the breadth of the lower face 9 $\frac{1}{2}$ minutes, that of the upper 12 $\frac{1}{2}$; the diſtance of two modilions at the upper faces is 20 minutes, and at the lower faces 23 minutes; the axis of the column paſſing through the middle of a modilion.

*Preparatory to the* directions for drawing either of the Orders, it may be proper, for the uſe of beginners, to ſhow how
*To draw the Mouldings in Architecture.*

The terminations, or ends, of flat members, are right lines.

The aſtragal, fuſarole, and torus, are terminated by a ſemicircle.

*To deſcribe the Torus.* Fig. 1. Plate 1.

On AB, its breadth, deſcribe a ſemicircle.

*To make an Ovolo, whoſe breadth is* AB. Fig. 2.

Let AC = $\frac{2}{3}$ or $\frac{3}{4}$ of AB, and draw CB.

Make the angle CBD equal to the angle BCD.

Then the interſection of BD with CA will give D the center of the arc BC.

Or, Deſcribe on BC an equilateral triangle; and make the vertex the center.

The former of theſe methods is the moſt graceful.

*To make a Cavetto, whoſe breadth is* AB. Fig. 3.

Let AC = $\frac{2}{3}$ or $\frac{3}{4}$ of AB; draw BC, and produce the bottom line towards D.

Make

Make an angle BCD equal to the angle CBD.

Then D, the interſection of CD with BD, is the center ſought.

Or, On BC deſcribe an equilateral triangle, and the vertex will be the center: But this method is inferior to the former.

*To make a Scotia, whoſe breadth is* AB. Fig. 4.

Make AF equal to ⅓ of AB.

On AF, deſcribe the ſquare AC, and on BF, deſcribe the ſquare BD.

Then C is the center of the arc EF, and D the center of the arc FG.

*To make a Cima, whoſe breadth is* AB. Fig. 5.

Let AC equal to about ⅞ of AB. Prob. XIV.

Draw the right line CB, which biſeſt in D.

On CD and DB, make iſoſceles triangles, whoſe legs DE, DF, may be (by Prob. XIV.) each ⅚ of the baſe CD, DB; and the vertexes E and F will be the centers of the arcs CD, DB.

Or, the centers E, F, of the arcs CD, DB, may be the vertices of equilateral triangles deſcribed on the right lines CD, DB: But the curvatures found by the former way, have the moſt agreeable appearance.

*To make a Cymaiſe, or Ogee, whoſe breadth is* AB. Fig. 6.

Let AC equal to about ⅞ of AB.

Draw the right line CB, which biſeſt in D.

Through D draw the right line EF, ſo, that the angle CDE may be equal to the angle DCE; meeting the upper and lower lines in E and F.

Then E is the center of the arc CD, and F the center of the arc DB.

*To deſcribe the curve joining the ſhaft of a column with its upper or lower fillet, the projeſtion of* AB *being given.* Fig. 7.

Make AC equal to twice AB.

Draw CD parallel to AB, and equal to ¼ of AC.

Then D is the center of the arc CB.

*To*

### *To draw the gradual diminution of a Column.* Fig. 8.

Draw the axis AB of the intended length of the fhaft; and parallel thereto, at half a module of diftance, draw CD; make CE equal to half the proper diminution, and draw EF parallel to BA.

Make AG equal to one third of AB; and fo high is the fhaft to be parallel to its axis: through G draw HI at right angles to AB.

On HI defcribe a femicircumference cutting the line EF at the point 4; divide the arc H4 into equal parts at pleafure, fuppofe 4; and through thofe points draw the lines 1,1; 2,2; 3,3; 4,4.

Divide the line GB into a like number of equal parts, as at the points *a, b, c*; and through thefe points draw lines parallel to IH; making *aa* = 1,1; *bb* = 2,2; *cc* = 3,3.

Then a curved line drawn through the extremities H, *a, b, c,* E, will limit the gradual diminution required.

*Palladio* defcribes another method, which is more ready in practice.

Lay a thin ruler by the points D, H, E, and the bending of the ruler will give the gradual diminution required.

### *To defcribe the Volute of the Ionic order.* Figs. 9, 10.

The altitude AB, which is $\frac{4}{9}$ of a module, or $26\frac{2}{3}$ minutes, is divided into 8 equal parts, *viz.* 4 from C to A, and 4 from C to B; upon CD = $3\frac{1}{3}$, one of thefe parts, a circle is defcribed, and called the eye of the volute, which correfponds with the aftragal of the column.

*Palladio* gives the following manner of finding the 12 centers of the volute, which he difcovered on an old unfinifhed capital. Fig. 9.

Within the eye of the volute infcribe a fquare, whofe diagonal is CD; in this fquare draw the two diameters 1,3; 2,4; and thefe four points 1, 2, 3, 4, are the centers of the arcs A1, 1B, B3, 34, which forms the firft revolution. The centers of the arcs forming the fecond and third revolutions are thus found; fee the eye of the volute drawn at large. Fig. 9.

Divide the radii O1, O2, O3, O4, each into 3 equal parts, as at the

the points 5, 6, 7, 8, 9, 10, 11, 12, and thefe will be the centers of the remaining arcs, the laft of which is to coincide with the point c, in the eye.

*Goldman* obferving, that in this conftruction, the ends and beginnings of the arcs were not at right angles to the fame radii, contrived the following conftruction. See Fig. 10. and its eye drawn at large.

Upon one half of CD, defcribe the fquare 1, 2, 3, 4; and draw the lines O2, O3; divide O1, O4, each into 3 equal parts; then lines drawn through thofe points parallel to 1,2, their interfections with 1,4; O,2; O,3; will be centers of the volute.

So the points, 1, 2, 3, 4, 5, 6, 7, 8, 9, 10, 11, 12, will be the centers of the twelve arcs which together form the outward curve of the volute.

In either method, the centers of the inner curve may be thus found.

Take O$a$ equal to $\frac{7}{8}$ of O1; divide O$a$ into three equal parts, and thefe divifions will give centers of the inner curve; the two eyes drawn at large will fhew how the 12 inner centers are found, where they are diftinguifhed by large points; the 12 centers of the outward curve being marked by the figures.

In the defcribing of thefe volute, it will frequently happen, that the laft quadrant will not fall on its true termination, occafioned by the radii of the feveral quadrants not being exactly taken by the compaffes: In order to avoid this inaccuracy, at leaft in fome degree, here is fubjoined a table, fhewing the length of each radius, computed from *Goldman*'s method: But it may alfo be applied to *Palladio*'s, the radius of the largeft quadrant not differing $\frac{3}{100}$ of a minute, or $\frac{1}{2000}$ of a module from the truth; and excepting the arc defcribed from the firft center, the reft may be made quadrants in the fame manner as fhewn in *Goldman*'s method.

The table is conftructed in the following manner.

For the outward curves.

CA $= (\frac{1}{2}$ AB $= 13\frac{1}{3} =) \frac{40}{3}$; 1. 4. $= ($OC $= \frac{1}{2}$ CD $= 1\frac{2}{3} =) \frac{5}{3}$.
1C $= \frac{1}{2}$ OC $= \frac{5}{6}$; then 1A $= \frac{80}{6} + \frac{5}{6} = \frac{85}{6}$; and 4. 4. $= \frac{55}{6}$.

Again

Again 4. 5. $= (\frac{5}{6}$ of $\frac{5}{3} =) \frac{25}{18}$; then $\frac{165}{18} - \frac{25}{18} = \frac{140}{18} = \frac{70}{9}$; and 8. 8. $= \frac{40}{9}$.

Alſo 8. 5. $= \frac{3}{6}$ of $\frac{5}{3} = \frac{15}{18}$; then $\frac{80}{18} - \frac{15}{18} = \frac{65}{18}$.

For the inward curve.

O$a = \frac{7}{8}$ of O1. and $a$1 $= \frac{1}{8}$ of $\frac{5}{6} = \frac{5}{48}$: Alſo the rim $= 1\frac{2}{3} = \frac{10}{6}$.

Now (1A or) $\frac{85}{6} - \frac{10}{6} = \frac{75}{6} = \frac{600}{48}$; and $\frac{600}{48} + \frac{5}{48} = \frac{605}{48} = 1$ſt radius.

And the reſt of the radius's are eaſily made out.

To uſe the firſt part of the table, a ſcale of $\frac{1}{4}$ of a module ſhould be made, and divided into 15 minutes, and the extreme diviſion decimally divided, whereby the lengths of the ſeveral radii may be taken: But as the ſector is an univerſal ſcale, there are two other columns added, applicable to the ſector; where the longer radius 14,166 is made a tranſverſe diſtance to 10 and 10, or 100 and 100, on the line of lines; and all the other radii of both curves are proportioned thereto: Now the centers of the curves being found as ſhewn in the eyes of the volute, the ſeveral radii may be taken from the ſector, and the curves more accurately deſcribed than by any other method.

By the help of the following table, the centers of the arcs may be found (without the trouble of dividing the eye of the volute) in the following manner.

Lay the firſt radius on the line AB, from A towards the eye; and it gives the center of the firſt arc A1: Through the ſaid center, draw, at right angles to the firſt radius, a line meeting the firſt arc A1 in 1; and on this line lay the ſecond radius from 1 towards the eye; and it gives the center of the ſecond arc 1.2. From this center, and at right angles to the laſt radius, draw a line meeting the ſecond arc 1.2 in 2, and on this line apply the third radius from 2 towards the eye, and it gives the center of the third arc 2.3. Through this laſt center, draw a line at right angles to the laſt radius, meeting the laſt arc 2.3 in 3; and to this line apply the fourth radius from 3 towards the eye, and it gives the center of the fourth arc 3.4. And in like manner the centers of all the arcs both of the outwards and inward curves of the volute may be expeditiouſly and accurately obtained by the help of the table.

*A* TABLE

*A* TABLE *of the lengths, in minutes, of the several radii of the outward and inner volutes.*

| Nᵒ Rad. | Outward Curve. | Inward Curve. | In parts of 1ft rad. | |
|---|---|---|---|---|
| | | | Outward. | Inward. |
| 1 | $\frac{85}{6} = 14{,}166$ | $\frac{605}{48} = 12{,}604$ | 100,000 | 88,969 |
| 2 | $\frac{75}{6} = 12{,}500$ | $\frac{535}{48} = 11{,}146$ | 88,235 | 78,677 |
| 3 | $\frac{65}{6} = 10{,}833$ | $\frac{465}{48} = 9{,}687$ | 76,468 | 68,379 |
| 4 | $\frac{55}{6} = 9{,}166$ | $\frac{395}{48} = 8{,}229$ | 64,705 | 58,087 |
| 5 | $\frac{70}{9} = 7{,}777$ | $\frac{1010}{144} = 7{,}014$ | 54,901 | 49,510 |
| 6 | $\frac{60}{9} = 6{,}666$ | $\frac{870}{144} = 6{,}041$ | 47,058 | 42,642 |
| 7 | $\frac{50}{9} = 5{,}555$ | $\frac{730}{144} = 5{,}069$ | 39,215 | 35,781 |
| 8 | $\frac{40}{9} = 4{,}444$ | $\frac{590}{144} = 4{,}097$ | 31,372 | 28,920 |
| 9 | $\frac{65}{18} = 3{,}611$ | $\frac{485}{144} = 3{,}368$ | 25,490 | 23,774 |
| 10 | $\frac{55}{18} = 3{,}055$ | $\frac{415}{144} = 2{,}882$ | 21,568 | 20,343 |
| 11 | $\frac{45}{18} = 2{,}500$ | $\frac{345}{144} = 2{,}395$ | 17,647 | 16,906 |
| 12 | $\frac{35}{18} = 1{,}944$ | $\frac{275}{144} = 1{,}909$ | 13,725 | 13,475 |

*To describe the Flutings and Fillets in channelled columns.* Fig. 11.

In the Doric, the circumference of the column being divided into 20 equal parts (here the ¼ circumference is divided

into

into 5), of which *ab* is one; on *ab* defcribe a fquare, and the center *c* of that fquare is the center of the channel or flute required.

In the Ionic, and Corinthian, divide the circumference of the column into 24 equal parts (here $\frac{1}{4}$ circumference is divided into 6), of which *ad* is one; divide *ad* into 4 equal parts, then $ae = \frac{3}{4} ad$ is the breadth of the flute, and $ed = \frac{1}{4} ad$ is the breadth of the fillet.

The flutes are femicircles defcribed on the chords of their arcs in the column.

In the three following tables are contained the heights and projections of the parts of each order; according to the proportions given by *Palladio*; the orders of this architect were chofen, becaufe the *Englifh*, at prefent, are more fond of copying his productions, than thofe of any other architect.

The firft table ferves for the pedeftal, the fecond for the column, and the third for the entablature, of each order. Each table is divided into feven principal columns: In the firft, beginning at the left hand, is contained the name of the primary divifions; in the fecond, thofe of the feveral divifions and members in the orders; and the other five, titled with *Tufcan, Doric, Ionic, Corinthian, Roman*, contain the numbers, expreffing the altitudes, and projections taken from the axis, or middle of the column, of the feveral members belonging to their correfponding orders.

The column containing each order, is divided, firft into two other columns, one fhewing the altitude, and figned Alt. and the other, the projections, and figned Proj. Each of thefe is alfo divided into two other columns, one containing modules, and marked Mo. and the other, the minutes and parts, and marked Mi.

Under the table of the pedeftal there is another table, fhewing the general proportions for the heights of the orders.

In each of the orders of architecture, the height of the order, and the diameter of the column, have a conftant relation to one another.

Therefore,

Therefore, if the diameter of the column be given, the height of the order is given alfo: And having determined by what fcale the order is to be drawn, fuch as ½ inch, 1 inch, 2 inches, &c. to a foot or yard, &c. Take from fuch fcale, the part or parts expreffing the diameter of the column, and make this extent a tranfverfe diftance to 6 and 6 (*i. e.* 60 and 60) on the fcales of lines, and the fector will be opened fo, that the feveral proportions of the order may be taken from it.

EXAM. *Suppofe the diameter of a column is to be 18 inches; and the drawing of the order is to be delineated from a fcale of an inch to a foot: that is, the diameter of the column in the drawing is to be an inch and half.*

Make the tranfverfe diftance of 6 to 6, on the fcale of lines, equal to 1 ½ inch, and the fector is fitted for the fcale.

If the height of the order is given, divide this height, by the height of the order in the table, and the quotient will be the diameter of the column.

EXAM. *What muft be the diameter of the column in the* Ionic *order, when the whole height of the order is fixed at 18 feet 6 inches.*

The height of the order in the table is 13 mo. 29 ¼ mi. = $13 \frac{29,25}{60} = 13,4875$ modules: And 18 f. 6 in. = 18,5 feet. Therefore $\frac{18,5}{13,4875} = 1,3709$ feet = 1 f. 4 ½ inches nearly: And the fector may be fitted to this, as before directed, according to the intended fize of the draught.

## *To delineate an Order by thefe Tables*

Having determined the diameter of the column at the bottom, and fet the fector to the intended fcale, draw a line to reprefent the axis or middle of the order.

On this line, lay the parts for the heights of the pedeftal,

column,

column, and entablature, taken from the table of general proportions.

Within each of thefe parts refpectively, lay the feveral altitudes taken from the tables of particulars, under the word Alt. Through each of the points marked on the axis, draw lines perpendicular to the axis, or draw one line perpendicular, and the others parallel thereto.

On the lines drawn perpendicular to the axis, lay the projections correfponding to the refpective altitudes; thefe projections are to be laid on both fides of the axis, for the pedeftal and column; and only one fide, for the entablature: join the extremities of the projections with fuch lines as are proper to exprefs the refpective mouldings and parts: And the order, exclufive of its ornaments, will be delineated.

As the altitudes of many of the parts are very fmall, it will not be convenient, if poffible, to take from the fcale of lines, fuch fmall parts alone; therefore, it may be beft to proceed as in the following example of the *Ionic* order.

### *To conftruct the Pedeftal.* Plate II.

In the line AD, which reprefents the axis of the order, take the bafe A$a$ = 42 $\frac{1}{2}$ min., the die $ad$ = 1 mod. 35 min.; and the capital $d$D = 22 $\frac{3}{4}$ min. Then to draw the fmall members in the bafe and cornice, proceed thus.

To the minutes in the bafe, 42 $\frac{1}{2}$, add fome even number of minutes, fuppofe 30, = $a$B, and the fum 72 $\frac{1}{2}$ is equal to AB; then compofe a table, fuch as the following one, wherein the alt. of the plinth is fubtracted out of the No. 72 $\frac{1}{2}$; then the torus out of this remainder; then the cyma out of this remainder; then the fillet out of this; and laftly, the cavetto out of this remainder. Thus,

|  |  | Min. |
|---|---|---|
| Bafe with 30 minutes – – – – – – – – – | | 72 $\frac{1}{2}$ |
| This lefs by the plinth, | 28 $\frac{1}{2}$, remains – – – | 44 |
| This lefs by the torus, | 4, remains – – – | 40 |
| This lefs by the fillet, | 0 $\frac{3}{4}$, remains – – – | 39 $\frac{1}{4}$ |
| This lefs by the cyma, | 5, remains – – – | 34 $\frac{1}{4}$ |

This

This lefs by the fillet,      o $\frac{3}{4}$, remains – – – 33 $\frac{1}{2}$

This lefs by the cavetto,   3 $\frac{1}{2}$, remains – – – 30,
     the minutes firft added.


Then the feveral numbers in the table may be taken from the line of lines on the fector, and applied from B towards A. Thus,

Make B1 = 44, B2 = 40, B3 = 39 $\frac{1}{4}$, B4 = 34 $\frac{1}{4}$, B5 = 33 $\frac{1}{2}$; draw lines through thefe points at right angles to AD, and on thefe lines lay the refpective projections, as fhewn in the general table; then the proper curvature or figure being drawn at the extremities of the numbers, the bafe of the pedeftal will be made.

It will be found moft convenient to lay off the numbers from the greater to the leffer ones; for then there is only one motion required in the joints of the compaffes, which is, to bring them clofer and clofer every diftance laid down.

And in the fame manner, for the cornice of the pedeftal, take a point C, 30 minutes below the cornice; and tabulate as before.

Cornice with 30. min. – – – – – – – 52 $\frac{3}{4}$ = CD

This lefs by the fillet or cap,  2 $\frac{1}{2}$, leaves   50 $\frac{1}{4}$ = C1

Ditto – – – – ogee – – – 3 $\frac{1}{2}$, ditto    46 $\frac{3}{4}$ = C2

Ditto – – – – corona  – – 4 $\frac{1}{2}$ – – – 42 $\frac{1}{4}$ = C3

Ditto – – – – fillet – – – 1 $\frac{3}{4}$ – – – 40 $\frac{1}{2}$ = C4

Ditto – – – – cyma   – – 5 $\frac{1}{4}$ – – – 35 $\frac{1}{4}$ = C5

Ditto – – – – fillet – – – 1 $\frac{3}{4}$ – – – 33 $\frac{1}{2}$ = C6

Ditto – – – – cavetto – – 3 $\frac{1}{2}$ – – – 30  = C*d*.


Thefe numbers laid from C towards D, give the altitudes of the members of the cornice.

In like manner the mouldings about the bafe and capital are laid down, by taking 30 minutes in the fhaft both above the bafe and below the capital; having firft fet on the axis, the refpective heights of bafe, fhaft, and capital.

*Thus*

### *Thus for the Base.*

The base 33 ½ min. with 30 added    $= 63\frac{1}{2} =$ SD
This less by the plinth 10 min. leaves    $53\frac{1}{2} =$ S1
Ditto – – – – torus   $7\frac{1}{2}$ – – – $46 =$ S2
Ditto – – – – fillet   $1\frac{1}{4}$ – – – $44\frac{3}{4} =$ S3
Ditto – – – – scotia   $4\frac{2}{3}$ – – – $40\frac{1}{12} =$ S4
Ditto – – – – fillet   $1\frac{1}{4}$ – – – $38\frac{5}{6} =$ S5
Ditto – – – – torus   $5\frac{1}{3}$ – – – $33\frac{1}{2} =$ s6
Ditto – – – – astragal $2\frac{1}{4}$ – – – $31\frac{1}{4} =$ S7
Ditto – – – – fillet   $1\frac{1}{4}$ – – – $30 =$ s8.

s8 is here supposed to be 30, though the plate is not high enough to admit 30 minutes to be laid in the shaft of the column.

### *For the Capital*

The capital $24\frac{1}{4}$ with 30 added, gives    $54\frac{1}{4} =$ FG
This less by the plateband   $1\frac{3}{4}$, leaves   $52\frac{1}{2} =$ FI
Ditto – – – – ogee   $3\frac{1}{3}$ – – – $49\frac{1}{6} =$ F2
This less by the rim of volute $1\frac{1}{3}$ – – – $47\frac{5}{6} =$ F3
Ditto – – – – hollow   $5\frac{1}{3}$ – – – $42\frac{1}{2} =$ F4
Ditto – – – – ovolo   $7\frac{1}{2}$ – – – $35 =$ F5
Ditto – – – – astragal   $3\frac{1}{3}$ – – – $31\frac{2}{3} =$ F6
Ditto – – – – fillet   $1\frac{2}{3}$ – – – $30 =$ F7.

### *To construct the Cornice.*

In the axis take GH $= 36$ for the architrave, HI $= 27$ for the freeze, and IK $= 46$ for the cornice. Then,

### *For the parts of the Architrave.*

To the freeze 27 add HG 36, gives    $63 =$ IG
This less by the first face   $6\frac{1}{2}$, leaves   $56\frac{1}{2} =$ I1
Ditto – – – – fusarole   $1\frac{1}{4}$ – – – $55\frac{1}{4} =$ I2
Ditto – – – – 2d face   $8\frac{1}{3}$ – – – $46\frac{11}{12} =$ I3
Ditto – – – – fusarole   $2$ – – – $42\frac{11}{12} =$ I4
Ditto – – – – 3d face   $10\frac{1}{2}$ – – – $35\frac{5}{12} =$ I5
Ditto – – – – ogee   $4\frac{3}{4}$ – – – $31\frac{2}{3} =$ I6
Ditto – – – – fillet   $2\frac{2}{3}$ – – – $27 =$ IH.

TABLE

A TABLE *shewing the Altitudes and Projections of*
*Order; according to the*

| Names of the Members. | | Tuscan. | | | | Doric. | | | |
|---|---|---|---|---|---|---|---|---|---|
| | | Alt. | | Proj. | | Alt. | | Proj. | |
| | | Mo. | Mi. | Mo. | Mi. | Mo. | Mi. | Mo. | Mi. |
| **CORNICE.** Fillet – – – – | | — | — | — | — | o | 3 ⅔ | o | 56 |
| Ogee – – – – | | — | — | — | — | — | — | — | — |
| Corona – – – | | — | — | — | — | — | — | — | — |
| Fillet – – – | | — | — | — | — | — | — | — | — |
| Cima – – – | | — | — | — | — | o | 9 | — | — |
| Fillet – – – – | | — | — | — | — | o | { 1 ¼ / 1 ¼ | o | { 47 / 45 ¾ |
| Aftragal – – – | | — | — | — | — | — | — | — | — |
| Ogee – – – – | | — | — | — | — | — | — | — | — |
| Cavetto – – – | | — | — | — | — | o | 5 | o | 41 ¼ |
| Fillet – – – | | — | — | — | — | — | — | — | — |
| The Cornice – – | | — | — | — | — | o | 26 ⅙ | — | — |
| THE DIE – – | | I | o | o | 42 | I | 20 | o | 40 |
| The Bafe – – – | | — | — | — | — | o | 40 | — | — |
| **BASE.** Fillet – – – – | | — | — | — | — | — | — | — | — |
| Cavetto – – – | | — | — | — | — | o | 5 | o | 41 ¼ |
| Ogee – – – – | | — | — | — | — | — | — | — | — |
| Aftragal – – – | | — | — | — | — | — | — | — | — |
| Fillet – – – – | | — | — | — | — | o | { 1 ¼ / 1 ¼ | o | { 46 / 47 ¼ |
| Cima – – – – | | — | — | — | — | — | — | — | — |
| Fillet – – – – | | — | — | — | — | — | — | — | — |
| Torus – – – – | | — | — | — | — | — | 5 | o | 50 |
| Plinth – – – – | | — | — | — | — | — | 27 ½ | o | 50 |

*A* TABLE *of general*

| | | Mo. | Mi. | Mo. | Mi. | Mo. | Mi. | Mo. | Mi. |
|---|---|---|---|---|---|---|---|---|---|
| The Order – – | | 9 | 44 ½ | — | — | 12 | 13 ⅙ | — | — |
| The Entablature | | I | 44 ½ | — | — | I | 53 | — | — |
| The Column – – | | 7 | o | — | — | 8 | o | — | — |
| The Pedeftal – – | | I | o | — | — | 2 | 20 ⅙ | — | — |

## FIRST.

*every Moulding and Part in the Pedeſtals of each Proportions given by* Palladio.

| Ionic. | | | | Corinthian. | | | | Roman. | | | |
|---|---|---|---|---|---|---|---|---|---|---|---|
| Alt. | | Proj. | | Alt. | | Proj. | | Alt. | | Proj. | |
| Mo. | Mi. | Mo. | Mi. | Mo. | Mi. | Mo. | Mi. | Mo. | Mi. | Mo. | Mi. |
| 0 | 2½ | 0 | 56¼ | 0 | 2½ | 0 | 57 | 0 | 2½ | 0 | 57 |
| 0 | 3½ | 0 | { 55¼<br>53¼ | 0 | 3½ | 0 | { 56<br>54¼ | 0 | 3½ | 0 | { 56<br>54¼ |
| 0 | 4½ | 0 | 52¼ | 0 | 4¾ | 0 | 53¼ | 0 | 5½ | 0 | 53½ |
| 0 | 1¾ | 0 | 51¾ | — | — | — | — | 0 | 1 | 0 | 52¾ |
| 0 | 5¼ | — | — | 0 | 4¼ | 0 | { 49¼<br>46 | 0 | 8½ | — | — |
| 0 | 1¾ | 0 | 44¾ | 0 | 0¾ | 0 | 46 | — | — | — | — |
| — | — | — | — | — | — | — | — | 0 | 3 | 0 | 46¾ |
| — | — | — | — | 0 | 3¾ | 0 | { 45<br>43 | — | — | — | — |
| 0 | 3½ | 0 | 41¾ | — | — | — | — | — | — | — | — |
| — | — | — | — | — | — | — | — | 0 | 1¾ | 0 | 44¾ |
| 0 | 22¾ | — | — | 0 | 19 | — | — | 0 | 25¾ | — | — |
| 1 | 35 | 0 | 41¼ | 1 | 36 | 0 | 42 | 2 | 6½ | 0 | 42 |
| 0 | 42½ | — | — | 0 | 38 | — | — | 0 | 50 | — | — |
| — | — | — | — | — | — | — | — | 0 | 1 | 0 | 45½ |
| 0 | 3½ | 0 | 41¾ | — | — | — | — | — | — | — | — |
| — | — | — | — | 0 | 4 | 0 | { 43<br>46 | — | — | — | — |
| — | — | — | — | — | — | — | — | 0 | 3 | 0 | 47 |
| 0 | 0¾ | 0 | 47¼ | 0 | 0¾ | 0 | 47 | — | — | — | — |
| 0 | 5 | — | — | 0 | 5 | — | — | 0 | 7½ | 0 | { 45¼<br>54¾ |
| 0 | 0¾ | 0 | 53¾ | 0 | 0¾ | 0 | 55 | 0 | 1 | 0 | 54¾ |
| 0 | 4 | 0 | 56¼ | 0 | 4 | 0 | 57 | 0 | 4½ | 0 | 57 |
| 0 | 28½ | 0 | 56¼ | 0 | 23½ | 0 | 57 | 0 | 33 | 0 | 57 |

*Proportions for the Orders.*

| | | | | | | | | | | | |
|---|---|---|---|---|---|---|---|---|---|---|---|
| 13 | 29¼ | — | — | 13 | 57 | — | — | 15 | 22¼ | — | — |
| 1 | 49 | — | — | 1 | 54 | — | — | 2 | 0 | — | — |
| 9 | 0 | — | — | 9 | 30 | — | — | 10 | 0 | — | — |
| 2 | 40¼ | — | — | 2 | 33 | — | — | 3 | 22¼ | — | — |

*A* TABLE, *shewing the Altitudes and Projections of*
*according to the Propor-*

| Names of the Members. | Tuscan. Alt. Mo. | Mi. | Proj. Mo. | Mi. | Doric. Alt. Mo. | Mi. | Proj. Mo. | Mi. |
|---|---|---|---|---|---|---|---|---|
| **CAPITAL.** | | | | | | | | |
| Angular Volutes — | — | — | — | — | — | — | — | — |
| Abacus { Ovolo | — | — | — | — | — | — | — | — |
| Abacus { Fillet — | — | — | — | — | o | 1 ¼ | o | 38 ¾ |
| Abacus { Cavetto | — | — | — | — | — | — | — | — |
| Basket Rim — — | — | — | — | — | — | — | — | — |
| Ogee — — — — | — | — | — | — | o | 2 ½ | o | { 37 ¾ 36 ¼ } |
| Abacus — — — | o | 10 | o | 30 | o | 6 ¼ | o | 35 ¾ |
| Vo- fillet or rim | — | — | — | — | — | — | — | — |
| lute chan. or hollow | — | — | — | — | — | — | — | — |
| Ovolo — — — — | o | 10 | o | 29 | o | 6 ½ | o | 34 ⅓ |
| Astragal — — — | — | — | — | — | — | — | — | — |
| Fillet — — — — | o | 1 ½ | o | 24 ½ | o | 1 ⅙ | o | 29 ¾ |
| | | | | | o | 1 1/9 | o | 28 ½ |
| | | | | | o | 1 1/9 | o | 27 ¼ |
| Collarino — — — | o | 8 ½ | o | 22 ½ | o | 10 | o | 26 |
| Middle Volute — | — | — | — | — | — | — | — | — |
| Cours. of leaves, 3d | — | — | — | — | — | — | — | — |
| folding half 2d | — | — | — | — | — | — | — | — |
| their height 1st | — | — | — | — | — | — | — | — |
| **SHAFT.** | | | | | | | | |
| Astragal — — — | o | 4 | o | 27 | o | 3 ½ | o | 30 |
| Fillet — — — — | o | 1 ½ | o | 24 ½ | o | 1 ½ | o | 28 ¼ |
| Body of the Column | 5 | 54 ½ | o | { 22 ½ 30 } | 6 | 53 ¾ | o | { 26 30 } |
| Fillet — — — — — | o | 2 ½ | o | 33 ¾ | o | 1 ¼ | o | 33 ½ |
| Astragal — — — | — | — | — | — | — | — | — | — |
| **BASE.** | | | | | | | | |
| Torus — — — — | — | — | — | — | o | 5 ½ | o | 36 ⅓ |
| Astragal — — — — | — | — | — | — | — | — | — | — |
| Fillet — — — — | — | — | — | — | o | 1 ¼ | o | 35 |
| Scotia — — — — | — | — | — | — | o | 4 ½ | o | 33 ⅓ |
| Fillet — — — — | — | — | — | — | o | 1 ¼ | o | 36 ⅔ |
| Astragal — — — | — | — | — | — | — | — | — | — |
| Fillet — — — — | — | — | — | — | — | — | — | — |
| Scotia — — — — | — | — | — | — | — | — | — | — |
| Fillet — — — | — | — | — | — | — | — | — | — |
| Torus — — — — | o | 12 ½ | o | 40 | o | 7 ½ | o | 40 |
| Plinth — — — — | o | 15 | o | 40 | o | 10 | o | 40 |
| Bafe — — — — | o | 27 ½ | — | — | o | 30 | — | — |
| Shaft — — — — | 6 | 2 ½ | — | — | 7 | 0 | — | — |
| Capital — — — | o | 30 | — | — | o | 30 | — | — |

# SECOND.

*every Moulding and Part in the Columns of each Order;*
*tions given by* Palladio.

| Ionic. | | | | Corinthian. | | | | Roman. | | | |
|---|---|---|---|---|---|---|---|---|---|---|---|
| Alt. | | Proj. | | Alt. | | Proj. | | Alt. | | Proj. | |
| Mo. | Mi. | Mo. | Mi. | Mo. | Mi. | Mo. | Mi. | Mo. | Mi. | Mo. | Mi. |
| 0 | $26\frac{2}{3}$ | 0 | $41\frac{2}{3}$ | 0 | 12 | 0 | 41 | 0 | $25\frac{2}{3}$ | 0 | 35 |
| — | — | — | — | 0 | 3 | 0 | 45 | 0 | 3 | 0 | 44 |
| 0 | $1\frac{3}{4}$ | 0 | $31\frac{1}{2}$ | 0 | $1\frac{1}{3}$ | 0 | 42 | 0 | $1\frac{1}{3}$ | 0 | $42\frac{1}{2}$ |
| — | — | — | — | 0 | $5\frac{2}{3}$ | 0 | 39 | 0 | $5\frac{2}{3}$ | 0 | 41 |
| — | — | — | — | 0 | $2\frac{1}{2}$ | — | — | — | — | — | — |
| 0 | $3\frac{1}{3}$ | 0 | $30\frac{3}{4}$<br>29 | — | — | — | — | — | — | — | — |
| — | — | — | — | — | — | — | — | — | — | — | — |
| 0 | $1\frac{1}{3}$ | — | — | — | — | — | — | — | — | — | — |
| 0 | $5\frac{1}{3}$ | — | — | — | — | — | — | — | — | — | — |
| 0 | $7\frac{1}{2}$ | 0 | 35 | — | — | — | — | 0 | $5\frac{1}{2}$ | 0 | 32 |
| — | — | — | — | — | — | — | — | 0 | 3 | 0 | 26 |
| — | — | — | — | — | — | — | — | — | — | — | — |
| — | — | — | — | — | — | — | — | 0 | $1\frac{1}{2}$ | 0 | 24 |
| — | — | — | — | — | — | — | — | — | — | — | — |
| — | — | — | — | — | — | — | — | — | — | — | — |
| — | — | — | — | 0 | $9\frac{1}{2}$ | — | — | — | — | — | — |
| — | — | — | — | 0 | 8 | — | — | 0 | 10 | — | — |
| — | — | — | — | 0 | 20 | 0 | 41 | 0 | 20 | 0 | 39 |
| — | — | — | — | 0 | 20 | 0 | 35 | 0 | 20 | 0 | 35 |
| 0 | $3\frac{1}{3}$ | 0 | 30 | 0 | $3\frac{2}{3}$ | 0 | 30 | 0 | 4 | 0 | 30 |
| 0 | $1\frac{2}{3}$ | 0 | $28\frac{1}{3}$ | 0 | $1\frac{1}{3}$ | 0 | 28 | 0 | $1\frac{1}{2}$ | 0 | 28 |
| 8 | $2\frac{1}{4}$ | 0 | 26<br>30 | 7 | $40\frac{3}{4}$ | 0 | 26<br>30 | 8 | 9 | 0 | 26<br>30 |
| 0 | $1\frac{1}{4}$ | 0 | 33 | 0 | $1\frac{3}{4}$ | 0 | $33\frac{1}{2}$ | 0 | 1 | 0 | 34 |
| 0 | $2\frac{1}{4}$ | 0 | $34\frac{1}{2}$ | 0 | $2\frac{1}{2}$ | 0 | $35\frac{1}{2}$ | 0 | 3 | 0 | $35\frac{1}{2}$ |
| 0 | $5\frac{1}{3}$ | 0 | 37 | 0 | 5 | 0 | $37\frac{1}{2}$ | 0 | $4\frac{1}{2}$ | 0 | 37 |
| — | — | — | — | 0 | $1\frac{1}{2}$ | 0 | $35\frac{1}{2}$ | — | — | — | — |
| 0 | $1\frac{1}{4}$ | 0 | $34\frac{1}{2}$ | 0 | $0\frac{2}{3}$ | 0 | 34 | 0 | $0\frac{2}{3}$ | 0 | $35\frac{1}{2}$ |
| 0 | $4\frac{2}{3}$ | — | — | 0 | $3\frac{3}{4}$ | — | — | 0 | 3 | — | — |
| 0 | $1\frac{1}{4}$ | 0 | 37 | 0 | $0\frac{3}{4}$ | 0 | 37 | 0 | $0\frac{1}{2}$ | 0 | $36\frac{1}{2}$ |
| — | — | — | — | 0 | $1\frac{3}{4}$ | 0 | $38\frac{1}{2}$ | 0<br>0 | 1<br>1 | 0<br>0 | 37<br>37 |
| — | — | — | — | — | — | — | — | 0 | $0\frac{1}{2}$ | 0 | $36\frac{1}{2}$ |
| — | — | — | — | — | — | — | — | 0 | 3 | — | — |
| — | — | — | — | — | — | — | — | 0 | $0\frac{2}{3}$ | 0 | $38\frac{1}{2}$ |
| 0 | $7\frac{1}{2}$ | 0 | $41\frac{1}{4}$ | 0 | 7 | 0 | 42 | 0 | 7 | 0 | 42 |
| 0 | 10 | 0 | $41\frac{1}{4}$ | 0 | $9\frac{2}{3}$ | 0 | 42 | 0 | $9\frac{2}{3}$ | 0 | 42 |
| 0 | 30 | — | — | 0 | 30 | — | — | 0 | $31\frac{1}{2}$ | — | — |
| 8 | $10\frac{3}{4}$ | — | — | 7 | 5 | — | — | 8 | $18\frac{1}{2}$ | — | — |
| 0 | $19\frac{1}{4}$ | — | — | 1 | 10 | — | — | 1 | 10 | — | — |

| A TABLE, shewing the Altitudes and Projections of Order; according to the Pro- | | | | | | | | |
|---|---|---|---|---|---|---|---|---|
| | Tuscan. | | | | Doric. | | | |
| Names of the Members. | Alt. | | Proj. | | Alt. | | Proj. | |
| | Mo. | Mi. | Mo. | Mi. | Mo. | Mi. | Mo. | Mi. |
| **CORNICE** — Fillet – – – – | 0 | 3½ | 1 | 6 | 0 | 2¼ | 1 | 16 |
| Cima – – – – | 0 | 10 | — | — | 0 | 6¾ | — | — |
| Fillet – – – – | 0 | 2 | 0 | 54¼ | 0 | 0¾ | 1 | 8 |
| Ogee – – – – | — | — | — | — | 0 | 3¼ | 1 / 1 | 7 / 5½ |
| Corona – – – | 0 | 10 | 0 | 52¼ | 0 | 8 | 1 | 4½ |
| Ovolo – – – – | 0 | 9 | 0 | 42 | 0 | 6 | 0 | 39½ |
| Fillet or Astragal | 0 | 1½ | 0 | 32 | 0 | 1 | 0 | 35 |
| Ogee – – – – | — | — | — | — | — | — | — | — |
| Modilion { 2d Face | — | — | — | — | — | — | — | — |
| Modilion { Ogee | — | — | — | — | — | — | — | — |
| Modilion { 1st Face | — | — | — | — | — | — | — | — |
| Fillet – – – – | — | — | — | — | — | — | — | — |
| Ovolo – – – – | — | — | — | — | — | — | — | — |
| Ogee – – – – | — | — | — | — | — | — | — | — |
| Fillet – – – – | — | — | — | — | — | — | — | — |
| Dentel – – – | — | — | — | — | — | — | — | — |
| Astragal – – – | — | — | — | — | — | — | — | — |
| Fillet – – – – | — | — | — | — | — | — | — | — |
| Ogee – – – – | — | — | — | — | — | — | — | — |
| Cavetto – – – | 0 | 7½ | 0 | 23½ | 0 | 5 | 0 | 31 |
| Trigliphs Capital | — | — | — | — | 0 | 5 | 0 | 30½ |
| The Cornice – – | 0 | 43½ | — | — | 0 | 38 | — | — |
| The FREEZE – | 0 | 26 | 0 | 22½ | 0 | 45 | 0 | 26 |
| The Architrave – | 0 | 35 | — | — | 0 | 30 | — | — |
| **ARCHITRAVE** — Fillet – – – – | 0 | 5 | 0 | 27½ | 0 | 4½ | 0 | 28 |
| Cavetto – – – | — | — | — | — | — | — | — | — |
| Ogee – – – – | — | — | — | — | — | — | — | — |
| Astragal or Fusarole | — | — | — | — | — | — | — | — |
| Third Face – – | — | — | — | — | — | — | — | — |
| Astragal or Fusarole | — | — | — | — | — | — | — | — |
| Second Face – – | 0 | 17½ | 0 | 24 | 0 | 14½ | 0 | 27 |
| Ogee – – – – | — | — | — | — | — | — | — | — |
| Astragal or Fusarole | — | — | — | — | — | — | — | — |
| First Face – – – | 0 | 12½ | 0 | 22½ | 0 | 11 | 0 | 26 |

# THIRD.

*every Moulding and Part in the Entablature of each*
*portions given by* Palladio.

| Ionic. | | | | Corinthian. | | | | Roman. | | | |
|---|---|---|---|---|---|---|---|---|---|---|---|
| Alt. | | Proj. | | Alt. | | Proj. | | Alt. | | Proj. | |
| Mo. | Mi. | Mo. | Mi. | Mo. | Mi. | Mo. | Mi. | Mo. | Mi. | Mo. | Mi. |
| 0 | 2½ | 1 | 12 | 0 | 2¼ | 1 | 14 | 0 | 2½ | 1 | 18½ |
| 0 | 7 | — | — | 0 | 6¼ | — | — | 0 | 8 | — | — |
| 0 | 1 | 1 | 4 | 0 | 0⅔ | 1 | 6½ | 0 | 1 | 1 | 10 |
| 0 | 3½ | { 1<br>1 | 3<br>0½ | 0 | 3 | { 1<br>1 | 5½<br>4 | 0 | 3¾ | { 1<br>1 | 9<br>6 |
| 0 | 8 | 0 | 59½ | 0 | 7⅓ | 1 | 3 | 0 | 9½ | 1 | 5 |
| — | — | — | — | — | — | — | — | 0 | 2½ | 0 | 55 |
| — | — | — | — | 0 | 0⅔ | 1 | 2 | 0 | 1¼ | 0 | 54 |
| 0 | 3 | 0 | { 55<br>53 | 0 | 2⅓ | { 1<br>0 | 1<br>59 | — | — | — | — |
| — | — | — | — | — | — | — | — | 0 | 6½ | 0 | 53 |
| 0 | 7½ | 0 | 52 | 0 | 7¼ | 0 | 40¼ | 0 | 1¾ | 0 | 52½ |
| — | — | — | — | — | — | — | — | 0 | 3¼ | 0 | 51 |
| 0 | 1½ | 0 | 37 | 0 | 1 | 0 | 40 | 0 | 1 | 0 | 51 |
| 0 | 6 | 0 | 36 | 0 | 4½ | 0 | 39 | — | — | — | — |
| — | — | — | — | — | — | — | — | 0 | 5 | 0 | { 35½<br>29 |
| — | — | — | — | 0 | 1 | 0 | 36 | — | — | — | — |
| — | — | — | — | 0 | 5½ | 0 | 35 | — | — | — | — |
| — | — | — | — | — | — | — | — | 0 | 2 | 0 | 30 |
| 0 | 1 | 0 | 31½ | 0 | 1 | 0 | 32 | 0 | 2 | 0 | 28½ |
| — | — | — | — | 0 | 4½ | 0 | { 31<br>27 | — | — | — | — |
| 0 | 5 | 0 | 27 | — | — | — | — | — | — | — | — |
| — | — | — | — | — | — | — | — | — | — | — | — |
| 0 | 46 | — | — | 0 | 47½ | — | — | 0 | 50 | — | — |
| 0 | 27 | 0 | 34 | 0 | 28½ | 0 | 26 | 0 | 30 | 0 | 35 |
| 0 | 36 | — | — | 0 | 38 | — | — | 0 | 40 | — | — |
| 0 | 2⅔ | 0 | 34 | 0 | 2½ | 0 | 34½ | 0 | 2⅛ | 0 | 35 |
| — | — | — | — | — | — | — | — | 0 | 4⅛ | 0 | 32 |
| 0 | 4¾ | 0 | { 33<br>30 | 0 | 5 | 0 | { 33½<br>30 | 0 | 3⅔ | 0 | { 31<br>29 |
| — | — | — | — | 0 | 2 | 0 | 29½ | — | — | — | — |
| 0 | 10½ | 0 | 29 | 0 | 10½ | 0 | 28 | — | — | — | — |
| 0 | 2 | 0 | 29 | 0 | 1¾ | 0 | 28 | 0 | 1 5/12 | 0 | 29 |
| 0 | 8⅓ | 0 | 27½ | 0 | 8¼ | 0 | 27 | 0 | 15 | 0 | 28 |
| — | — | — | — | — | — | — | — | 0 | 2⅔ | 0 | { 27½<br>26½ |
| 0 | 1¼ | 0 | 27½ | 0 | 1¾ | 0 | 27 | — | — | — | — |
| 0 | 6½ | 0 | 26½ | 0 | 6¼ | 0 | 26 | 0 | 11 | 0 | 26 |

*For the Cornice.*

To the freeze 27 add the cornice 46, gives 73　　= HK

This lefs by the fillet　　　　2½, leaves　　70½ = HI

Ditto – – – – cima　　　7　– – –　63½ = H2

Ditto – – – – fillet　　　1　– – –　62½ = H3

Ditto – – – – ogee　　　3½ – – –　59　= H4

Ditto – – – – corona　　8　– – –　51　= H5

Ditto – – – – ogee　　　3　– – –　48　= H6

Ditto – – – – modilion　7½ – – –　40½ = H7

Ditto – – – – fillet　　　1½ – – –　39　= H8

Ditto – – – – ovolo　　6　– – –　33　= H9

Ditto – – – – fillet　　　1　– – –　32　= H10

Ditto – – – – cavetto　5　– – –　27　= HI.

Tables may be made in like manner for either of the orders, to be taken from the fector: The projections from the axis being all of them large numbers, they may be taken from the fector eafily enough after it is fet to the diameter of the column, as before fhewn.

A little reflection will make this very clear, and perhaps more fo, than by beftowing more words thereon.

## SECT. XIII.

### *Some Ufes of the Scales of Polygons.* Pl. VI.

## PROBLEM XVI.

*In a given circle, whofe diameter is* AB, *to infcribe a regular octagon.* Fig. 22.

SOLUTION. Open the legs of the fector, till the tranfverfe diftance of 6 and 6, be equal to AB: Then will the tranfverfe diftance of 8 and 8, be the fide of an octagon which will be infcribed in the given circle.

In

In like manner may any other polygon not exceeding 12 fides, be infcribed in a given circle.

## PROBLEM XVII.

*On a given line* AB, *to defcribe a regular pentagon.* Fig. 23.

SOLUTION. 1ft. Make AB a tranfverfe diftance to 5 and 5.

2d. At that opening of the fector, take the tranfverfe diftance of 6 and 6; and with this radius, on the points, A, B, as centers, defcribe arcs cutting in C.

3d. On C as a center, with the fame radius, defcribe a circumference paffing through the points A, B; and in this circle may the pentagon, whofe fide is AB, be infcribed.

By a like procefs may any other polygon, of not more than 12 fides, be defcribed on a given line.

The fcales of chords will folve thefe two problems, or any other of the like kind: Thus,

*In a circle whofe diameter is* AB, *to defcribe a regular polygon of* 24 *fides.* Fig. 24.

SOLUTION. 1ft. Make the diameter AB, a tranfverfe diftance to 60 and 60, on the fcales of chords.

2d. Divide 360 by 24; the quotient gives 15.

3d. Take the tranfverfe diftance of 15 and 15, and this will be the chord of the 24th part of the circumference.

As there are great difficulties attending the taking of divifions accurately from fcales; therefore in this problem, where a diftance is to be repeated feveral times, it will be beft to proceed thus.

With the chord of 60 degrees, divide the circumference into fix equal parts.

In every divifion of 60 degrees, lay down 1ft. The chord of 15 degrees. 2d. The chord of 30 degrees. 3d. The chord of 45 degrees, beginning always at the fame point.

If methods like this be purfued in all fimilar cafes, the error in taking diftances, will not be multiplied into any of the divifions following the firft.

SECT.

## S E C T.  XIV.

### *Some Ufes of the Scales of Chords.*

THESE double fcales of chords, are more convenient than the fingle fcales, fuch as defcribed on the plain fcale; for on the fector, the radius with which the arc is to be defcribed, may be of any length between the tranfverfe diftance of 60 and 60, when the legs are clofe, and that of the tranfverfe diftance of 60 and 60, when the legs are opened as far as the inftrument will admit of. But with the chords on the plain fcale, the arc defcribed, muft always be the fame radius.

## PROBLEM XVIII.

*To protract, or lay down, a right lined angle,* BAC, *which fhall contain a given number of degrees.* Pl. VI.

CASE I. *When the degrees given are under 60: Suppofe* 46. Fig. 25.

1ft. At any opening of the fector, take the tranfverfe diftance of 60 and 60, (on the chords;) and with this opening, defcribe an arc BC.

2d. Take the tranfverfe diftance of the given degrees 46, and lay this diftance on the arc from any point B, to C; marking the extremities B, C, of the faid diftance.

3d. From the center A of the arc, draw two lines AC, AB, each paffing through one extremity of the diftance BC, laid on faid arc; and thefe two lines will contain the angle required.

CASE II. *When the degrees given are more than 60: Suppofe* 148.

1ft. Defcribe the arc BCD as before.

2d. Take the tranfverfe diftance of $\frac{1}{2}$ or $\frac{1}{3}$, of the given degrees 148; fuppofe $\frac{1}{3} = 49\frac{1}{3}$ degrees; lay this diftance on the

arc

arc thrice; *viz.* from B to *a*, from *a* to *b*, from *b* to D.

3d. From the center A, draw two lines AB, AD, and the angle BAD will contain the degrees required.

*When an angle containing lefs than 5 degrees, fuppofe* 3 $\frac{1}{2}$, is to be made, it is moft convenient to proceed thus.

1ft. Defcribe the arch DG with the chord of 60 degrees.

2d. From fome point D, lay the chord of 60 degrees to G; and the chord of 56 $\frac{1}{2}$ degrees (= 60° − 3° $\frac{1}{2}$) from D to E.

3d. Lines drawn from the center A, through G and E, will form the angle of AGE, of 3 $\frac{1}{2}$ degrees.

If the radius of the arc or circle is to be of a given length; then make the tranfverfe diftance of 60 to 60, equal to that affigned length.

Thefe fcales of chords on either leg of the fector, may be ufed fingly; in the manner directed in the ufe of chords on the plain fcale.

From what has been faid about the protracting of an angle to contain a given number of degrees, it will be eafy to fee how to find the degrees which are contained in a given angle already laid down.

## PROBLEM XIX.

*To delineate the vifual lines of a furvey; by having given, the bearings and diftances from each other, of the ftations terminating thofe vifual lines.*

EXAM. Suppofe in the field-book of a furvey the bearings and diftances of the ftations were expreffed as follows:

⊙ fignifies Station.

B ——— Bearing.

D ——— Diftance.

⊙ I.

⊙ 1. B  70° 50′ D 1080 links.

⊙ 2. B 128   10  D  580.

⊙ 3. B  32   15  D  605.

⊙ 4. B 287   30  D  766.

⊙ 5. B  50   45  D  940.

⊙ 6. B 273   55  D 1085.

⊙ 7. B 183   25  D  700.

Return to D 314 in ⊙ 7.  ⊙ 8. B 133   30  D  510 to ⊙ 5.

⊙ 9. B 186   30  D  390 to ⊙ 2.

Return to D 700 in ⊙ 7.  ⊙ 10. B 209   20  D  668 cutting 1ſt D.

Return to ⊙ 10.  ⊙ 11. B 275   30  D  800.

⊙ 12. B 171   50  D  784 to ⊙ 1.

The bearings are counted from the North, Eaſtward. Therefore all the bearings under 90 degrees fall between the N. and E. or in the 1ſt quadrant.

Bearings between 90° and 180°, fall between E. and S. or in the 2d quadrant.

Thoſe between 180° and 270°, fall between the S. and W. or in the 3d quadrant.

And thoſe between 270° and 360°, fall between the W. and N. or in the 4th quadrant.

SOLUTION. 1ſt. Take from the chords the tranſverſe diſt-ance of 60 and 60, (the ſector being opened at pleaſure, the larger, the better) with this radius deſcribe a circumference, and draw the diameters NS. WE. at right angles. Pl. VI. Fig. 31.

2d. The firſt bearing 70° 50′ is in the firſt quadrant; but being more than 60°, take the tranſverſe diſtance of the half of 70° 50′, and apply this extent in the circumference twice from N. towards E, and the point correſponding to the 1ſt bearing will be obtained, which mark with the figure 1.

3d. The ſecond bearing 128° 10′, falls in the ſecond quadrant; its ſupplement to 180° is 51° 50′, that is, 51° 50′ from the S. point. Now take the tranſverſe diſtance of 51° 50′, and apply it to the circumference from S. towards E, and the point correſponding

correfponding to the fecond bearing will be found, which mark
with the figure 2.

4th. The 3d bearing 32° 15′, is to be applied from N. to 3:
The 4th bearing 287° 30′, is in the 4th quadrant; therefore take
it from 360°, and the remainder 72° 30′, is to be applied from N.
towards W. and the point 4, reprefenting the 4th bearing, will
be known.

In this manner proceed with all the other bearings, and
mark the correfponding points in the circumference with the
numbers 5, 6, 7, &c. agreeable to the number of the bearing or
ftation.

5th. Chufe fome convenient point on the paper to begin at,
as at the place markt ⊙ 1. Lay a parallel ruler by C the center of
the circle, and the point in its circumference marked 1, and (by
the help of the ruler) draw a parallel line thro' ⊙ 1, the point
chofe for the firft ftation, in the direction of the (fuppofed)
radius C1; and on this line lay the firft diftance; that is, take
from a convenient fized fcale of equal parts the extent of 1080,
and transfer this extent from ⊙ 1 to ⊙ 2; and this line will
reprefent the firft diftance meafured, laid down according to its
true pofition in refpect to the circle firft defcribed.

6th. Lay the ruler by the center C, and the point in the
circumference noted by the figure 2, and parallel to this
pofition of the ruler, draw thro' the point ⊙ 2, a line ⊙ 2 ⊙ 3, in
the direction of the (fuppofed) radius C2, and on this line lay
from ⊙ 2 to ⊙ 3 the extent 580 taken from the fame fcale of
equal parts the 1080 was taken from; and this line fhall
reprefent the fecond meafured diftance laid down in its true
pofition relative to the firft diftance.

Proceed in this manner from ftation to ftation until the line
⊙ 7 ⊙ 10 is drawn.

7th. Take from the fcale of equal parts 314, and apply this
extent in the line ⊙ 7 ⊙ 10 from ⊙ 7 to ⊙ 8, and the relative
point, where the eighth ftation was taken, will be reprefented
by the point ⊙ 8; then by the parallel ruler draw the line ⊙ 8
⊙ 5, in the direction of, and parallel to, the (fuppofed) radius
C8; and if the preceding work is accurately performed, this line
will

will not only pafs through the point ⊙ 5, but the length of the line ⊙ 8 ⊙ 5 will be equal to 510, as the ftation line was meafured in the field.

8th. Now as the 9th ftation falls on the fame point as the 5th ftation did, draw the line ⊙ 9 ⊙ 2, and this line will not only be parallel to the (fuppofed) radius C9, but will alfo meafured on the fcale of equal parts 390, the length meafured in the field from the 9th ftation.

9th. The 10th ftation is taken from the end of the line 700 meafured from the 7th ftation; therefore drawing from ⊙ 10 a line parallel to the (fuppofed) radius C 10, this line will concur with the firft meafured line at the diftance of 668 from the point ⊙ 10.

10th. Returning to ⊙ 10 again, the fame point is taken for the 11th ftation, and the line ⊙ 11 ⊙ 12 is to be drawn parallel to the (fuppofed) radius C 11, and to be made of the length of 800 from the fcale of equal parts; and this will give the point ⊙ 12 for the 12th ftation: Then drawing the line ⊙ 12 ⊙ 1, if the operation is every where truly done, this line will not only be parallel to the (fuppofed) radius C 12, but will alfo meafure on the fcale of equal parts 784, the fame as was meafured in the field in proceeding from ⊙ 12 to ⊙ 1.

By fuch methods as thefe, the furveyor obtains a cheque on his work, and can make his *furvey clofe* (as 'tis called) as he proceeds.

The drawing of the vifual lines of a furvey is, tho' an effential part, but a fmall ftep towards making a plan; for the remaining part of the work, the reader is refer'd to the treatifes already extant on that fubject.

What has been faid about the delineating of the vifual lines of a furvey, may be applied to navigation in the conftruction of a figure to reprefent the various courfes and diftances a fhip has failed in a given time, called traverfe failing; for the courfes are the bearings from the Meridian, and the diftances failed are of the fame kind as the diftance between ftation and ftation in a furvey.

S E C T.

# SECT. XV.

## *Some Uſes of the Logarithmic Scale of Numbers.*

BEFORE any operations can be performed by this ſcale, the notation, or the eſtimating of the values of the ſeveral diviſions, muſt be well known.

Let the ſector be quite opened, like a ſtreight ruler.

If the 1, at the beginning of the ſcale, or at the left hand of the firſt interval, be taken for unity, or 1; then the 1, in the middle, or at the end of the firſt interval and beginning of the ſecond, will expreſs the number 10; and the 10, at the end of the right hand end of the ſecond interval, or end of the ſcale, will repreſent the number 100. So that the diviſions of the beginning, middle and end, will repreſent numbers in the ratio of 1, 10, 100: So that

If the firſt is    10,   the middle is    100,   and the laſt   1000

             100, − − − − 1000, − − − 10000

Or − − − $\frac{1}{10}$ − − − − 1 − − − 10

            $\frac{1}{100}$ − − − − $\frac{1}{10}$ − − − 1

And the primary and intermediate diviſions in each interval, muſt be eſtimated according to the values ſet on their extremities, *viz.* at the beginning, middle and end of the ſcale.

In arithmetical multiplication, or diviſion; the parts may be conſidered as proportional terms; for in ſimple multiplication; as unity of 1, is to one factor, ſo is the other factor, to the product: And in diviſion; as the diviſor, is to unity; ſo is the dividend, to the quotient; or, as the diviſor, to the dividend; ſo is unity to the quotient.

Now as the common logarithms of numbers, expreſs how far the ratios of their correſponding numbers are diſtant from unity; it follows, that of thoſe numbers which are proportional, that is, have equal ratios; their correſponding logarithms will have equal intervals, or diſtances: and hence ariſes the rule for

working

working proportionals on the logarithmic fcale.

RULE. Set one foot of the compaffes on the point or divifion reprefenting the firft term, and extend the other foot to the point reprefenting the fecond term: Keep the compaffes thus opened; fet one foot on the point expreffing the third term, and the other foot will fall on the fourth term, or number fought.

EXAM. I. *What is the product of* 3 *by* 4 ?

SOLUTION. Set one foot on the 1 at the beginning, and extend the other to 3, in the firft interval; with this opening, fet one foot on 4, in the firft interval, and the other foot will reach to 12, found in the fecond interval.

*Obferve.* In this EXAM. the 1, 3, and 4, are values as units in the firft interval; and the one in the middle is 10; the diftance between this 1 or 10, and the 2 or 20, in the fecond interval, is divided into 10 principal parts, exprefs'd by the longer ftrokes; every one in the Exam. is taken as an unit; now as the point of the compaffes falls on the fecond of thefe principal parts, that is on 2 units beyond 10, therefore this point is efteemed in this Exam. as 12.

EXAM. II. *What is the product of* 40 *by* 3 ?

SOLUTION. In the firft interval, take the diftance between 1 and 3; and this diftance will reach from (4 or) 40 in the firft interval to (12 or) 120 in the fecond interval.

*Obferve.* The 1 and 3 in the firft interval, are taken as units: but as the values given to the primary divifions in either interval, may as well be call'd tens, as units; and the 4 being taken as 40, the 1 at the beginning of the fecond interval will be 100; and the 2 in the fecond interval will be 200; confequently the principal divifions between this 1 and 2 will exprefs 10; and fo the fecond of them will be 20, which with the 100, exprefs'd by the 1, makes 120.

EXAM. III. *What is the product of* 35 *by* 24 ?

SOLUTION. The diftance from 1 in the firft interval, to 24 in the fecond, will reach from 35 in the firft interval, to 840 in the fecond.

fecond.

*Obferve.* In the firft application of the compaffes, the primary divifions in the firft interval are taken as units, and thofe in the fecond interval, as tens: But in the fecond application, the primary divifions in the firft interval are reckon'd as tens; and thofe in the fecond, as hundreds.

As the extent out of one interval into the other, may fometimes be inconvenient, it will be proper to fee in fuch cafes, how the example may be folved in one interval. Thus,

In either interval, take the extent from 1 to 2 $\frac{4}{10}$ (i. e. 24) and this extent, (in either interval) will reach from 3 $\frac{5}{10}$ (i. e. 35) to 8 $\frac{4,0}{10,0}$ (i. e. 840.)

In this operation; the fecond term is reckoned a tenth higher than the firft term; therefore, as it falls in the fame interval, the fourth term muft be a tenth higher than the third term.

EXAM. IV. *What is the product of 375 by 60 ?*

SOLUTION. The extent from 1 to 6, (or 60) in the firft interval will reach from 3 $\frac{7\frac{1}{2}}{10}$ ($= 3 \frac{75}{100}$ or 375) in the firft interval, to 2 $\frac{25}{100}$ in the fecond interval; which divifion muft be reckoned 22500: For had the point fell in the firft interval, it would have been one place more than the 375, becaufe 60 is one place more than 1; but as it falls in the fecond interval, every of whofe divifions is one place higher than thofe in the firft interval, therefore, it muft have two places more than 375, which is taken in the firft interval.

If the operations in thefe examples be well confidered, it will not be difficult to apply others to the fcale, and readily affign the value of the refult.

EXAM. V. *What will be the quotient of 36 divided by 4 ?*

SOLUTION. The extent from 4 to 1, in the firft interval, will read from 36 in the fecond interval to nine in the firft.

It is to be obferved, that when the fecond term is greater than

than the firſt term; the extents are reckoned from the left hand towards the right: and when the ſecond term is leſs than the firſt, the extents are taken from the right hand towards the left: that is, the extents are always counted the ſame way towards which the terms proceed.

EXAM. VI. *If* 144 *be divided by* 9; *what will be the quotient ?*
SOLUTION. The extent from 9 to 1, will reach from 144 to 36.

EXAM. VII. *If* 1728 *be divided by* 12; *what will be the quotient ?*
SOLUTION. The extent from 12 to 1, will reach from 1728 to 144.

EXAM. VIII. *To the numbers* 3, 8, 15; *find a fourth proportional.*
SOLUTION. The extent from 3 to 8; will reach from 15 to 40.

EXAM. IX. *To the numbers* 5, 12, 38; *find a 4th proportional.*
SOLUTION. The extent from 5 to 12; will reach from 38 to 91 $\frac{1}{5}$.

EXAM. X. *To the numbers* 18, 4, 364; *find a 4th proportional.*
SOLUTION. The extent from 18 to 4; will reach from 364 to 80 $\frac{8}{9}$.

EXAM. XI. *To two Numbers* 1 *and* 2; *to find a ſeries of continued proportions.*
SOLUTION. The extent from 1 to 2, will reach from 2 to 4; from 4 to 8 in the firſt interval; from 8 to 16 in the ſecond interval, from 16 to 32; from 32 to 64; &c. Alſo the ſame extent will read from 1 $\frac{1}{2}$ to 3; from 3 to 6; from 6 to 12; from 12 to 24; from 24 to 48; &c. And the ſame extent will reach from 2 $\frac{1}{2}$ to 5; from 5 to 10; from 10 to 20; from 20 to 40; &c. And in the like manner proceed if any ratio was given beſides that of 1 to 2.

This

This example is of ufe, to find if the divifions of the line of numbers, are accurately laid down on the fcale.

There are many other ufes to which this fcale of log. numbers are applicable, and on which feveral large treatifes have been wrote; but the defign here, is not to enter into all the ufes of the fcales on the fector, only to give a few examples thereof: but after all that has been faid, when examples are to be wrought whofe refults exceeds three places, 'tis beft to do it by the pen; for on inftruments, altho' they be very large ones, the loweft places of the anfwers, at beft, are but guefs'd at.

## SECT. XVI.

### *Some Ufes of the Scales of Log. Sines and Log. Tangents.*

THESE fcales are chiefly ufed in the folution of the cafes of plain and fpherical trigonometry, which will be fully exemplified hereafter: But in this place, it will be proper to fhew, how proportional terms are applied to the fcales.

In plane trigonometrical proportions, there are always four terms under confideration; fuppofe two fides and two angles, whereof, only three of the terms are given, and the fourth is required: Now the fides in plane trigonometry are always applied to the fcale of log. numbers; and the angles are either applied to the log. fines, or to the log. tangents; according as the fines or tangents are concerned in the proportion. Therefore, when among the three things given, if two of them be fides, and the other an angle; or if two terms be angles, and the other a fide.

RULE. On the fcale of log. numbers, take the extent between the divifions expreffing the fides; and this extent applied from the divifion expreffing the angle given, will reach to the divifion fhewing the angle required.

Or, the extent of the angles, taken on the fines or tangents, will reach from the fide given to the fide required, on the line of numbers.

So

So in fpherical trigonometry, where fome of the cafes are worked wholly on the fines, others partly on fines, and partly on tangents; the extent taken with the compaffes, between the firft and fecond terms, when thofe terms are of the fame kind, will reach from the third term to the fourth.

Or the extent from the firft term to the third, when they are of the fame kind, will reach from the fecond term to the fourth.

# SECT. XVII.

## *Some Ufes of the double Scales of Sines, Tangents, and Secants.*

# PROBLEM XX.

*Given the radius of a circle (fuppofe equal to 2 inches) required the fine, and tangent of* 28° 30' *to that radius.*

SOLUTION. Open the fector fo that the tranfverfe diftance of 90 and 90, on the fines; or of 45 and 45 on the tangents; may be equal to the given radius; *viz.* 2 inches: Then will the tranfverfe diftance of 28° 30', taken from the fines, be the length of that fine to the given radius; or if taken from the tangents, will be the length of that tangent to the given radius.

*But if the fecant of* 28° 30' *was required?*

Make the given radius two inches, a tranfverfe diftance to 0 and 0, at the beginning of the line of fecants; and then take the tranfverfe diftance of the degrees wanted, *viz.* 28° 30'.

*A Tangent greater than* 45 *degrees (fuppofe* 60 *degrees) is found thus.*

Make the given radius, fuppofe 2 inches, a tranfverfe diftance to 45 and 45 at the beginning of the fcale of upper tangents; and then the required degrees 60° 00' may be taken from this fcale.

The fcales of the upper tangents and fecants do not run quite to 76 degrees; and as the tangent and fecant may

fometimes

fometimes be wanted to a greater number of degrees than can be introduced on the fector, they may be readily found by the help of the annexed table of the natural tangents and fecants of the degrees above 75; the radius of the circle being unity.

| Degrees. | Nat. Tangent. | Nat. Secant. |
|---|---|---|
| 76 | 4,011 | 4,133 |
| 77 | 4,331 | 4,445 |
| 78 | 4,701 | 4,810 |
| 79 | 5,144 | 5,241 |
| 80 | 5,671 | 5,759 |
| 81 | 6,314 | 6,392 |
| 82 | 7,115 | 7,185 |
| 83 | 8,144 | 8,205 |
| 84 | 9,514 | 9,567 |
| 85 | 11,430 | 11,474 |
| 86 | 14,301 | 14,335 |
| 87 | 19,081 | 19,107 |
| 88 | 28,636 | 28,654 |
| 89 | 57,290 | 57,300 |

Meafure the radius of the circle ufed, upon any fcale of equal parts. Multiply the tabular number by the parts in the radius, and the product will give the length of the tangent or fecant fought, to be taken from the fame fcale of equal parts.

EXAM. *Required the length of the tangent and fecant of* 80 *degrees to a circle whofe radius, meafured on a fcale of* 25 *parts to an inch, is* 47 ½ *of thofe parts.*

Againft

|                              | tangent. | fecant. |
|------------------------------|----------|---------|
| Againſt 80 degrees ſtands     | 5,671    | 5,759   |
| The radius is                | 47,5     | 47,5    |

|          |          |
|----------|----------|
| 28355    | 28795    |
| 39697    | 40313    |
| 22684    | 23036    |

|            |            |
|------------|------------|
| 269,3725   | 273,5525   |

So the length of the tangent on the twenty-fifth ſcale will be 269 $\frac{1}{3}$ nearly. And that of the fecant about 273 $\frac{1}{2}$.

Or thus. The tangent of any number of degrees may be taken from the fector at once; if the radius of the circle can be made a tranſverſe diſtance to the complement of thoſe degrees on the lower tangent.

EXAM. *To find the tangent of 78 degrees to a radius of 2 inches.*

Make two inches a tranſverſe diſtance to 12 degrees on the lower tangents; then the tranſverſe diſtance of 45 degrees will be the tangent of 78 degrees.

In like manner the fecant of any number of degrees can be taken from the fines, if the radius of the circle can be made a tranſverſe diſtance to the cofine of thoſe degrees. Thus making two inches a tranſverſe diſtance to the fine of 12 degrees; then the tranſverſe diſtance of 90 and 90 will be the fecant of 78 degrees.

From hence it will be eaſy to find the degrees anſwering to a given line, expreſſing the length of a tangent or fecant, which is too long to be meaſured on thoſe ſcales, when the fector is fet to a given radius.

Thus. For a tangent, make the given line a tranſverſe diſtance to 45 and 45 on the lower tangents; then take the given radius and apply it to the lower tangents; and the degrees where it becomes a tranſverſe diſtance is the cotangent of the degrees anſwering to the given line.

And for a fecant. Make the given line a tranſverſe diſtance to 90 and 90 on the fines. Then the degrees anſwering to the given radius, applied as a tranſverſe diſtance on the fines, will
be

be the co-fine of the degrees anfwering to the given fecant line.

## PROBLEM XXI.

*Given the length of the fine, tangent, or fecant, of any degrees; to find the length of the radius to that fine, tangent, or fecant.*

Make the given length, a tranfverfe diftance to its given degrees on its refpective fcale: Then,

*In the fines.* The tranfverfe diftance of 90 and 90 will be the radius fought.

*In the lower tangents.* The tranfverfe diftance of 45 and 45, near the end of the fector, will be the radius fought.

*In the upper tangents.* The tranfverfe diftance of 45 and 45 taken toward the center of the fector on the line of upper tangents, will be the radius fought.

*In the fecant.* The tranfverfe diftance of o and o, or the beginning of the fecants, near the center of the fector, will be the radius fought.

## PROBLEM XXII.

*Given the radius and any line reprefenting a fine, tangent, or fecant; to find the degrees correfponding to that line.*

SOLUTION. Set the fector to the given radius, according as a fine, or tangent, or fecant is concerned.

Take the given line between the compaffes; apply the two feet tranfverfely to the fcale concerned, and flide the feet along till they both reft on like divifions on both legs; then will thofe divifions fhew the degrees and parts correfponding to the given line.

## PROBLEM XXIII.

*To find the length of a verfed fine to a given number of degrees, and a given radius.*

Make the tranfverfe diftance of 90 and 90 on the fines, equal

to

to the given radius.

Take the tranſverſe diſtance of the ſine complement of the given degrees.

If the given degrees are leſs than 90, the difference between the ſine complement and the radius, gives the verſed ſine.

If the given degrees are more than 90, the ſum of the ſine complement and the radius, gives the verſed ſine.

## PROBLEM XXIV.

*To open the legs of the ſector, ſo that the correſponding double ſcales of lines, chords, ſines, tangents, may make, each, a right angle.*

*On the lines,* make the lateral diſtance 10, a diſtance between 8 on one leg, and ſix on the other leg.

*On the ſines,* make the lateral diſtance 90, a tranſverſe diſtance from 45 to 45; or from 40 to 50; or from 30 to 60; or from the ſine of any degrees, to their complement.

*Or on the ſines,* make the lateral diſtance of 45 a tranſverſe diſtance between 30 and 30.

## PROBLEM XXV.

*To deſcribe an Ellipſis, having given* AB *equal to the longeſt diameter; and* CD *equal to the ſhorteſt diameter.*

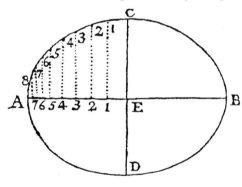

SOLUTION. 1ſt. Set the two diameters AB, CD, at right angles to each other in their middles at E.

2d. Make AE a tranſverſe diameter to 90 and 90 on the ſines; and take the tranſverſe diſtances of 10°, 20°, 30°, 40°, 50°, 60°, 70°, 80°, ſucceſſively, and apply thoſe diſtance to AE from E towards A, as at the points 1, 2, 3, 4, 5, 6, 7, 8; and thro' thoſe thofe points draw lines parallel to EC.

3d. Make EC a tranfverfe diftance to 90 and 90 on the fines; take the tranfverfe diftances of 80°, 70°, 60°, 50°, 40°, 30°, 20°, 10°, fucceffively, and apply thofe diftances to the parallel lines from 1 to 1, 2 to 2, 3 to 3, 4 to 4, 5 to 5, 6 to 6, 7 to 7, 8 to 8, and fo many points will be obtained thro' which the curve of the ellipfis is to pafs.

The fame work being done in all the four quadrants, the elliptical curve may be completed.

This Problem is of confiderable ufe in the conftruction of folar Eclipfes; but inftead of ufing the fines to every ten degrees, the fines belonging to the degrees and minutes correfponding to the hours, and quarter hours are to be ufed.

## PROBLEM XXVI.

*To defcribe a Parabola whofe parameter fhall be equal to a given line.*

SOLUTION.    1ft. Draw a line to reprefent the axis, in which make AB equal to half the given parameter; divide AB like a line of fines to every ten degrees, as to the points 10, 20, 30, 40, 50, &c. and thro' thefe points draw lines at right angles to the axis AB.

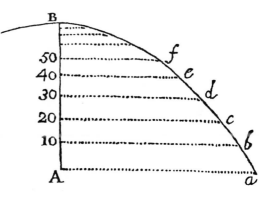

2d. Make the lines A*a*, 10*b*, 20*c*, 30*d*, 40*e*, &c. refpectively equal to the chords of 90°, 80°, 70°, 60°, 50°, &c. to the radius AB, and the points *a*, *b*, *c*, *d*, *e*, &c. will be in the curve of the parabola.

The like work may be done on both fides of the axis when the whole curve is wanted.

As the chords on the fector run no farther than 60°, thofe of

7°,

70, 80 and 90 may be found by taking the tranfverfe diftance of the fines of 35°, 40°, 45° to the radius AB, and applying thofe diftances twice along the lines 20*c*, 10*b*, &*c.*

## PROBLEM XXVII.

*To defcribe an Hyperbola, the vertex* A *and affymtopes* BH, BI, *being given.*

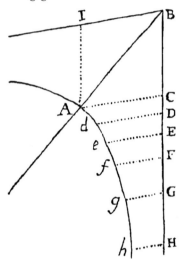

SOLUTION. 1ft. The affymtopes BH, BI, being drawn in any pofition, the line BA, bifecting the angle IBH, and the vertex A taken, draw AI, AC, parallel to BH, BI.

2d. Make AC a tranfverfe diftance to 45 and 45 on the upper tangents, and apply to the affymptotes from B, fo many of the upper tangents taken tranfverfely as may be thought convenient, as BD 50°, BE 55°, BF 60°, BG 65°, BH 70°, &*c.* and draw D*d*, E*e*, &*c.* parallel to AC.

3d. Make AC a tranfverfe diftance to 45 and 45 on the lower tangents, take the tranfverfe diftance of the co-tangents before ufed, and lay them on thofe parallel lines; thus make D*d* = 40°, E*e* = 35°, F*f* = 30°, G*g* = 25°, H*h* = 20°, &*c.* and thro' the points A, *d*, *e*, *f*, *g*, *h*, &*c.* If a curve line be drawn it will be the hyperbola required.

There are many other methods of conftructing the curves in the three laft problems, and a multitude of entertaining and ufeful properties fubfifting among the lines drawn within and about thefe curves; which the inquifitive reader may find in the treatifes on conic fections.

PROBLEM

# PROBLEM XXVIII.

*To find the diftance of places on the terreftrial globe, by having given their latitude and longitudes.*

This problem confifts of fix cafes.

CASE I. If both the places are under the equator.
Then the difference of longitude is their diftance.

CASE II. When both places are under the fame meridian.
Then the difference of latitude is their diftance.

CASE III. When only one of the places has latitude, but both have different longitudes.

EXAM. *Ifland of* Bermudas, *lat.* 32° 25′ N. *longit.* 68° 38′ W. *Ifland of* St. Thomas, *lat.* o o, *longit.* 1° o E. *Required their diftance.*

SOLUTION. 1ft. With the chord of 60° defcribe a circle reprefenting the equator, wherein take a point C to reprefent the beginning of longitude.

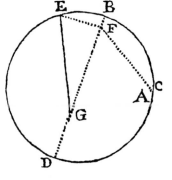

2d. From C apply the chord of *Bermudas* longitude 68° 38′ to B, and that of *St. Thomas's* longitude to A, the arc AB, being the difference of the longitude.

3d. From B, the place having latitude, draw the diameter BD, apply the chord of the latitude 32° 25′ from B to E, and draw EF at right angles to BD.

4th. Draw FC, make FG, equal to FC, and draw EG meafured on the chords will give the diftance fought, about 73 degrees.

CASE IV. When the given places are in the fame parallel of latitude.

EXAM.

EXAM. *Required the diftance between the* Lizard *and* Pengwin *Ifland, both in latitude* 49° 56′ N. *the longitude of the* Lizard *being* 5° 14′ W. *and that of* Pengwin *Ifland* 50° 32′ W.

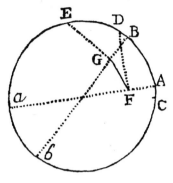

SOLUTION. 1ft. From C, the commencement of the longitude, apply the chord of the *Lizard*'s longitude to A, and of *Pengwin*'s longitude to B, and draw the diameters A*a*, B*b*.

Apply the chord of the common latitude 49° 56′ from A to D, and from B to E; draw DF and EG at right angles to A*a*, B*b*, and join GF; then GF meafured on the chords will give the diftance fought, about 29 degrees.

CASE V. When the given places are on the fame fide of the equator, but differ both in latitude and longitude.

EXAM. *What is the diftance between* London *in latitude* 51° 32′ N. *longitude,* 0° 0′ *and* Bengal *in latitude* 22° 0′ N. *longitude* 92° 45′ E.

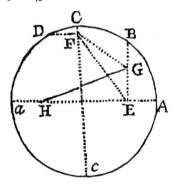

SOLUTION. 1ft. From A, *London*'s longitude, apply *Bengal*'s longitude 92° 45′ to C, taken from the chords; alfo apply the chord of *London*'s latitude from A to B, and of *Begnal*'s latitude from C to D.

2d. Draw the diameters A*a*, C*c*, and BE, DF, at right angles to A*a*, C*c*, and join FE.

3d. Make BG equal to DF, and EH equal to EF, join GH; Then GH meafured on the chords will give the diftance required, which is about 72 degrees.

CASE VI. When the places are on contrary fides of the equator, and differ both in latitude and longitude.

EXAM. *What is the diftance between* London *in latitude* 51°

32′

32′ N. *longitude* 0° 0′ *and* Cape-Horn *in latitude* 55° 42′ S. *longitude* 66° 0′ W.

SOLUTION. 1ſt. From A, *London*'s longitude, apply the chord of *Cape-Horn*'s longitude to C, draw the diameters Aa, Cc, alſo apply the chords of *London*'s latitude from A to B, and of *Horn*'s latitude from C to D.

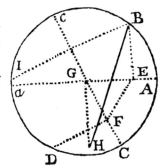

2d. Draw BE and DF at right angles to Aa, Cc; join EF and make EG equal to EF.

3d. At right angles to Aa, draw GH, and make it equal to DF; join BH, which meaſured on the chords will give the diſtance required, which is about 123 degrees.

*To meaſure* BH *on the chords*; apply BH from B to I, and meaſure the arc BcI.

## S E C T.  XVIII.

### *The Uſe of ſome of the ſingle and double Scales, applied in the Solution of the Caſes of plain Trigonometry.*

## P R O B L E M  XXIX.

*I*N *a right lin'd triangle, any three of the ſix terms, viz. ſides and angles, (provided one of them be a ſide) being given, to find the other three.*

This problem conſiſts of three caſes.

CASE I. When among the things given, there be a ſide and its oppoſite angle.

CASE II. When there is given two ſides and the included angle.

CASE III. When the three ſides are given.

SOLUTION

## SOLUTION *of* C A S E  I.

The Solution of the examples falling under this cafe depend on the proportionality there is between the fides of plane triangles, and the fides of the oppofite angles.

### EXAMPLE I. Pl. VI. Fig. 26.

In the triangle ABC: Given $\begin{array}{l} \text{AB} = 56 \\ \text{AC} = 64 \end{array}$ } equal parts.

$$\angle\text{B} = 46° \ 30'$$

Required $\angle$C, $\angle$A, & BC.

The proportions are as follow,

As fide AC : fide AB :: fine $\angle$B : fine $\angle$C.

Then the fum of the angles B and C being taken from 180° will leave the angle A.

And as fine $\angle$B : fine $\angle$A :: fide AC : fide CB.

#### *Firft by the logarithmic fcales.*

#### *To find the angle* C.

The extent from 64 (= AC) to 56 (= AB) on the fcales of logarithm numbers, will reach from 46° 30' (= $\angle$B) to 39° 24', (= $\angle$C) on the fcale of logarithmic fines.

And the fum of 46° 30' and 39° 24' is 85° 54'.

Then 85° 54' taken from 180°, leaves 94° 6' for the angle A.

#### *To find the fide* BC.

The extent from 46° 30' (= $\angle$B) to 85° 54' the fupplement of 94° 6' (= $\angle$A) on the fcale of log. fines, will reach from 64 (= AC), to 88 (= BC), on the fcale of logarithm numbers.

#### *Secondly by the double Scales.*

#### *To find the Angle* C.

1. Take the lateral diftance of 64 (= AC) from the lines.

2. Make

2. Make this a tranfverfe diftance of 46° 30′ (= ∠B) on the fines.

3. Take the lateral diftance of 56 (= AB) on the lines.

4. Find the degrees to which this extent is a tranfverfe diftance on the fines, *viz.* 39° 24′; and this is the angle fought.

### To find the fide BC.

1. Take the lateral diftance of 64 (= AC) from the lines.

2. Make this a tranfverfe diftance of 46° 30′ (= ∠B) on the fines.

3. Take the tranfverfe diftance of 85° 54′ (the fupplement of 94° 6′ = ∠A) on the fines.

4. Find the lateral diftance this extent is equal to on the lines; and this diftance, *viz.* 88, will be the fide required.

Ex. II. In the triangle ABC, Pl. VI. Fig. 27.

Given BC = 74
∠B = 104° 0′
∠C =  28  0

Required AB & AC.

Now the fum of 104° 0′ and 28° 0′ is 132° 0′.

And 132° 0′ taken from 180, leaves 48° 0′ for the angle A.

As fine ∠A : fine ∠C :: fide BC : fide AB.

And as fine ∠A : fine ∠B :: fide BC : fide AC.

### Firft, by the Logarithmic Scales.

### To find AB.

The extent from 48° 0′ (= ∠A) to 28° 0′ (= ∠C) on the fcale of logarithm fines, will reach from 74 (= BC) to 46,75, (= AB,) on the fcale of logarithm numbers.

### To find AC.

The extent from 48° 0′ to 76° 0′ (= fupplement of 104° 0′) on the fcale of log. fines, will reach from 74 to 96,6 (= AC) on the fcale of logarithm numbers.

*Secondly*

*Secondly by the double Scales.*

### *To find* AB.

1. Take the lateral diſtance of 74 (= BC) from the lines.

2. Make this extent a tranſverſe diſtance to 48° o′ (= ∠A) on the ſines.

3. Take the tranſverſe diſtance of 28° o′ (= ∠C) on the ſines.

4. To this extent find the lateral diſtance on the lines, *viz.* 46,75 and this will be the length of AB.

### *To find* AC.

1. Take the lateral diſtance of 74 (= BC) from the lines.

2. Make this extent a tranſverſe diſtance to 48° o′ (= ∠A) on the ſines.

3. Take the tranſverſe diſtance to 76° o′ the ſupplement of 104° o′ (= ∠B) on the ſines.

4. To this extent, find the lateral diſtance on the lines, *viz.* 96,6, and this will be the length of AC.

## SOLUTION *of* CASE II.

The ſolution of this caſe depends on a well known theorem, *viz*.

As the ſum of the given ſides

Is to the difference of thoſe ſides,

So is the tangent of the half ſum of the unknown angles.

To the tangent of the half difference of thoſe angles.

And the angles are readily found, their half ſum and half difference being known.

Ex. III. In the triangle ABC, Pl. VI. Fig. 28.

Given BC = 74

BA = 52

∠B = 68° o′

Required ∠A; ∠C; & AC.

*Preparation.*

### *Preparation.*

Take the given angle 68° 0′ from 180°, and half the remainder, *viz.* 56° 0′ is the half fum of the unknown angles, which call z; and let x ftand for the half difference of thofe angles.

Alfo, find the fum of the given fides, *viz.* BC + BA = 126.

And take the difference of thofe fides, *viz.* BC − BA = 22.

Then the proportions are

As BC + BA : BC − BA :: *tan.* Z : *tan.* X.

Then the fum of Z and X gives the greater angle A.

The difference of Z and X gives the leffer angle C.

And as fine ∠C : fine ∠B :: fide BA :: fide AC.

### *Firft, by the Logarithmic Scales.*

#### *To find the tangent of* X.

Take the extent from 126 (= fum of the given fides) to 22 (= diff. of thofe fides) on the fcale of logarithm numbers; lay this extent from 45° 0′ to the left, on the logarithm tangents; ftay the loweft point, and bring that which refted on 45 degrees, to 56° 0′; remove the compafs, and this extent laid from 45° 0′ towards the left, gives 14° 31′ equal X.

Then the fum of 56° 0′ and 14° 31′ or 70° 31′ is the angle A.

And 14° 31′ taken from 56° 0′ leaves 41° 29′ for the angle C.

#### *To find* AC.

The extent from 41° 29′ (= ∠C) to 68° 0′ (= ∠B) on the logarithmic fines, will reach from 52 (= BA) to 72,75 (= AC) on the fcale of logarithm numbers.

In finding the tangent of (X, or) the half difference of the unknown angles, there were two applications of the compaffes to the fcale of tangents: Now this happens becaufe the upper tangents which fhould have been continued beyond 45°, or to the right hand, are laid down backwards, or to the left hand, among the lower tangents (the logarithmic tangents afcending

and

and defcending on both fides of 45°), and thereby the length of the fcale is kept within half the length neceffary to lay down all the tangents in order, from the left towards the right. But fuppofing they were fo laid down; then the point 56° 0′ will reach as far to the right of 45° as it does now to the left; and the extent on the numbers from 126 to 22 would reach from the point 56° taken on the right of 45°, to 14° 31′ at one application; the faid extent being applied from 45° downwards, will reach as far beyond 14° 31′, as is the diftance from 45° to 56°; therefore the legs of the compaffes being brought as much clofer as is that interval, will reach from 45° to the degrees wanted.

Indeed when the half fum is lefs than 45°, then the extent from the fum of the fides to their difference, will reach from the tangent of the half fum, downward, to the tangent of the half difference, at once.

And when the half fum of the unknown angles, and their half diftance, are both greater than 45°, then the extent from the fum of the fides to their difference, will reach from the tangent of the half fum of the angles, upwards (or to the right) to the tangent of the half difference of thofe angles, at once.

## *Secondly by the double Scales.*

Becaufe 126 the fum of the fides will be longer than the fcales of lines, therefore take 63, the half of 126, and 11, the half of 22, the difference of the fides; for the ratio of 63 to 11, is the fame as that of 126 to 22. Then,

1. Take the lateral diftance 63 on the fcales of lines.

2. Make this extent a tranfverfe diftance to 56 degrees, on the upper tangents.

3. Take the tranfverfe diftance of 45° on the upper tangents, and make this extent a tranfverfe diftance to 45° on the other tangents.

4. Take the lateral diftance 11, on the lines.

5. To this extent, find the tranfverfe diftance on the tangents, and this will be 14° 31′ = X.

And

And this is the manner of operation, when z is greater than 45 degrees, and x is lefs.

But when z { greater } than 45
& x are each { or lefs } degrees.

Then the third article of the foregoing operation is omitted.

Now having found the angles A and C, the fide AC may be found as in the firft or fecond examples.

But in this cafe, the third fide AC may be found without knowing the angles. Thus,

1. Take the lateral diftance of 34 deg. (the half of 68,) the given angle, from the fines.

2. Make this extent a tranfverfe diftance, to 30 on the fines.

3. With the fector thus opened, take the diftance from 74 on one leg, to 52 on the other leg, each reckon'd on the lines.

4. The lateral diftance, on the lines, of this extent, gives the fide AC = 72,75.

From the two firft articles of this operation, is learn'd how to fet the double fcales to any given angle.

When the included angle B is 90 degrees, the angles A and C are more readily found, as in the following example, whofe folution depends on this principle. That one of the given fides has the fame proportion to radius, as the other given fide has to the tangent of its oppofite angle.

Ex. IV. In the triangle ABC: Fig. 29.
Given AB = 45
BC = 65
∠B = 90°
Required ∠A; ∠C; & AC.

The proportions are,
*For the Angle* A.

As fide AB : fide BC :: *radius* : *tan.* ∠A.

And the ∠A taken from 90° leaves the ∠C, then AC may be found as directed in the laft examples.

*Firft*

### *Firſt by the logarithmic Scales.*

The extent from 45 (= AB) to 65 (= BC) on the numbers, will reach from 45 degrees to 55° 18′ (= ∠A) on the tangents.

Here the angle A is taken equal to 55° 18′, becauſe the ſecond term BC is greater than the firſt term AB: But if the terms were changed, and it was made BC to AB, then the degrees found would be 34° 42′ = ∠C.

### *Secondly by the double Scales.*

1. Take the lateral diſtance of the firſt term, from the lines.

2. Make this a tranſverſe diſtance to 45 deg. on the tangents.

3. Take the lateral diſtance of the ſecond term, from the lines.

4. The tranſverſe diſtance of this extent, found on the tangents, gives the degrees in the angles ſought.

If the firſt term is greater than the ſecond, then the lateral diſtance of the firſt term, muſt be ſet to 45 degrees on the lower tangents, and the lateral diſtance of the ſecond term, muſt be reckon'd on the ſame tangents.

But if the firſt term is leſs than the ſecond, then the lateral extent of the firſt term muſt be ſet to 45° on the upper tangents, and the lateral extent of the ſecond term muſt be reckon'd on the ſame tangents.

## Solution *of* CASE III.

In the triangle ABC: Fig. 30.

Given BC = 926

BA = 558

AC = 702

Requir'd ∠B, ∠C, ∠A.

There are uſually given for the ſolution of this caſe, by the logarithmic ſcales, two methods; the one beſt when all the

angles

angles are to be found, the other beft when one angle only is wanted; both methods will be here delivered.

FIRST. *When all the angles are wanted.*

Suppofe a perpendicular AD (Pl. VI. Fig. 30) drawn to the greateft fide BC, from the angle A oppofite thereto; then AD divides the triangles ABC into two right angled triangles BDA, CDA; in which if CD and DB were known, the angles would be found as in the folution of Cafe I.

Take the fum of the fides AC and AB, which is 1260.

Alfo their difference, which is 144.

Then on the fcale of numbers, the extent from 926 (= BC) to 1260, will reach from 144 to 196.

And the half fum of 926 and 196, is 561 = DC.

And the half difference of 926 and 196 is 365 = DB.

The extent from 558 (= BA) to 365 (= BD) on the numbers, will reach on the log. fines from 90° (= ∠BDA) to 40° 52′ (= ∠BAD.)

Then 40° 52′ taken from 90°, leaves 49° 8′ for ∠B.

And the extent from 702 (= CA) to 561 (= CD) on the numbers, will reach from 90° (= ∠CDA) to 53° 04′ (= ∠CAD) on the fcale of log. fines.

Then 53° 4′ taken from 90°, leaves 36° 56′ for the ∠C.

Alfo the fum of 40° 52′ and 53° 4′ gives 93° 56′ for the ∠CAB.

SECONDLY, *To find either angle; fuppofe* B.

Preparation.

Take the difference between BC and BA, the fides including the angles fought, and call it D = 368.

Find the half fum of AC and D, call it Z = 535.

And the half diff. of AC and D, call it X = 167.

Then as $1 : \sqrt{\dfrac{Z \times X}{AB \times BC}} ::$ radius : fine $\frac{1}{2}$ ∠B.

1. The

1. The extent on the log. numbers from 1 to 535 (= z), will reach from 167 (= x) to a 4th point = 89300; mark it and call it G.

2. The extent from 1 to 558 (= AB), will reach from 926 (= BC) to a fourth point = 516000; mark it and call it H.

3. The extent from the point H 516, to the point G 89,3, will reach from 1, downward, to a 4th point, 0,173 nearly; mark it and call it K.

4. The extent from K, to the middle point, above 0,415, between it, and the 1 next above K, taken on the log. numbers, will reach on the log. fines from 90° to 24° 34′, which doubled gives 49° 8′ for the angle B.

But the fcale of log. verfed fines being ufed, the work will be confiderably fhortened. Thus,

1. On the log. numbers take the extent from 535 (= z) to 926 (= BC), this will reach from 558 (= BA) to a 4th point, where let the foot of the compaffes reft.

2. Then the extent from that 4th point to 167 (= x), will reach on the line of verfed fines from 0 degrees (at the end) to 130° 52′, which taken from 180° leaves 49° 8′ for the angle B.

## By the double, or fectoral, Scales.

1. Take the lateral diftance 702 (= AC, the fide oppofite to the angle B) from the lines.

2. Open the legs of the fector until this extent will reach from 926 (= CB) on one fcale of lines, to 558 (= AB) on the other fcale of lines.

3. The fector being thus opened, take the tranfverfe diftance between 30° and 30° on the fines, this diftance meafured laterally on the fines, one foot being on the center, will give 24° 34′ for the half angle B.

The other angles may be found as ∠B was, or according to the directions in fome of the preceding cafes.

Although in thefe examples, oblique triangles were taken as being the moft general; yet it may be readily feen, that thofe concerning right-angled triangles are only particular cafes, and

may

may be for the general, more eafily folved.

Variety of other examples, fhewing the ufes of thefe fcales, might be given in various parts of the mathematics, which the reader may of himfelf fupply: However here will be fubjoined a few in fpherical trigonometry, as they will include fome operations not only curious, but perhaps not to be met with elfewhere; and they will be followed by a few examples in perfpective.

## SECT. XIX.

### *The Conftruction of the feveral cafes of Spherical Triangles by the Scales on the Sector.*

## PROBLEM XXX.

*In a fpherical Triangle, any three of the fix terms, viz. fides and angles, being given, to find the other three.*

THE cafes of fpherical triangles contained in this Problem are fix.

CASE I. Given two fides, and an angle oppofite to one of them.

CASE II. Given two angles, and a fide oppofite to one of them.

CASE III. Given two fides, and the included angle.

CASE IV. Given two angles, and the included fide.

CASE V. Given the three fides.

CASE VI. Given the three angles.

Thefe fix cafes include all the variety that can arife in fpherical triangles.

In the following folutions, are given three conftructions to every cafe, whereby each fide is laid on the plane of projection, or (as it is commonly called, the) primitive circle.

To abbreviate the directions given in the following conftructions,

ftructions, it is to be underftood, that the primitive circle is always firft defcribed, and two diameters drawn at right angles.

The fector is alfo fuppofed to be fet to the radius wanted, on the fcale ufed; and the tranfverfe diftance of the degrees propofed is to be taken from the chords, or fecants, or tangents, &c. according to the name mentioned in the conftruction.

## SOLUTION *of* C A S E  I.

EXAM. In the fpherical triangle ABD.
         Given AB = 29° 50′
               DB = 63  59
               ∠D = 25  55
    Required the triangle.

I. *To put* DB *on the primitive circle.* Fig. 1. 1. Pl. VII.

1ft. Make DB = chord of 63° 59′, and draw the diameter BE.

2d. From D, with the fecant of the ∠D, 25° 55′, cut the diameter ⊙ I in C: on C as a center, with that radius, defcribe the circumference DA, and the angle BDA will be 25° 55′.

3d. Make B*d* equal to AB, with the chord of 29° 50′.

4th. With the tangent of AB, 29° 50′, from *d*, cut ⊙ B produced in *b*; and from *b*, with that radius, cut DA in A or *a*.

5th. Through B, A, E, defcribe a circumference, and the triangle BDA will be that required; whofe parts DA, ∠B, and ∠A may be thus meafured.

### *To meafure* DA.

6th. Make ⊙ P equal to the tangent of half the angle BDA, *viz.* 12° 57 ½′; then a ruler on P and A, gives *e*; and D*e* meafured on the chords, gives the degrees, in DA, *viz.* 42° 9′.

### *To meafure* ∠B.

7th. Draw the diameter FG at right angles to BE, cutting the circumference BAE in *s*; a ruler by B & *s* gives *f*; make *fg* equal to the chord of 90 deg. a ruler on *g* and B, gives *p* in the dia-

meter

meter of FG. Then E*g* on the chords gives the angle B = 36° 9′.

### *To meafure* ∠A.

8th. A ruler on A and P, gives *n*; and on A and *p*, gives *m*; and *nm* meafured on the chords, gives 52° 9′, for the fupplement of the angle DAB, which is 127° 51′.

### II. *To put* DA *on the primitive circle*, Fig. 2. 1.

1ft. With the fecant of the angle D, 25° 55′, from D, cut the diameter in C; and on C, with the fame radius, defcribe the arc DB, and the angle BDA will be 25° 55′.

2d. Make ⊙ P equal to the tangent of half the angle D; *viz.* 12° 57 $\frac{1'}{2}$.

3d. On the primitive circle, make D*d* equal to the given fide DB, with the chord of 63° 59′.

4th. A ruler on P and *d*, gives B; then will BD = 63° 59′.

5th. Draw ⊙ B *r*, cutting the primitive circle in *r*.

6th. Make *rx* = the chord of 90°; or twice the chord of 45°.

7th. A ruler on *x* and B, gives *m* on the primitive circle.

8th. Make *mq* = *mp* = chord of 29° 50′.

9th. A right line through *x* & *p*, *x* & *q*, gives *f* & *e* in ⊙ *r*.

10th. On *fe* as a diameter, defcribe a circumference, cutting the primitive circle in A, *a*.

11th. A ruler on A & ⊙, gives F.

12th. Through A, B, F, defcribe a circumference, and the triangle ABD is conftructed with DA on the primitive circle as required.

### III. *To put* AB *on the primitive circle.* Fig. 3. 1.

1ft. Make AB = the chord of 29° 50′; and draw the diameter BF.

2d. In A*b*, drawn perpendicular to AG, take A*b* = fine of AB 29° 50′.

3d. Make the angle *b*A*g*, = ∠D 25° 55′; from A draw A*e* at right angles to A*g*, and from *d*, the middle of A*b*, draw *de* perpendicular to A*b*, cutting A*e*, in *e*; from *e*, with the radius *e*A, defcribe a circumference A*fb*.

4th.

4th. From *b*, with the fine of BD, 63° 59′, cut the circumference A*fb* in *f*; and draw A*f*.

5th. From A, draw AC at right angles to *f*A, meeting E ⊙ (perpendicular to A ⊙,) continued, in C; and on C, with the radius CA, defcribe a circumference ADG.

6th. Make B*m* = BD, with the chord of 63° 59′; from *m*, with the tangent of 63° 59′ cut ⊙ B produced in *n*; on *n*, with the fame radius, cut ADG in D.

7th. Through B, D, F, defcribe a circumference, and the triangle ABD will be that which was required.

### *Computation by the logarithmic fcales.*

### *To find the angle* A.

The fines of the angles of the fpheric triangles are proportional to the fines of their oppofite fides.

Then the extent of the compaffes on the line of fines from 29° 50′ (= AB) to 25° 55′ (= ∠D); will reach from the fine of 63° 59′ (= DB) to the fine of 52° 9′ (= ∠A).

But by conftruction the ∠A is obtufe; therefore 127° 51′ (the fupplement of 52° 9′) is to be taken for the angle A.

### *To find the angle* B.

Say, as radius, to the cofine of DB.

So tang. ∠D, to the cotang of a fourth arc.

And as tang. AB, to the tang. of DB.

So cofine of the 4th arc, to the cofine of a 5th arc.

Then the difference between the 4th and 5th arcs gives ∠B.

The extent from the fine of 90° to the fine of 26° 1′ (= comp. of 63° 59′), will, on the tangents, reach from 25° 55′ to 12° 2′: But the 4th arc is to be a cotangent; therefore 77° 58′ (the comp. of 12° 2′) is the 4th arc.

The extent from the tangent of 29° 50′ to the tangent of 63° 59′, will reach on the lines of fines from 12° 2′ (= comp. of 77° 58′) to 48° 9′.

But the 5th arc is to be a cofine; therefore 41° 51′ (the comp. of 48° 9′) is the fifth arc.

And

And 41° 51′ taken from 77° 58′ leaves 36° 7′ for the angle B.

The extent from the tangent of 29° 50′ to the tangent 63° 59′ is thus taken. Set one foot on the tangent 29° 50′, and extend the other to the tangent of 45°; Apply this extent on the tangents from 63° 59′ towards the left; reſt the left hand foot, and extend to the other to 45°, and the compaſs will then have the required extent.

### *To find* AC.

Say, as radius, to the coſine of the angle D.

So is the tangent of DB, to the tangent of a 4th arc.

And as coſine of DB, to the coſine of AB.

So is the coſine of the 4th arc, to the coſine of the 5th arc.

Then the difference between the 4th and 5th arcs will give the ſide AD.

The extent on the ſines from 90° to 64° 5′ (the comp. of 25° 55′) will reach on the tangents from 63° 59′ towards the right to 61° 31′ the 4th arc.

Alſo the extent on the ſines from 26° 1′ (= comp. of 63° 59′) to 60° 10′ (= comp. of 29° 50′) will reach from the ſine of 28° 29′ (the complement of 61° 31′) to the ſine of 70° 37′.

But the 5th arc is to be a coſine, therefore 19° 23′ is the fifth arc.

And 19° 23′ taken from 61° 31′ leaves 42° 8′ for the ſide AD.

## SOLUTION *of* CASE II.

EXAM. In the ſpherical triangle ABD.

Given AD = 42° 9′
$\angle$A = 127  50
$\angle$B = 36   8

Required the triangle.

I. *To put* DB *on the primitive circle.* Fig. 1. 2. Pl. VII.

1ſt. From B, with the ſecant of $\angle$B, 36° 8′, cut the diameter ⊙ E in C; on C, with the ſame radius, deſcribe the circumference B*a*F: then the angles DBF = the given $\angle$B.

2d.

2d. Make the angle *naq* equal to 37° 50′, the difference between 127° 50′ and 90°.

3d. Make *aq* = tangent of DA, 42° 9′; on ⊙ with the fecant of 42° 9′ defcribe an arc *q*Q: on C with C*q*, cut the arc *q*Q in Q.

4th. Draw Q ⊙ G cutting the primitive circle in D, and BD will be a fide of the triangle.

5th. From Q with Q*a*, cut B*a*F in A; and through D, A, G, defcribe a circumference, and the triangle BAD is that required. Whofe parts BD, BA and ∠B are thus meafured.

6th. BD meafured on the chords, gives 64 degrees.

7th. Make ⊙ P = tangent of half ∠B, *viz.* 18° 4′; a ruler on P and A gives *x*; then B*x* meafured on the chords gives 29° 50′, for BA.

8th. Draw a diameter perpendicular to GD, cutting the circumference DAG in *s*; a ruler on D and *s* gives *m*; make *mn* 90 degrees, then G*n* meafured on the chords, gives 25° 55′ for the ∠D.

## II. *To put* AB *on the primitive circle.* Fig. 2. 2.

1ft. From A, with the fecant of the fupplement of the ∠A, *viz.* 52° 10′, cut the diameter ⊙ F continued in C; on C, with the fame radius, defcribe a circumference A*a*E.

2d. Make ⊙ P = the tangent of half the fupplement of ∠A, *viz.* 26° 5′; and make A*x* = chord of AD, 42° 9′: a ruler on P and *x*, gives D; then is AD equal to 42° 9′.

3d. On ⊙, with the tangent of the angle B, 36° 8′, defcribe an arc *mc*; on D, with the fecant of ∠B, 36° 8′, cut the arc *mc* in *c*; on *c*, with the fame radius, defcribe a circumference DB, then the triangle ADB, will be that required.

## III. *To put* DA *on the primitive circle.* Fig. 3. 2.

1ft. Lay down AD with the chord of 42° 9′: Draw the diameter DF; and another ⊙ H, perpendicular to DF.

2d. On A, with the fecant of the fupplement of ∠A, *viz.* 52° 10′, cut the diameter E ⊙ in C; and on C, with the fame radius, defcribe the circumference ABG.

3d. Make ⊙ P equal to the tangent of half the fupplement

∠A,

∠A, *viz.* 26° 5′, a ruler by G and P gives *x*.

4th. Make *xm* = *xn* with the chord of ∠B, 36° 8′; a ruler by G and *n* gives *r*, by G and *m* gives *s*; on *b* the middle of *rs*, with the radius *bs*, cut ⊙ H in *p*.

5th. A ruler on F and *p*, gives *h*; make *hk* = *h*D; a ruler on F and *k* gives *c*; with the radius *c*D, defcribe the circumference DBF; and the triangle ABD, is that fought.

## *Computation by the Logarithmic Scales.*

### *To find the fide* BD.

Say, as the fine of ∠B, is to the fide AD;
So is the fine of ∠A, to the fide BD.

Then the extent from the fine of 36° 8′ to the fine of 42° 9′, will reach from the fine of 52° 10′ (the fupplement of 127° 50′) to the fine of 63° 59′ = fide BD.

### *To find the fide* AB.

Say, as the radius, is to the cofine of the ∠A.
So is the tangent of AD, to the tangent of the 4th arc.
And, as the tangent of ∠B, to the tangent of ∠A;
So is the fine of the 4th arc, to the fine of the 5th arc.

Then the difference between the 4th and 5th arcs will be equal to the fide AB.

The extent from the radius, or the fine of 90° to the fine of 37° 50′ (the complement of 52° 10′), will reach on the tangents from 42° 9′ to 29° 02′ = 4th arc.

And the extent from the tangent of 36° 8′ to the tangent of 52° 10′, will reach on the fines from 29° 02′, to 58° 54′ = 5th arc.

Then the difference between 58° 54′ and 29° 02′, gives 29° 52′ for the fide AB.

The extent from the tangent of 36° 8′ to the tangent of 52° 10′ is taken as fhewed in the fecond operation of the firft cafe.

### *To find the* ∠D.

Say, as the radius is to the cofine AD.

So

So is the tangent of ∠A, to the tangent of a 4th arc.

And as the cofine of ∠A, to the cofine of ∠B;

So is the fine of the 4th arc, to the fine of the 5th arc.

Then the difference between the 4th and 5th arcs will give the ∠D.

Now the extent from the fine of 90° to the fine of 47° 51′ (the complement of 42° 09′) will reach from the tangent of 52° 10′ to the tangent of 43° 40′. But the 4th arc being a cotangent will be 46° 20′, the complement of 43° 40′.

Alfo the extent from the fine of 37° 50′ (the complement of 52° 10′) to the fine of 53° 52′ (the complement of 36° 08′), will reach from the fine of 46° 20′ to the fine of 72° 15′ the 5th arc.

Then the difference between 72° 15′ and 46° 20′, *viz.* 25° 55′ will be the angle D.

In applying the firft extent, *viz.* from the fine of 90° to the fine of 47° 51′, to the tangents; fet one foot on the tangent of 45° and let the other foot reft where it falls; move the foot from 45° to 52° 10′; then this extent will reach from 45° to 43° 40′.

## SOLUTION *of* CASE III.

Ex. In the fpherical triangle ABD:

Given AB = 29° 50′

BD = 63   59

∠B = 36    8

Required the triangle.

I. *To put* AB *on the primitive circle.* Fig. 1. 3. Pl. VII.

1ft. Make AB = chord of 29° 50′, draw the diameter BF, and another ⊙ E perpendicular thereto.

2d. From B, with the fecant of ∠B, 36° 8′ cut ⊙ E in C, the center of BDF.

3d. From ⊙, with the tangent of half ∠B, *viz.* 18° 4′ cut ⊙ E in P, the pole of BDF.

4th. Make Bx = BD, 63° 59′; a ruler on P and x gives D. Through A, D, G, defcribe a circumference, and the triangle ADB is that required, whofe parts AD, ∠A, and ∠D may be thus meafured.

meafured.

5th. A ruler on A and *s* gives *z*, make *zy* = chord of 90°; a ruler on A and *y* gives *p* the pole of A*s*G; a ruler on *p* and D, gives *n*, and A*n* meafured on the chords gives 42° 8′ for AD.

6th. G*y* meafured on the chords, gives 52° 11′ for the fupplement of ∠A; therefore ∠A = 127° 49′.

7th. A ruler on D and *p* gives *r*, on D and P, gives *m*; and *rm*, meafured on the chords gives 25° 56′ for the angle BDA.

II. *To put* DB *on the primitive circle.* Fig. 2. 3.

1ft. Make DB = chord of 63° 59′: draw the diameter BF, and perpendicular thereto, the diameter ⊙ G.

2d. From B, with the fecant of ∠B, 36° 8′, cut ⊙ G in C; on C with CB, defcribe the circumference BAF.

3d. Make ⊙ P = tangent of half ∠B, 18° 4′, and D*x* = chord of AB 29° 50′, a ruler on P and *x* gives A; through D, A, E, defcribe a circumference, and the triangle ABD is that required.

III. *To put* AD *on the primitive circle.* Fig. 3.3.

1ft. In a right line *ed*, touching the primitive circle in any point *b*, take *bd* = tangent of BD, 63° 59′; and *be* = tangent of AB, 29° 50′.

2d. Make the angles *dba* = ∠B, 36° 8′, and make *ba* = *be*.

3d. From *d*, ⊙, with D*a*, ⊙ *e*, defcribe arcs croffing in *x*; from *x*, *d*, draw the diameters AE, DF; and others OG, OH, perpendicular to AE, FD.

4th. From *d*, *x*, with *bd*, *eb*, defcribe arcs croffing in B; and draw *d*B, *x*B.

5th. From B draw BC, perpendicular to *x*B, and meeting in ⊙ G produced in C; alfo draw B*c* perpendicular to *d*B, and meeting ⊙ H in *c*; then C is the center of a circumference through A, B, E; and *c* the center of that through D, B, F; and the triangle ABD is that required.

*Computation*

## *Computation by the Logarithmic Scales.*

### *To find the angles* A *and* C.

Say as the fine of half the fum of the given fides
To the fine of half their difference;
So is the cotangent of half the given angle
To the tangent of half the difference of the required angles.
And, as the cofine of half the fum of the given fides
To the cofine of half their difference;
So is the cotangent of half the given angle
To the tangent of half the fum of the required angles.

Then the half difference of the required angles added to their half fum will give the greater angle A.

And the half difference of thofe angles taken from their half fum will give the leffer angle D.

Now the fum of the given fides 63° 59′ and 29° 50′ is 93° 49′, their difference is 34° 09′; the half fum = 46° 54½′, and the half difference is 17° 04½′.

Alfo half the given angle is 18° 04′.

Then the extent from the fine of 46° 54′ to the fine of 17° 4′, will reach from the tangent of 71° 56′, (the complement of 18° 4′) to the tangent of 50° 57′ the half difference of the required angles.

Here the extent on the fines is from right to left or decreafing; fo the extent on the tangents muft be from left to right, which in this cafe is decreafing.

Alfo, the extent from the fine of 43° 6′ (the complement of 46° 54′) to the fine of 72° 56′ (the complement of 17° 04′), will on the fcale on tangents reach from 71° 56′ (the complement of 18° 4′) to 76° 53′ the half fum of the required angles.

Then the fum of 76° 53′ and 50° 57′ = 127° 50′ = ∠A.

And the difference of 76° 53′ and 50° 57′ = 25° 56′ = ∠C.

The angles being known, the other fide may be found by oppofite fides and angles, and is 42° 08′.

Or the other fide may be found without knowing the angles.

Say,

Say, as radius is to the cofine of the given angle;

So is the tangent of either given fide, to the tangent of a 4th arc.

Which 4th arc will be like the fide ufed when the given angle is acute; otherwife it will be of a contrary kind with the fide ufed.

Then take the difference between the 4th arc and the other given fide, call the remainder a 5th arc.

And as the cofine of the 4th arc is to the cofine of a 5th arc;

So is the cofine of the fide ufed in the former proportion

To the cofine of the fide required.

Now the extent from the fine of 90° to the fine of 53° 52′ (= complement of 36° 08′) will reach from the tangent of 29° 50′ to the tangent of 24° 51′ the 4th arc.

And 24° 51′ taken from 63° 59′ leaves 39° 8′ for the 5th arc.

Then the extent from the fine of 65° 09′ (the complement of 24° 51′) to the fine of 50° 52′ (the complement of 39° 08′) will reach from the fine of 60° 10′ (the complement of 29° 50′) to the fine of 47° 51′; whofe complement, *viz.* 42° 09′ is the fide required.

## Solution *of* C A S E  IV.

Ex. In the fpherical triangle ABD:
$$\text{Given } \angle D = 25° 55'.$$
$$\angle B = 36° 08'.$$
$$DB = 63° 59'.$$
Required, The triangle.

I. *To put* DB *on the primitive circle.* Fig. 1. 4. Pl. VII.

1ft. Make DB = chord of 63° 59′; draw the diameter BF, and draw ⊙ G perpendicular to BF.

2d. From B, with the fecant of ∠B, 36° 8′, cut ⊙ G in C; and C will be the center of BAF.

3d. From D, with the fecant of ∠D, 25° 55′; cut ⊙ H in *c*, and *c* will be the center of DAE; and the triangle DAB is that which was required; whofe parts DA, BA, and ∠A, are thus meafured.

4th.

4th. Make ⊙ $p$ = tangent of $\frac{1}{2}$ ∠D, 12° 57 $\frac{1}{2}'$, a ruler on $p$ and A gives $x$; then D$x$ meaſured on the chords gives 42° 10′ for AD.

5th. Make ⊙ P = tangent of $\frac{1}{2}$ ∠B, 18° 4′, a ruler on P and A, gives $z$; then B$z$ meaſured on the chords, gives 29° 54′ for AB.

6th. A ruler on A and $p$, gives $n$, on A and P, gives $m$; and $nm$ meaſured on the chords gives 52° 10′ the ſupplement of the angle A. Therefore ∠A = 127° 50′.

II. *To put* DA *on the primitive circle.* Fig. 2. 4.

1ſt. From D, with the ſecant of ∠D, 25° 55′; cut ⊙ F in C; and C is the center of the circumference DBE.

2d. Make ⊙ P = tangent of $\frac{1}{2}$ ∠D, 12° 57 $\frac{1}{2}'$; and make D$x$ = chord of BD, 63° 59′; a ruler on P, $x$, gives B; and DB is 63° 59′.

3d. make the angle CB$c$ = ∠B, 36° 8′; through C, draw $mc$ perpendicular to B ⊙, cutting B$c$ in $c$; on $c$, with the radius $c$B, deſcribe the circumference ABG; and the triangle ABD, is that which was required.

III. *To put* AB *on the primitive circle.* Fig. 3. 4.

1ſt. From B, with the ſecant of ∠B, 36° 8′ cut ⊙ F in C; and C is the center of the circumference of BDE.

2d. Make B$x$ = chord of BD, 63° 59′; and ⊙ P = tangent of $\frac{1}{2}$ ∠B, 18° 4′; a ruler on P and $x$ gives D; then is BD = 63° 59′.

3d. Make the angle CD$c$ = ∠D, 25° 55′; then $mc$ drawn perpendicular to ⊙ D, meeting D$c$ in $c$, gives $c$ the center of the circumference ADG; and the triangle ABD will be that required.

### *Computation by the Logarithmic Scales.*

#### *To find the angle* A.

Say, as the radius is to the coſine of the given ſide;

So is the tangent of either given angle to the cotangent of a 4th arc.

Call the difference between the other given angle and the 4th arc, the 5th arc.

And as the ſine of the 4th arc, is to the ſine of the 5th arc;

So is the coſine of the angle uſed in the former proportion

To

To the cofine of the required angle.

The 4th arc will be of the fame kind with the angle firft ufed, if the given fide is lefs than 90°; but of a contrary kind if that fide is greater than 90°.

Arcs are faid to be of the fame kind, when both are lefs, or both greater, than 90 degrees.

The required angle will be of the fame kind with the angle ufed in the proportions, if the 4th arc is lefs than the other angle; but of an unlike kind when the 4th arc is greater than the other angle.

Now the extent from the fine of 90° to the fine of 26° 01′ (the complement of 63° 59′) will reach from the tangent of 25° 55′ to the tangent of 12° 02′: But this is the complement of the 4th arc, which is 77° 58′.

And 36° 08′ taken from 77° 58′ leaves 41° 50′ for the 5th arc.

Then the extent from the fine of 77° 58′ to the fine of 41° 50′, will reach from the fine of 64° 5′ (the complement of 25° 55′) to the fine of 37° 50′, which is the complement to 52° 01′.

But as the 4th arc was greater than 36° 08′, the angle fought is to be of a contrary kind to 25° 55′ (= ∠D,) that is, that A is to be obtufe; fo 127° 50′ (the fupplement of 52° 10′) is to the taken for the angle A.

Now all the angles and one fide being known, the other fides may be found by the proportion fubfifting between the fines of angles, and the fines of their oppofite fides.

Or fay,

As the fine of half the fum of the given angles
Is to the fine of half the difference of thofe angles;
So is the tangent of half the given fide
To the tangent of half the difference of the required fides.

And

As the cofine of half the fum of the given angles
Is to the cofine of half the difference of thofe angles;
So is the tangent of half the given fide,
To the tangent of half the fum of the required fides.

Then the half difference added to the half fum, gives the greater of the fought fides.

And

And the half difference fubtracted from the half fum, gives the leffer of the fought fides.

Now the half fum of the given angles, *viz.* ½ ∠D + ½ ∠B = 31° 01 ½',

And the half difference of thofe angles, *viz.* ½ ∠D – ½ ∠B = 5° 6½',

Alfo the half of the given fide DB, is 31° 59 ½'.

Then the extent from the fine of 31° 1', to the fine of 5° 6';

Will reach from the tangent of 31° 59', to the tangent of 6° 3'.

And the extent from the fine of 58° 59' (= complement of 31° 01') to the fine of 84° 54' (the complement of 5° 6'), will reach from the tangent of 31° 59' to the tangent of 35° 58'.

Then the fum of 35° 58' and 6° 3', *viz.* 42° 01' = AD.

And the difference of 35° 58' and 6° 3', *viz.* 29° 55' = AB.

## SOLUTION *of* C A S E  V.

EX. In the fpherical triangle ABD.
          Given  AB = 29° 50'
                 AD = 42    9
                 BD = 63   59
     Requir'd, The triangle.

I. *To put* AB *on the primitive circle.* Fig. 1. 5. Pl. VII.

1ft. Make AB = chord of 29° 50'; draw the diameter BF.

2d. Make A*n* = chord of AD, 42° 9'; and B*m* = chord of BD, 63° 59'.

3d. From *n*, with the tangent of AD, 42° 9', cut EA produced in C; and from C, with that radius, defcribe the arc *nm*; from *m*, with the tangent of BD, 63° 59', cut FB produced in *c*; and from *c*, with the radius *cm*, cut the arc *nm* in D.

4th. Through A, D, E; B, D, F, defcribe the circumferences, and the triangle ADB is that which was required; whofe angles A, B, D, are thus meafured.

5th. A ruler on A and *a*, gives *x*; on B and *b*, gives *z*; make *xy*, *zv*, each 90°; a ruler on A and *y* gives P, in a radius
                                              perpendicular

perpendicular to AE; and a ruler on B and *v* gives *p*, in a radius perpendicular to BF.

6th. E*y* meafured on the chords, gives 52° 12′ for the fupplement of the ∠A; therefore ∠A = 127° 48′.

7th. F*v* meafured on the chords, gives 36° 10′ for the angle B.

8th. A ruler on D and P gives *t*, and on D and *p* gives *s*; then *ts* meafured on the chords, gives 25° 58′ for the angle D.

The fides AD, DB, are put on the primitive circle, by a conftruction fo like the foregoing one, that it is needlefs to repeat it. See figures 2. 5. and 3. 5.

### *Computation by the Logarithmic Scales.*

#### *To find the angle* A.

The fides including angle A are    AD = 42° 09′
And AB = 29   50
_____
Their difference call X   = 12   19
The fide oppofite the ∠A is BD = 63   59

Then the fum of BD and X is 76° 18′; the half fum is 38° 09′.

And the difference of BD and X is 51° 40′; the half difference is 25° 50′.

Now take the extent on the line of fines, from the half fum 38° 9′ to either of the containing fides, as to 29° 50′; apply this extent from the other containing fide 42° 09′ towards the left, there let the foot reft, and extend the other point (*viz.* that which was fet on 42° 09′) to the half difference 25° 50′; then this extent applied to the line of verfed fines, will reach from o degrees (at the beginning) to 52° 12′; the fupplement of which, or 127° 48′ will be the degrees in the angle A.

#### Again. *To find the angle* D.

The fides including angle D, are   BD = 63° 59′
And AD = 42   09
_____
Their difference call X   = 21   50
The fide oppofite the ∠D is AB = 29   50

Then

Then the fum of AB and X is $51°$ $40'$; the half fum is $25°$ $50'$.

And the difference of BA and X is $8°$ $0'$; the half difference is $4°$ $00'$.

Then the extent on the fines from $25°$ $50'$ to $63°$ $59'$ will reach from the fine of $42°$ $09'$ to fome point beyond $90°$; therefore apply the extent between $25°$ $50'$ and $63°$ $59'$ from the fine of $90°$ downwards, let the point reft where it falls, and bring that point which was fet on $90°$ to $42°$ $09'$; then will the diftance between the feet fhew how far the firft extent would reach paft $90°$: Now apply this extent on the fines from the point oppofite the middle 1 on the line of numbers, the other foot falling upwards to the right, let it reft there, and extend the other foot to the half difference $4°$ $0'$: Then this extent applied to the verfed fines, one foot being fet on the point oppofite the middle 1 on the line of numbers, the other foot will fall on $154°$ $5'$; the fupplement whereof, *viz.* $25°$ $55'$ will be the angle D.

## SOLUTION *of* CASE VI.

Ex. In the fpherical triangle ABD:
> Given $\angle A = 127°$ $50'$.
> $\angle B = 36°$ $8'$.
> $\angle D = 25°$ $55'$.
Required, The triangle.

I. *To put* AB *on the primitive circle.* Fig. 1. 6. Pl. VII.

1ft. From B, with the fecant of $\angle B$, $36°$ $8'$, cut ⊙ F in C, and C will be the center of the circumference through B, D, E.

2d. From ⊙, with the tangent of $52°$ $10'$ the fupplement of $\angle A$, defcribe an arc *xc*.

3d. Make an angle C*aq* = $\angle D$, $25°$ $55'$; make *aq* equal B*x* (= fecant of $52°$ $10'$.)

4th. From C, with the radius C*q*, cut *xc* in *c*: From *c*, with the radius *qa*, defcribe a circumference ADG; and the triangle ABD, is that which was required: whofe fides AB, BD, DA, are meafured as follows.

5th.

5th. A ruler on B and *a* gives *d*, and on A and *b*, gives *f*; make *dg*, *fh*, each 90 degrees; a ruler on *g* and B gives P, and on *h* and A, gives *p*, in ⊙ F, ⊙ H drawn perpendicular to BE, AG.

6th. A ruler on P and D gives *n*, and on *p* and D, gives *m*.

7th. Then BA, B*n*, A*m*, meafured on the chords, gives 29° 50′; 63° 59′; 42° 9′; for the refpective meafures of BA, BD, AD.

The directions for the conftruction may be eafily applied to the putting either of the other fides on the primitive circle. Fig. 2. 6. and 3. 6. Pl. VII.

## *Computation by the Logarithmic Scales.*

### *To find the fide* BD:

The angles including the fide BD, are ∠B = 36° 08′

And ∠D = 25   55
_____

Their difference call X = 10   13

The fupplement of the ∠ oppofite to BD is 52   10

The fum of the fupplement of ∠A and X is 62° 23′; the half fum is 31° 11 ½′.

The difference of the fupplement of ∠A and X is 41° 57′; the half difference is 20° 58 ½′.

Now on the fines, the extent from the half fum 31° 11 ½′ to 25° 55′ will reach from 36° 08′ to a fourth fine; and the extent from that fourth fine to the fine of the half difference 20° 58 ½′ will reach on the verfed fines from the beginning to about 64° the fide fought.

And in like manner may the other fides be found.

S E C T.

## SECT. XX.

### *The use of the Sector in drawing the Perspective representations of Objects.*

IT may be of use, to beginners, to explain briefly a few terms and notions used in this art, relative to the examples which follow.

1. The PICTURE, or *plane*, upon which the representation is to be exhibited, is supposed to be transparent, like a plate of glass; and to stand upright upon the ground, between the object seen upon the ground, or upon a plane parallel to it, and the eye which is observing that object; and that every imaginary straight line coming from the object to the eye, intersects the picture in a point: The art of finding these points upon the picture, is the most considerable part of PERSPECTIVE.

2. The ORIGINAL PLANE, or GEOMETRIC PLANE, is the ground, floor, or ceiling, upon which rests the object to be represented.

3. The GROUND LINE, or INTERSECTION, is the line in which the *original plane* meets the *picture*; and is the bottom, or top, line of the picture, usually called the SEAT of all points and lines in the *original plane*, when the picture stands vertically to that plane.

4. The POINT OF SIGHT, is that point where the spectator's eye ought to be placed, to look at the picture.

5. The VANISHING LINE, usually called the HORIZONTAL LINE, is a line in the picture parallel to the ground line; and is the intersection of a plane, supposed to pass through the point of sight in a parallel position to the original plane.

6. The CENTER OF THE VANISHING LINE, is that point in it, which is perpendicularly opposite to the point of sight; and is called the CENTER OF THE PICTURE; when in a plane vertical to the ground line.

7. The DISTANCE OF THE PICTURE, is the distance between
the

the center and the place of the eye.

8. The VANISHING POINT, of an original line, is a point in the vanishing line, where it is interfected by a line drawn through the eye parallel to the original line.

9. In the following examples, (fee Plate VIII.) two parallel lines are drawn at a given diftance from one another, fuppofe 5 feet, that diftance being taken as the height of the eye above the floor on which the picture ftands: The lower line reprefents the interfection, or ground line, and the upper line reprefents the vanifhing line. The point C is taken as the center, as well of the vanifhing line, as of the picture; and the vertical line CF being drawn, the point F reprefents its foot.

Alfo, the eye is conceived to be the center; its diftance from the picture to be the radius; and the vanifhing line to be taken as a line of tangents proceeding from the center C of the picture, as well to the left hand as to the right.

10. The inclination of any original line to the picture being known, its vanifhing point will be known, by applying the tangent of the complement of the degrees in that inclination, on the vanifhing line, from its center: And the fecant of the complement of that inclination being applied from that vanifhing point towards the center, gives what may be called the VISUAL POINT of that line.

11. The tangents, of any number of degrees, when applied to the vanifhing line, from a given point in it, muft always be reckoned from its center. Thus. Take the difference between the degrees to be applied, and thofe in the diftance between the center and the point from whence they are to be applied: When this diftance contains the moft degrees, the faid difference is to be laid from the center towards the faid point; but when the diftance is the leaft, the diftance is laid from the center, the contrary way; always taking the faid difference from the tangents, the fector being fet to the proper radius.

12. The eye is fuppofed to be before the picture, and the objects viewed, to be behind, or on the other fide, beyond the picture. The neareft diftance from the picture, of a point in the original plane, may be called the NORMAL DISTANCE; and the

diftance

distance of that point taken sideways, either to the right or left of the foot F, may be called the LATERAL DISTANCE of that point.

13. In any object, those lines which are parallel to the *ground line*, and to the picture, will have their representations in the picture parallel to the vanishing line.

14. Those lines which are vertical to the original plane, or floor, and parallel to the picture, will have their representations at right angles to the vanishing line.

15. Those lines which are normal to the picture, will be represented by lines tending to the center of the picture, which then becomes the vanishing point of those lines.

16. Lines which are parallel to the original plane, and inclined to the picture, do all tend to one and the same vanishing point, in the common vanishing line.

17. Parallel lines, which are inclined to both the picture and original plane, will have one and the same vanishing point, in a line parallel to the horizontal line, either above or below it.

18. EXERCISE I. *To find the point* A *in the picture; which shall be the representation of a point on the original plane, normally distant* 3 *feet, and laterally distant* 2 *feet to the left.* Fig. 1. Pl. VIII.

SOLUTION. Set the sector to any convenient radius on the tangents, to represent the distance between the eye and center C (suppose it equal to the height CF); and apply that radius, or tangent of 45° from C to V, and V', on the vanishing line VV'.

On the intersection, or seat F*b*, apply the lateral distance 2 feet from F to *a*, and the normal distance 3 feet, from *a* to *b*: Then the lines C*a* and V*b*, or V'*b*', being drawn, their intersection will give the point A, for the representation required.

19. EXERCISE II. *From a given point* A *in the picture, to draw a line, which will represent one on the original plane, or floor, inclined to the picture in a given angle; suppose of* 25 *degrees.* Fig. 1. Pl. VIII.

SOLUTION. Make the radius CV a transverse distance to 45°,

on

on the tangents; take the tangent of 65°, the complement of
the given inclination 25°, and apply it from C, on the vanifhing
line, gives *v* the vanifhing point of that line. Then a line drawn
from A to *v* will be the reprefentation required.

20. EXERCISE III. *At a given point* A, *in the picture, to form
an angle, which fhall reprefent an angle on the floor, of a given
number of degrees, fuppofe* 70°; *one leg of the angle being inclined to
the picture in a given pofition, as of* 25 *degrees.* Fig. 2. Pl. VIII.

SOLUTION. Draw the line A*v* (by Exer. II.) reprefenting the
line inclined to the picture in an angle of 25 degrees.

From the point *v*, apply the tangent of 70° towards C; and it
gives the point *v'*; that is, C*v'* is the tangent of 5°, the
difference between 70° and 65°.

Draw the line A*v'*, and the angle *v*A*v'*, will be the reprefentation required.

21. EXERCISE IV. *In the reprefentation* A*v*, *of an original line,
to apply, from a given point* A, *the meafure of any propofed length;
fuppofe of* 4 *feet.* Fig. 2.

SOLUTION. Through A draw A*p* parallel to CV; a ruler by C
and A gives *a*, in the feat F*c*; in which take *ac* of 4 feet; then a
line C*c*, cuts A*p* in *p*.

Meafure the diftance C*v* on the fectoral tangents tranfverfely; fuppofe it 65°; take the fecant of thofe degrees, and fet
this diftance from *v* to *x*; then a line drawn from *x* to *p*, cuts A*v*
in B; and AB is the reprefentation of the length propofed; of 4
feet.

As C*v'* is equal to the tangent of 5°; then the fecant of 5° fet
from *v'*, gives *x'*; and a line drawn from thence to *p'*, cuts A*v'*, a
line AB', which is alfo the reprefentation of 4 feet.

22. EXERCISE V. *To defcribe the reprefentation of a regular
polygon, the magnitude of one fide; and its pofition to the picture
being given; as alfo the normal and lateral diftances of the neareft
end of that fide.*

EXAMPLE

EXAMPLE I. In the equilateral triangle. Fig. 3. Pl. VIII.

Let the fide be 4 feet; the inclination 40°; the normal diftance 2 feet, and the lateral diftance 2 feet to the left.

SOLUTION. Find the point A, by Exer. I. the pofition of A*v*, by Exer. II. and the length of AB, by Exer. IV.

The angle of an equilateral triangle being 60°, apply its tangent from *v*, the vanifhing point of AB, towards C, that is, make C*v*` = tangent of 10°, the difference between 60° and 50°, gives *v*` the vanifhing point of another fide AE.

The tangent of 60° alfo, being applied from *v*` to *v*`` (by Art. II. that is making C*v*`` equal to the tangents of 70°); then *v*`` becomes the vanifhing point of another fide EB.

The meeting of A*v*` and B*v*`` in E, is the third angular point; and the triangle ABE is the reprefentation of the equilateral triangle, as required.

If more of fuch triangles, contiguous to one another, were to be reprefented; then the lines drawn from *v*`` through the interfections of *v*E, *v*`B, &c. will form a number of equilateral triangles, which may reprefent a pavement of fuch figures.

Hence it will be eafy to find the reprefentation of any plane triangle, by having a fufficient data among the fides and angles.

23. EXAM. II. In the fquare. Fig. 4.

Let the fide be 4 feet; the inclination 40°; the normal diftance 2 feet, and lateral diftance 2 feet to the right.

SOLUTION. Find the point A, with the pofition and length of AB, by Exer. I. II. IV. *n* being the vanifhing point of AB.

The angle of a fquare being 90°, apply the tangent of the complement of C*n* from C to *n*`, which is the vanifhing point of the fides of the fquare paffing through A and B.

As the diagonal of a fquare makes an angle of 45° with its fide AB, apply the tangent of 45° from *n* to *n*`` (by Art. II; that is, make C*n*`` = tang. of 5°), then *n*`` is the vanifhing point of the diagonal AE; meeting *n*`B in E; then *n*E meeting *n*`A in D, forms the fquare ABED, as required.

If more of fuch fquares, contiguous to one another, were to be reprefented; the interfections of lines from the vanifhing

points

points $n$, $n'$, with thofe from the vanifhing point $n''$ of the diagonals, will form a number of perfpective fquares, which together may reprefent a pavement compofed of fquares.

Hence it will be eafy to find the reprefentation of any quadrilateral right lined figure; by having a proper data among the lines and angles in that figure.

24. EXAM. III. In the Pentagon. Fig. 5. Pl. VIII.

Let the fide be 4 feet; the inclination 40°; the normal diftance 2 feet, and lateral diftance 2 feet, to the left.

SOLUTION. Find the point A, with the pofition and length of AB, by Exer. I. II. IV. $v$ being the vanifhing point of AB.

The angle of a pentagon being 108°; the two diagonals drawn thence to oppofite angles, divides the 108° into three equal parts of 36° each: Then as C$v$ is the tangent of 50°; 50° leffened by 36°, leaves 14°, make C$v'$ the tangent of 14°, and $v'$ is the vanifhing point of a diagonal to A; alfo 36° leffened by 14°, leaves 22°; then C$v''$ being made equal to the tangent of 22°, gives $v''$ for the vanifhing point of another diagonal to A; and the fum of 22° and 36° is 58°; make C$v'''$ the tangent of 58° and draw $v'''$A, $v''$A, $v'$A.

The external angle of a Pentagon being 72°, which is equal to the angle $v$B$v''$; therefore $v''$ is the vanifhing point of a fide through B; then drawing B$v''$, it cuts $v'$A in the point D, an angular point of the pentagon: Alfo drawing B$v'''$, cutting A$v''$ in E, another angular point of the pentagon: laftly, drawing $v'$E, its meeting of A$v'''$ in G, is the fifth point.

So ABDEG is the reprefentation of the pentagon, as required.

By the directions here given, the perfpective appearance of an irregular pentagonal figure may be exhibited, a fufficient number of lines and angles in that figure being known.

25. EXAM. IV. In a Hexagon. Fig. 6. Pl. VIII.

Let the fide be 4 feet; the inclination 20°; the normal diftance 2 feet; and the lateral diftance 5 feet, to the right.

SOLUTION. Find the point A, with the pofition and length of AB, by Exer. I. II. IV. $n$ being the vanifhing point of AB.

In

In a Hexagon the intern angle is 120°, and the extern angle is 60°, therefore the tangent of 60° applied from *n* towards C (Art. II.) gives *n*‛ the vaniſhing point of lines through B and A: Alſo the tangent of 60° applied from *n*‛ (Art. II.) will reach to *v*; ſo that *n, n*‛ and *v*, are all the vaniſhing points wanted; each belonging to a diameter, and two oppoſite ſides.

Draw *v*A, *v*B; *n*‛A, *n*‛B; and where *v*B, *n*‛A, cut in O, is the repreſentation of the center of the Hexagon: A line through *n* and O, cuts *n*‛B, *v*A, in D and I, two angular points of the figure.

Draw *n*‛I, its meeting with *v*B in G, is another angular point. Laſtly, drawing *n*G, and it gives *n*‛A the point E, the ſixth angular point. So the figure ABDEGI is the repreſentation of the Hexagon as required.

It is eaſy to ſee how, by the help of the three vaniſhing points, *n, n*‛, *v*, other hexagonal figures may be annexed.

If in any of theſe examples, the given ſide was parallel to the vaniſhing line, or was normal to the picture, and ſo vaniſhed in the center, the ſolution would readily follow from what has already been ſaid.

26. EXERCISE VI. The repreſentation AB of a diameter of a circle being given; to find that of another diameter normal to the picture, or directed towards its center. Fig. 7. Pl. VIII.

SOLUTION. Find *v*, the vaniſhing point of AB; then C*v* applied tranſverſely to the tangents, CV being radius, gives 50° for the complement of the inclination of that diameter repreſented by AB; and make *vx* = ſecant of 50 degrees.

A ruler by *x* and A, B, cuts the ſeat F*b*, in *a, b*; alſo a ruler by *x*, and *d*, the middle of *ab*, gives in AB, the point *c* the place of the center: draw a line through C and *c*.

Make C*v*‛ = tangent of half the degrees in C*v*: then a ruler by *v*‛ and A, *v*‛ and B, will cut C*c* in D and E, the extremities of the diameter ſought.

27. EXERCISE VII. To deſcribe the repreſentation of a circle, whoſe diameter of 8 feet is inclined to the picture in an angle of 20 degrees; the neareſt end of that diameter being
normally

normally diftant 3 feet, and laterally 5 feet to the right. Fig. 8.

SOLUTION. Find the point A, with the pofition and magnitude of AB, by Exer. I. II. IV. *n* being the vanifhing point of AB.

Make C*n`* = tangent of 20°; then the points *n n`* are 90° diftant.

Make C*n"* = tangent of 25°; then *n"* is 45° diftant from *n* and *n`*.

Then *n`*A, *n`*B; *n"*E, being drawn, they meet in E and D; and through thefe points, *n*E, *n*D, being drawn, the reprefentation of a fquare HEGD, circumfcribing that circle, will be formed, where O reprefents the center.

A ruler by *n`* and A, *n`* and B, gives *e* and *d* in the feat F*d*; and *f* is the middle of *ed*.

Make *fe* or *fd*, a tranfverfe diftance to 90 and 90 on the fectoral fines; and on thefe lines apply, on both fides of *f*, the fines and cofines of fuch degrees as may be judged proper, as of 20°, 30°, and 40°; or, as in this example, of 25° and 40°.

Lines from *n`* to each of the divifions of *ed*, will interfect the diagonal *n`*E in as many points, which mark like thofe of *ed*; call thefe *fine lines*.

Lines from *n*, through the faid marked points in the diagonal, will cut the former lines through thofe points; call thefe latter *cofine lines*.

Mark the points of interfection, where the *fine lines* and their *cofine lines* meet; and thefe interfections will be points in the periphery.

Then a fmooth and uniform line defcribed through thofe points, will be the ellipfis, reprefenting the circumference of the circle, as required.

Many other inftances of the ufe of the fector, in drawing the perfpective appearance of objects, might be produced: But thefe examples well underftood, will enable the inquifitive to apply the precepts to other examples, which may be found in the books wrote on the fubject of perfpective.

SECT.

## S E C T. XXI.

### *Of the proportional Compaſſes.*

THOSE compaſſes are called proportional, whoſe joint lies between the points terminating each leg; in ſuch manner, that when the compaſſes are opened, the legs form a croſs.

Such compaſſes are either ſimple or compound.

Simple proportional compaſſes, are ſuch, whoſe center is fixed: One pair of theſe, ſerve only for one proportion.

Thus, if a right line is to be divided into 2, 3, 4, 5, &c. equal parts; or the chord of $\frac{1}{3}, \frac{1}{5}, \frac{1}{7}$, &c. part of a circumference is to be taken; there muſt be as many ſuch compaſſes, as there are diſtinct operations to be performed.

In each caſe, take the length of the right line, or of the radius of the circle, between the longer points of the legs; and the diſtance of the ſhorter points will be the part required.

Compound proportional compaſſes are thoſe wherein the center is moveable; ſo that one pair of theſe, will perform the office of ſeveral pairs of the ſimple ſort.

In the ſhanks of theſe compaſſes are grooves, wherein ſlides the center, which is made faſt by a nut and ſcrew.

On each ſide of theſe grooves, ſcales are placed; which may be of various ſorts, according to the fancy of the buyer: But the ſcales which the inſtrument-makers commonly put on theſe compaſſes, are only two, *viz.* lines and circles.

By the ſcale of lines, a right line may be divided into a number of equal parts, not exceeding the greateſt number on the ſcale; which is generally 12.

EXAM. I. To divide a given right line, (ſuppoſe of $7\frac{1}{2}$ inches long,) into a propoſed number of equal parts, (as 11.)

OPERATION. Shut the compaſſes; unſcrew the button; move the ſlide until the line acroſs it, coincides with the 11th diviſion on the ſcale of lines; ſcrew the button faſt; open the

                                                        compaſſes,

compaſſes, until the given line can be received between the longer points of the legs; then will the diſtance of the ſhorter points be the 11th part of the given line, as required.

By the ſcale of circles, a regular polygon may be inſcribed in a given circle; provided the number of ſides in the polygon, do not exceed the numbers on the ſcale, which commonly proceed to 24.

EXAM. II. To inſcribe in a circle of a known radius, (ſuppoſe 6 inches) a regular polygon of 12 ſides.

OPERATION. Shut the compaſſes; unſcrew the button; ſlide the center until its mark coincides with the 12th diviſion on the ſcale of circles; ſcrew the button faſt; take the given radius between the longer points of the legs; then will the diſtance of the ſhorter points, be the ſide of the polygon required.

Theſe ſcales are applicable to ſeveral other uſes beſide the foregoing ones, in the ſame manner, as the like lines on the ſector are.

From theſe operations it is evident, that the lengths of the longer and ſhorter legs, (reckoned from the center,) muſt always be proportional to the diſtance of their extremities.

Therefore, to divide a right line into 2, 3, 4, 5, 6, 7, 8, &c. equal parts; the lengths of each leg, from the center, will be expreſſed by the following ſeries, the whole length of the inſtrument being taken for unity.

Longer leg, $\frac{2}{3}, \frac{3}{4}, \frac{4}{5}, \frac{5}{6}, \frac{6}{7}, \frac{7}{8}$, &c.

Shorter leg, $\frac{1}{3}, \frac{1}{4}, \frac{1}{5}, \frac{1}{6}, \frac{1}{7}, \frac{1}{8}$, &c.

Theſe diviſions may be very accurately laid on the legs of the compaſſes by the help of a good ſector. (See Prob. 14.)

Or, the diviſions of this ſcale of lines may be found by the following conſtruction.

In the two lines AB, A*a*, meeting in any angle at A, take AB for the length of the ſcale from whence the proportions are taken; and A*a* for the length of the ſhank of the compaſſes; and through *a* draw the indefinite right line DE, parallel to AB.

Draw

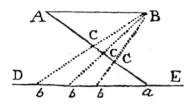

Draw any right line B$b$, cutting A$a$, D$a$, in $c$, $b$. Then A$c$ : $ca$ :: AB : $ab$.

Therefore, to find the divifions of A$a$, fo that $ab$ may be a given part of AB, fuppofe the $n$th part; or that $n$ times $ab$ be equal to AB.

Suppofe the line A$a$ to contain P equal parts of AB.

Now  A$c$ : $ca$ :: AB : $\dfrac{1}{n}$AB.

Or      A$c + ca$ : $ca$ :: AB $+ \dfrac{1}{n}$AB : $\dfrac{1}{n}$AB.

Or      P         : $ca$ :: $\overline{1 + \dfrac{1}{n}} \cdot$ AB : $\dfrac{1}{n} \cdot$ AB.

Or      P         : $ca$ :: $\left(1 + \dfrac{1}{n} : \dfrac{1}{n} ::\right) n + 1 : 1$

So $ca = \dfrac{1}{n+1} \times$ P; and  A$c = \dfrac{n}{n+1} \times$ P; when the mark on the flider (or moveable center) is oppofite to the fcrew-pin. But if the center of the fcrew-pin be different from the mark in the flider by a known quantity, fuppofe the $m$th part of P.

Then $ac = \left(\dfrac{P}{n+1} \pm \dfrac{P}{m} =\right) \dfrac{n+1+m}{n+1} \times \dfrac{1}{m}$P.

Ex. If P $= 10000$, $m = 400$, and $n = 1$, or 2, or 3, &c.

Then $ac = 5000$, or 3333, or 2500, &c. when the divifions on the fhank refpect the center pin.

And $ac = \begin{cases} 5025 \text{ or } 3358 \text{ or } 2525, \text{ &c.} \\ 4975 \text{ or } 3308 \text{ or } 2475, \text{ &c.} \end{cases}$

when the divifions refpect a mark in the flider, diftant from the center pin, $\frac{1}{25}$ of the length of the Inftrument.

The fcale for dividing the circle, or the divifions for regular polygons may be found thus.

Find the angles at the center, of as may regular polygons as are to be defcribed on the compaffes.

Seek the fines belonging to the half of each angle, to the radius 1.

To

To each of thefe fines doubled, add the radius 1.

Then will the reciprocal of thefe numbers, be the lengths of the polygonal divifions, on the legs of the compaffes, reckoned from the longer point; the length of the inftrument being accounted unity.

For the longer and fhorter legs, (or points) are in the fame ratio, as are the radius and chord of the angle at the center.

And as the fum of the radius and chord, is to the radius; fo is the fum of the longer and fhorter legs, (or points) to the length of the longer point.

And hence was the following table compofed, which fhews the decimal parts on the leg, from the longer point to the center.

| N° Sides. | Length on the Leg. | N° Sides. | Length on the Leg. | N° Sides. | Length on the Leg. |
|---|---|---|---|---|---|
| 3 | 0,3333 | 11 | 0,6396 | 19 | 0,7523 |
| 4 | 0,4142 | 12 | 0,6589 | 20 | 0,7617 |
| 5 | 0,4597 | 13 | 0,6763 | 21 | 0,7706 |
| 6 | 0,5000 | 14 | 0,6921 | 22 | 0,7785 |
| 7 | 0,5354 | 15 | 0,7063 | 23 | 0,7860 |
| 8 | 0,5665 | 16 | 0,7193 | 24 | 0,7931 |
| 9 | 0,5940 | 17 | 0,7313 | | |
| 10 | 0,6180 | 18 | 0,7423 | | |

Thefe divifions may be truly laid off by the help of a good fector; making the whole length of the proportional compaffes, a tranfverfe diftance to 10 and 10, on the line of lines.

The complements, to unity, of the numbers in the table, will give the diftances of the divifions from the other point of the inftrument.

If the mark in the flider, is at fome diftance from the center, as it commonly is, then this diftance, which is always known,

muft

muſt be added to, or ſubtracted from, the foregoing numbers, according to the ſide of the center the mark is on; and the ſums, or remainders, will give the diſtances of the diviſions from one of the points.

About *Michaelmas*, 1746, was finiſhed a pair of proportional compaſſes, with the addition of a very curious and uſeful contrivance; (ſee the plate fronting the title page) *viz.* into one of the legs (A) at a ſmall diſtance from the end of the groove, was ſcrewed a little pillar *(a)* of about ⅓ of an inch high, and perpendicular to the ſaid leg; through this pillar, and parallel to the leg, went a ſcrew pin *(bb)*; to one end of this ſcrew, was ſoldered a ſmall beam *(cc)* nearly the length of the groove in the compaſſes; the beam was ſlit down the middle lengthwiſe, which received a nut *(f)* that ſlid along the ſlit *(dd)*; this nut could be ſcrewed to the beam, faſt enough to prevent ſliding; one end *(e)* of the ſcrew of the nut *(f)* falls into a hole in the bottom of the ſcrew to the great nut *(g)* of the compaſſes; the ſcrew pin *(bb)* paſſed through an adjuſter *(h)*.

To uſe this inſtrument:

Shut the legs cloſe, ſlacken the ſcrews of the nuts *g* and *f*; move the nuts and ſlider *k* to the diviſion wanted, as near as can be done readily by the hand, and ſcrew faſt the nut *f*: Then by turning the adjuſter *h*, the mark on the ſlider *k*, may be brought exactly to the diviſion: ſcrew faſt the nut *g*; open the compaſſes; gently lift the end *e*, of the ſcrew of the nut *f*, out of the hole in the bottom of the nut *g*; move the beam round its pillar *a*, and ſlip the point *e*, into the hole in the pin *n*, which is fixed to the under leg; ſlacken the ſcrew of the nut *f*; take the given line between the longer points of the compaſſes, and ſcrew faſt the nut *f*: Then may the ſhorter points of the compaſſes be uſed without danger of the legs changing their poſition; this being one of the inconveniencies that attended the proportional compaſſes before this ingenious contrivance; which was made by the late Mr. *Thomas Heath*, Mathematical Inſtrument-maker in the *Strand, London*.

The proportional compaſſes had not long been invented before there were ſeveral learned and ingenious perſons who

contrived

contrived a variety of fcales to be put thereon; but thefe are here omitted, becaufe the credit of the proportional compaffes is greatly fallen, fince the invention of the fector, the latter being a much more ufeful inftrument than the former, and not fo fubject to be put out of order; for if one of the points of thefe compaffes fhould be blunted or broke, the inftrument cannot be ufed, until the damaged point be replaced by a new one. However, thofe who are defirous of knowing the conftruction and ufe of fuch fcales on the proportional compaffes, may be amply fatisfied in confulting *Hulfius, Horfcher, Galgemaire, Bion*, and others mentioned in the preface to this book.

APPENDIX

# A P P E N D I X.

## CONTAINING

The DESCRIPTION and USE of the

## GUNNERS CALLIPERS.

A Pair of Callipers is an inftrument ufed to take the diameters of convex and concave bodies.

The inftrument called the Gunners Callipers, confifts of two thin rulers or plates, which are moveable quite round a joint, by the plates folding one over the other.

The length of each ruler or plate is ufually between the limits of fix inches and a foot, reckoned from the center of the joint; and from one to two inches broad: But the moft convenient ufeful fize is about nine inches long. The figure is beft feen in the plate. IX.

On thefe rulers are a variety of fcales, tables, proportions, &c. fuch as are efteemed ufeful to be known by gunners and other perfons employed about artillery: But except for the taking of the calibre of fhot and cannon, and the meafuring of the magnitude of *faliant* and *entring angles*, there are none of the articles with which the callipers are ufually filled, effential to this inftrument; the fcales are, or may be, put on the fector; and the tables, precepts, &c. may be put into a pocket-book, where they will not need fo much contraction: However, for the fake of thofe who are defirous of having a fingle inftrument perform many things, the following articles and their difpofition on the callipers are here offered: Some of which were propofed many years ago by the late Mr. *Charles Labelye*, engineer to the works of *Weftminfter-bridge*.

*Articles*

*Articles to be put on the Gunners Callipers.*

I. The meafures of convex diameters in inches.

II. The meafures of concave diameters in inches.

III. The weights of iron fhot from given diameters.

IV. The weight of iron fhot proper to given gun bores.

V. The degrees of a femicircle.

VI. The proportion of Troy and Averdupoife weight.

VII. The proportion of Englifh and French feet and pounds.

VIII. Factors ufeful in circular and fpherical figures.

IX. Tables of the fpecific gravity and weights of bodies.

X. Tables of the quantity of powder neceffary for proof and fervice of brafs and iron guns.

XI. Rules for computing the number of fhot or fhells in a finifhed pile.

XII. Rules concerning the fall of heavy bodies.

XIII. Rules for the raifing of water.

XIV. The rules for fhooting with cannon or mortars.

XV. A line of inches.

XVI. Logarithmic fcales of numbers, fines, verfed fines, and tangents.

XVII. A fectoral line of equal parts, or the line of lines.

XVIII. A fectoral line of plans or fuperficies.

XIX. A fectoral line of folids.

The Callipers propofed for the reception of the foregoing articles is nine inches long, and each leg two inches broad at the head, and at the points; part of the breadth between the ends is hollowed away in a curve, in order to contain the curvature of the ball, whofe diameter is taken between the points; one of ten inches diameter is the largeft that can conveniently be taken with a nine inch Calliper; thofe of fix inches cannot well be applied to a fhot of more than feven inches diameter.

For the eafe of reference; it will be convenient to diftinguifh the four faces of the Callipers by the letters A, B, C, D: Each of the faces A and D confift of a circular head and a leg;

the

the other faces B and C confift each of a leg only.

# ARTICLE I.

### *Of the meafures of convex diameters.*

On part of the circular head joining to the leg of the face A, are divifions diftinguifhed by the title of *fhot diameters*: Thefe are to fhew the diftance in inches, and tenth parts of an inch, of the points of the Callipers when they are opened.

### THE USE.

Open the points of the Callipers fo, that they may take in the greateft diameter of the ball: then will the bevil edge marked E fhew among the forefaid divifions, the diameter of that ball in inches and tenth parts, not exceeding ten inches.

*Thefe divifions may be thus laid down by the fector.*

Open the fector until the radius of the circle, whereupon is marked the fcale of divifions on the head of the Callipers, taken with the compaffes, falls tranfverfely in the fcale of lines, on the divifions fhewing the diftance between the center of the Callipers and its points: Then the tranfverfe diftances of the feveral divifions on the fcales of lines, being applied like chords to the circle of divifions on the head of the Callipers will give the divifions required.

Thus in the nine inch Callipers, the radius of the head, or circle of divifions, being one inch, and the breadth at the points two inches; the diftance between the center and points will be $(\sqrt{82} = )$ 9,055385: Then one inch being made a tranfverfe diftance on the fcale of lines to $9\frac{5}{100}$; the tranfverfe diftances of 10, 9, 8, 7, 6, &c. being applied to the circle on the head of the Callipers appropriated for the fcale, from the mark where the divifions will commence, will give the feveral points, which being cut by the bevil edge E will fhew how far the points of the Callipers are diftant.

The workmen generally lay thefe divifions down by trial.

ARTICLE

## ARTICLE II.

*Of the weights of iron shot.*

On the circular bevil part E of the face B, is a scale of divisions denominated by ℔ *weight of iron shot.* These are to shew the weights of iron shot when the diameter is taken between the points of the Callipers: For then the number cut by the inner edge of the leg A, shews the weight of that iron shot in pounds averdupoise, when the weight is among the following ones, *viz.*

℔. ½. 1. 1 ½. 2. 3. 4. 5 ¼. 6. 8. 9. 12. 16. 18. 24. 26. 32. 36. 42.

Observing that the figures nearest the bevil edge answer to the short lines; and those figures behind them answer to the divisions marked with the longer strokes or lines.

These divisions are to be laid down from a table shewing the diameters of iron shots to given weights. Such a table is computed by knowing the weight of one shot of a given diameter: Thus an iron shot of four inches diameter is found to weigh nine pounds: Then the weights of spheres being to one another as the cubes of their diameters, Say As 9 ℔ is to 64, the cube of 4.

So is any other weight, to the cube of its diameter.

Then the cube root being taken will give the diameter.

Now setting the points of the Callipers to touch one another, make a mark on the bevil edge E opposite to the inner edge of the leg A; and this mark will be the beginning of this scale of weights: The other divisions will be obtained by opening the points of the Callipers to the distances respecting the weights to be introduced, as shewn by the table, and marking the division opposite to the inner edge of the leg A.

## ARTICLE III.

*Of the measures of concave diameters.*

On the lower part of the circular head of the face A, and to the

the right hand of the divifions for the diameters of fhot, is another fcale of divifions, againft which ftands the words *Bores of Guns.*

*To find the calibre, or the diameter of the bore of a cannon.*

Slip the legs of the Callipers acrofs each other, until the fteel points touch the concave furface of the gun in its greateft breadth; then will the bevil edge F, of the face B, cut a divifion in the fcale fhewing the diameter of that bore in inches and tenth parts.

In the nine inch Callipers thefe divifions may be extended to 18 inches diameter, but 14 inches is fufficient for both cannon and mortars: And in the fix inch Callipers a diameter greater than 10 inches cannot be conveniently introduced.

*Thefe divifions may be thus laid down by the fector.*

Set one inch the radius of the circle on which the divifions are to be put, as a tranfverfe diftance to the divifion $9\frac{5}{100}$ on the fcale of lines on the fector: Set the points of the Callipers together, and make a mark on the circular head where it is then cut by the bevil edge F: Then the feveral tranfverfe diftances taken from the fector, and applied on the circumference of the circular head of the Callipers, from the faid mark, the feveral divifions fhewing the diftance of the points of the Calliper are thereby obtained.

Workmen find thefe divifions by actually fetting the points to the diftance.

# ARTICLE IV.

*Of the weights of fhots to given gun bores.*

Within the fcales of fhot and bore diameters on the circular part of the face A are divifions marked *Pounders.*

When the bore of a gun is taken between the points of the Callipers, the bevil edge F will cut one of thefe divifions, or be

very

very near one of them: Then the number ſtanding againſt it will ſhew the weight of iron ſhot proper for that gun; not exceeding 42 pounds.

The inner figures, $\frac{1}{2}$, $1\frac{1}{2}$, 3, $5\frac{1}{4}$, 8, 12, 18, 26, 36, belong to the longeſt ſtroke or lines; and the figures 1, 2, 4, 6, 9, 16, 24, 32, 42 belong to the ſhort ſtrokes.

The diameters given by theſe pounders are larger than thoſe given for the ſame weights of ſhot; becauſe there is an allowance made, *called Windage*, that the ſhot may roll eaſily along the chace.

# ARTICLE V.

### *Of the degrees in the ſemicircular head.*

Theſe degrees are placed on the upper half of the circular head of the face A, where are three concentric ſcales of degrees: The outward ſcale has 180 degrees numbered from the right to left, with 10, 20, 30, 40, &c. to 180: The middle ſcale is numbered in the ſame manner, but the contrary way: And the inmoſt ſcale begins in the middle with 0, and is numbered from thence both ways with 10, 20, 30, &c. to 90 degrees.

### THE USE.
### *Firſt to meaſure an entring, or internal, angle.*

Apply the legs of the Callipers ſo that its outſide edges coincide with the legs of the given angle; then will the bevil edge F cut the degrees ſhewing the meaſure of that angle in the outſide ſcale.

### *Secondly. To meaſure a ſaliant, or external, angle.*

Slip the legs of the Callipers acroſs each other, ſo as their outſide edges may coincide with the legs of the given angle; then will the bevil edge E cut the degrees ſhewing the meaſure of that angle: Theſe degrees are to be counted on the middle ſcale.

Hence an angle of any number of degrees may be readily laid down by the Callipers, either on paper, or in the field.

Thus.

Thus. Open the Callipers, the legs being croffed, until the edge E cuts the degrees on the middle fcale; the croffing edges of the inftrument will then form the fides of that required angle: The Callipers then laid flat on the paper or ground, lines drawn by the ftrait fides will exprefs that angle.

*Thirdly. To find the elevation of cannon and mortars, or of any other oblique plane or line.*

Pafs one end of a fine thread into the notch on plate B, and to the other end tie a bullet, or other weight: Apply the ftrait fide of the plate A to the fide of the body whofe inclination is wanted; hold the plate A in the pofition, and move the plate B until the thread falls upon the line near the center marked *Perp.* Then will the bevil edge F cut the degrees, counted on the inner fcale, fhewing the inclination which that body makes with the horizon.

*Note.* When the edge F cuts o on the inner fcale; and the ftring cuts the *Perp.* mark, then the ftrait fide of the leg A is horizontal: If the head of the Callipers is elevated above the other end, then the edge F muft flide downwards towards the ftraight fide of the leg A: But if the head of the Callipers is held lower than the other end, then muft the edge F flide the contrary way.

As the outfide of a cannon or mortar is not parallel to its bore; therefore a ftrait ftick muft be applied to the bottom or top of the bore, and projecting beyond it; and the fide of the Callipers be laid on that ftick.

## A R T I C L E  VI.

*Of the proportion of Troy and Averdupoife Weights.*

On the face C near the point of the Callipers is a little table fhewing the number of pounds that are contained in an equal weight expreffed in pounds Troy; and the contrary.

Thefe numbers are taken from very accurate experiments made in the year 1744 by the late *Martin Folkes*, Efq; Prefident of the Royal Society, affifted by feveral other gentlemen of

that

that learned Body.

### THE TABLE.

| ℔ Troy | ℔ Averd. | oz. Troy | oz. Averd. |
|---|---|---|---|
| 576,00000 = | 700 | 82 | = 90 |
| 1,00000 = | 0,82274 | 1,00000 = | 1,09707 |
| 1,21545 = | 1,00000 | 0,91152 = | 1,00000 |

### THE USE.

EXAMPLE I. *What weight in pounds Troy is equal to a brafs gun weighing* 18 *Cwt.*

Now 18 C wt. is equal to 2016 ℔ (= 18 × 112).

Then        1 : 1,21545 :: 2016 : 2450 ℔ Troy.

Or, 0,82274 : 1        :: 2016 : 2450 ℔ Troy.

Or,      576 : 700     :: 2016 : 2450 ℔ Troy.

Either of thefe methods may be ufed as the operator pleafes.

EXAMPLE II. *What is the worth of a ton of gold; fuppofing* 1 ℔ *Troy makes* 44½ *guineas.*

Now 1 Ton = 2240 ℔ Averd. (= 20 × 112).

And 1 : 1,21545 :: 2240 : 2722,6 ℔ Troy.

Alfo 44½ Guineas, makes 46,725 £. fterling.

Then 1 : 2722,6 :: 46,725 : 127213,485 £.

Or, 127213*l.* 9*s.* 8*d.* ½.

But if Troy pounds were given to be converted into Averdupoife pounds, then the numbers in the Troy column muft be the firft terms of the proportions.

EXAMPLE III. *If a brafs gun weighs* 2450 ℔ *Troy; What is its weight in Averdupoife ?*

Then      1 : 0,82274 :: 2450 : 2015,7 ℔ Ave.

Or, 1,21545 : 1,00000 :: 2450 : 2015,7

Or,      700 :   576   :: 2450 : 2016.

Although the Averdupoife pound is heavier than the Troy pound, yet the Troy ounce is heavier than the Averdupoife ounce, nearly in the proportion of 90 to 82.

EXAMPLE

EXAMPLE IV. *In a cheſt of ſilver containing* 4380 *pieces of eight, each piece weighing* $\frac{4}{5}$ *of an ounce Troy: How many ounces Averdupoiſe.*

Then  82    :    90   :: 4380 × $\frac{4}{5}$ : 3845,88
Or,    1    : 1,09707 :: 4380 × $\frac{4}{5}$ : 3845,88
Or,  0,91152 :    1   :: 4380 × $\frac{4}{5}$ : 3845,88

Cloſe to the former table is another, ſhewing the number of cubic inches in a gallon, both in wine and beer meaſures; and conſequently their proportions: One uſe is ſhewn by the following Example.

*How long will 33 butts of beer ſerve a crew of* 324 *men, allowing to each man* 3 *wine quarts a day ?*

Now 33 butts contain 3564 beer gall. (= 108 × 33)
And 231 : 282 :: 3564 : 4350 $\frac{6}{7}$ wine gallons,
And 4350 $\frac{6}{7}$ gallons makes 17403 $\frac{3}{7}$ quarts,
Then 17403 divided by 324 gives very near 54.

Conſequently $\frac{1}{3}$ of 54, or 18 days, is the time that the beer will ſerve.

If wine gallons were to be converted into beer gallons,
Say 282 : 231 :: wine gallons : beer gallons.
Or  94 : 77 :: W. G.    : B. G.

## ARTICLE VII.

*Of the proportion of the Engliſh and French feet and pounds.*

Near the point of the face D of the Callipers are two tables ſhewing the proportion between the pound weights of *London* and *Paris*, and alſo between the lengths of the foot meaſure of *England* and *France*. Theſe are according to the accurate ſtandards ſettled between the Royal Societies of *London* and *Paris* about the year 1743.

THE

## THE TABLES.

| Eng. ℔. | | F. ℔. | | Eng. Ft. | | Fr. Ft. |
|---|---|---|---|---|---|---|
| 1,08 | = | 1,00 | | 114 | = | 107 |
| 1,00 | = | 0,926 | | 1,000 | = | 0,9386 |
| 108 | = | 100 | | 1,0654 | = | 1,0000 |

### THE USE.

EXAMPLE I. *Suppofe a crew of 54 Englifh failors were to attack a French fort, and carry off 6 pieces of Brafs cannon weighing one with another 980 ℔ French: How much would each John's fhare come to, fuppofing they could fell the cannon at 8l. a hundred weight Englifh?*

     ℔ F.    ℔ E.    ℔ F.

Now  100 : 108  :: 980 × 6 : 6350,4 ℔ Engl.

       ℔     £.     ℔

And  112 :  8  :: 6350,4 :  453,6 £. fterling.

      M.    £.     M.

Then  54 : 453,6 ::  1  :  8,4 £.

So that the fhare of each will be 8 guineas.

EXAMPLE II. *How many Englifh yards are equal to 180 French toifes or fathoms ?*

Now 1 : 1,0654 :: 180 : 191,672 Eng. Fa.

Then 180 French Fathoms are equal to about 383 yards 1 foot.

## ARTICLE VIII.

*Factors ufeful in circular and fpherical figures.*

Near the point of the Callipers on the face A is a table containing four rules of the circle and fphere.

                                                    THE

## THE TABLE.

| Diam. | × 3,1416 = circumf. | }  of a circle |
| Sq. Diam. | × 0,7854 = area | } |
| Sq. Diam. | × 3,1416 = furface | }  of a fphere |
| Cube Diam. | × 0,5236 = folidity | } |

## THE USE.

EXAMPLE I. *What is the circumference of a circle whofe diameter is* 12 *inches.*

Then (3,1416 × 12 = ) 37,6992 is the circumfer.

EXAMPLE II. *What is the area of a circle whofe diameter is* 12 *inches ?*

Now the fquare of 12 is 144.

Then (0,7854 × 144 =) 113,0976 is the area.

EXAMPLE III. *What is the fuperficies of a fphere whofe diameter is* 12 *inches ?*

Now the fquare of 12 is 144.

Then (3,1416 × 144 =) 452,3904 the fuperficies of the fphere.

EXAMPLE IV. *Required the folidity of a fphere whofe diameter is* 12 *inches.*

Now the cube of 12 is 1728.

Then (0,5236 × 1728 =) 904,7808 is the folidity.

Upon the circular heads of the Callipers were ufually placed certain mathematical figures with numbers fet to them; which figures and their numbers may be placed near the points of the Callipers here defcribed, the circular head being appropriated for another ufe.

*The*

*The figures are thefe.*

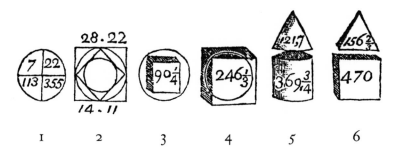

The numbers in figure 1, are ufeful for finding the circumference of a circle by knowing its diameter; or to find the diameter by knowing the circumference. Thus.

Say As     7 : 22 :: any given diameter : its circumference
And As    22 :    7 :: any given circumference : its diameter
Or As    113 : 355 :: any given diameter : its circumference
And As 355 : 113 :: any given circumference : its diameter

Fig. 2. There is a circle infcribed in a fquare; a fquare within that circle, and a circle within the inner fquare: To this figure are fet the numbers 28. 22. 14. 11. Thefe numbers fignify, that if the area of the outward figure is 28, the area of the infcribed circle is 22; the area of the fquare infcribed in that circle is 14, and the area of its infcribed circle is 11.

### THE USE.

EXAMPLE. *What is the area of a circle whofe diameter is* 12?

Now the fquare of 12 is 144.

Then As 28 : 22 :: 144 : 113,1 the area.

Or    As 14 : 11 :: 144 : 113,1.

It may be obferved that the fquares are in proportion to one another as 2 to 1; and the two circles are alfo in the fame proportion.

*Figure* 3. Reprefents a cube infcribed in a fphere; the number 90 $\frac{1}{4}$ fixed to it fhews, that a cube of iron, infcribed in a fphere of 12 inches in diameter, weighs 90 $\frac{1}{4}$ pounds weight.

*Figure*

*Figure* 4. Is to exprefs a fphere infcribed in a cube: Now this figure with its number 246 ⅓ is to fhew the weight in pounds of an iron fphere 12 inches in diameter; or of a fphere infcribed in a cube whofe fide is 12 inches.

*Figure* 5. Reprefents a cylinder and cone, whofe diameters and heights are each one foot: To the cylinder is annexed the number 369 $\frac{3}{14}$ fhewing the weight in pounds of an iron cylinder of 12 inches diameter and 12 inches height: And the number 121 $\frac{7}{100}$ joined to the cone fhews that an iron cone the diameter of whofe bafe is 12 inches, and the height 12 inches, weighs 121 $\frac{7}{100}$ pounds.

*Figure* 6. Shews that an iron cube, whofe fide is 12 inches, weighs 470 pounds; and that a fquare pyramid of iron, whofe bafe is a fquare foot, and its height 12 inches, weighs 156 ⅔ pounds.

Thefe numbers which have hitherto been fixed to the four laft figures are not ftrictly true.

For by experiment, an iron fhot of four inches diameter, weighs 9 pounds.

And the weights of fpheres being to one another as the cubes of their diameters.

Therefore 64 (= 4 × 4 × 4) : 9 :: 1728 : (= 12 × 12 × 12) : 243 pounds, for the weight of a fphere of iron which is 12 inches in diameter: Confequently the number 243 fhould be ufed inftead of 246 ¼ in the 4th figure.

Again the folidity of a cube infcribed in a fphere of 12 inches in diameter, is 332,55 cubic inches *.

And

* See Robertson's Menfuration, p. 335. 3d. Ed. 1767.

Or the folidity may be thus found.

The diameter of the sphere is equal to the diagonal of the inscribed cube, or to the hypothenuse of a right angled triangle, one leg being the side of the cube, and the other leg the diag. of one face of the cube.

Let $x$ = side of the cube; then the diag. of one face is $\sqrt{2xx}$, and the diag. of the cube 12 = ($x \sqrt{3}$ =) $x$ × 1,732. And the folidity of the cube $x^3 = \dfrac{1728}{1,732} = 332,55.$

And the weights of bodies of a like matter being in the proportion of their folidities.

Therefore, As 904,7808 : 243 :: 332,55 : 89,315 pounds.

Confequently the number 90 $\frac{1}{4}$ ufed at figure 3, fhould be 89 $\frac{1}{3}$.

Here 904,7808 is the folidity of a fphere of 12 inches diameter.

At figure 5, the weight of the iron cylinder fhould be 364,5 inftead of 369 $\frac{3}{14}$, and the weight of the cone fhould be 121,5.

For the folidity of a cylinder of 12 inches diameter, and 12 inches high, is 1357,1712 cubic inches.

Then 904,7808 : 243 :: 1357,1712 : 364,5 pounds.

And cylinders and cones having equal bafes and heights, are in proportion as 3 to 1.

Therefore the $\frac{1}{3}$ of 364,5, or 121,5 pounds is the weight of the cone.

The numbers at figure 6 annexed to the cube fhould be 464 pounds.

And that fixed to the pyramid fhould be 154 $\frac{2}{3}$ pounds.

For the cube inches in a foot cube are 1728.

Then 904,7808 : 243 :: 1728 : 464.

And a pyramid is $\frac{1}{3}$ of a cube, the bafes and height being equal.

Therefore the $\frac{1}{3}$ of 464 is 154 $\frac{2}{3}$ pounds for the weight of the pyramid.

Although it is ufually reckoned that a four inch iron fhot weighs nine pounds; and from thence it is deduced that the cube foot weighs 464 pounds; yet by the table of fpecific gravity on the callipers, which is framed from the moft accurate experiments, a cubic foot of caft iron weighs almoft 446 pounds; which is 18 pounds lefs than the weight derived from the 4 inch fhot, and 24 pounds lefs than that heretofore graved on the callipers; therefore all the weights found from the faid 4 inch fhot, fhould be diminifhed in the proportion of 464 to 446.

For

For the numbers at figures 3, 4, 5, 6.

As 464 : 446 :: 89,315 : 85,85.

As 464 : 446 :: 243        :233,5.

As 464 : 446 :: 364,5      :350,3.

So 85 $\frac{4}{5}$ lb. is the weight of an iron cube infcribed in a fphere of 12 inches in diameter.

And 233 $\frac{1}{2}$ lb. is the weight of an iron fphere of 12 inches diameter.

Alfo 350 $\frac{1}{3}$ lb. is the weight of an iron cylinder of a foot in diameter and height.

And 116 $\frac{2}{3}$ lb. is the weight of an iron cone of a foot in diameter and height.

Again 446 lb. is the weight of a cubic foot of iron.

And 148 $\frac{2}{3}$ is the weight of an iron pyramid, having its bafe a fquare foot, and its height equal to 12 inches.

# A R T I C L E   IX.

### *Of the fpecific gravities and weights of bodies.*

On the leg B of the callipers is a table fhewing the weights of a cubic inch or foot of various bodies in pounds averdupoife. To the table here annexed is joined the fpecific gravities of thofe bodies, which are omitted on the callipers for want of room.

In the following table is contained fuch bodies as practical engineers, and others, may have occafion to know their refpective weights; there are indeed a great number of other bodies whofe fpecific gravity have been determined by ingenious men: But thofe only which were apprehended to be the moft ufeful were felected for this fubject.

*A* TABLE

*A* TABLE *shewing the weights of bodies and their specific gravities.*

| Bodies. | | | Weights. | Spe.Gravity. |
|---|---|---|---|---|
| Fine Gold. | | Inch | 0,710359 | 19,640 |
| Standard Gold. | | Inch | 0,706018 | 19,520 |
| Quickfilver. | | Inch | 0,497657 | 13,762 |
| Lead { | | Foot | 707,0458 } | 11,313 |
|  | | Inch | 0,409170 } | |
| Fine Silver. | | Inch | 0,401150 | 11,091 |
| Standard Silver. | | Inch | 0,384440 | 10,629 |
| Copper { | | Foot | 548,0628 } | 8,769 |
|  | | Inch | 0,317166 } | |
| Brafs. | | F. | 506,2746 | 8,104 |
| Steel. | | F. | 490,6241 | 7,850 |
| Bar Iron. | | F. | 485,2500 | 7,764 |
| Block Tin. | | F. | 452,3731 | 7,238 |
| Caft Iron. | | F. | 445,9363 | 7,135 |
| White Marble. | | F. | 168,8757 | 2,702 |
| Glafs. | | F. | 162,4994 | 2,600 |
| Stone { | Flint. | F. | 161,3745 } | 2,582 |
|  | Portland. | F. | 160,6245 } | 2,570 |
|  | Free. | F. | 158,2485 } | 2,352 |
| Brick. | | F. | 125,0000 | 2,000 |
| Brimftone. | | F. | 112,5000 | 1,800 |
| Clay. | | F. | 112,0000 | 1,792 |
| River Sand. | | F. | 110,0000 | 1,760 |
| Sea Water. | | F. | 64,3732 | 1,030 |
| Rain Water { | Cubic | F. | 62,5000 } | 1,000 |
|  | Cubic | Inch | 0,036169 } | |
|  | Cylindric | F. | 49,080000 } | |
|  | Cylindric | Inch | 0,028403 } | |
| Port Wine. | | F. | 61,8000 | 0,988 |
| Brandy. | | F. | 58,0000 | 0,928 |
| Olive Oil. | | F. | 57,0624 | 0,913 |
| Dry Oak. | | F. | 57,1875 | 0,915 |
| Lime. | | F. | 52,0000 | 0,832 |
| Elm and Afh. | | F. | 50,0000 | 0,800 |
| Wheat. | | F. | 50,0000 | 0,800 |
| Yellow Fir. | | F. | 41,0625 | 0,657 |
| White Deal. | | F. | 35,5624 | 0,569 |
| Gun Powder { | | F. | 69,1200 } | 1,106 |
|  | | In. | 0,0400 } | |

Every

Every one will readily conceive how the column of weight may be obtained, namely by procuring maſſes of a cubic inch or foot of the ſolids, and carefully weighing them in nice ſcales to the ſmalleſt degree of averdupoiſe weight: And for the fluids, their weights may be determined by having cubical or cylindrical veſſels made to hold a known quantity of cubical inches, and in them to weigh the fluids.

The ſpecific gravity of a body being the relation which that body has to ſome other body fixed upon a ſtandard to compare by; and rain water being found to be alike, or very nearly ſo, in all places; and therefore choſen by philoſophers as the proper ſtandard; conſequently by the word ſpecific gravity of a body is meant no more, than that it is ſo many times heavier or lighter than water, when compared together in equal bulk.

Thus fine ſilver is ſomething more than 11; that is, a maſs of fine ſilver will weigh ſomething above eleven times the weight of an equal maſs of water: And, ſo a common brick weighs twice as much as the rain water that would fill a mould fitted to the brick.

Now the weights of equal maſſes of ſeveral bodies being determined, their ſpecific gravities may be readily found, they being in the ſame proportion to one another as their weights: And as the compariſon is made to rain water, of which, by repeated experiments, it has been found that a cubic foot weighed 62 ½ pounds averdupoiſe; therefore *dividing the weight of a cubic foot of any body, by 62 ½; the quotient will be the ſpecific gravity of the body*, relative to rain water whoſe ſpecific gravity is repreſented by unity.

The difficulty of procuring maſſes of metals and other bodies in all parts homogenous, and of having both them and the veſſels of capacity conſtructed to a mathematical exactneſs, has rendered this method of eſtimating the ſpecific gravities from the weights of equal bulks, liable to exception: And therefore another method has been contrived to come at theſe ſpecific gravities, hydroſtatically.

It is a well known thing that any body will weigh leſs when it is immerſed in water than when it is weighed in the open air; and

and from a very little reflection, it will be feen that the difference between the weights of any body when weighed in air and in water, will be equal to the weight of fo much water as is equal in bulk to the body immerfed: But the difference between the weights of a body in air and in water, will fhew the weight of a bulk of water equal to the body fo weighed: *Therefore to find the fpecific gravity of any body, find its weight in air and in rain water, and take the difference of thofe weights; then the weight in air divided by that difference, will give the fpecific gravity required.*

If the folid whofe fpecific gravity is wanted, be lighter than water, fo that it cannot fink by its own weight, let it be joined to another fo weighty that the compound may fink: But firft let the lofs of weight which the heavy body alone fuftains in water be found as before; and then let the lofs of weight which the compound body fuftains be difcovered; from which take the lofs of weight of the heavier, and the remainder is the lofs of weight fuftained by the lighter; by which dividing the weight in air of the lighter body, and the quotient will fhew the fpecific gravity.

When the fpecific gravity of fluids are to be compared to each other; take a folid of any matter and fhape, fuppofe a glafs ball, hung by a horfe hair, and immerfe this folid in each fluid, and find the lofs of weight of the folid in each fluid, the weight of the body in air being firft known; then will thefe loffes exprefs the fpecific gravities of thofe fluids: For fince the lofs of weight in each liquor is equal to the weight of as much of the liquor as is equal in bulk to the body weighed; therefore by taking the loffes of weight fuftained by the fame body in the feveral liquors, the abfolute weights are obtained of fuch proportions as are equal in bulk, and confequently the fpecific gravities of thofe liquors.

In this method of finding the fpecific gravity of folids, it is not neceffary that they fhould be reduced to any regular fhape; neither is there wanted a veffel of a known figure and capacity to contain the fluids; and confequently the fpecific gravities of bodies, whether folids or fluids, may be very eafily come at:

But

But from the fpecific gravities to find the abfolute weights of any affigned mafs of feveral bodies, there muft be another experiment made, which is to find the lofs of weight in water, of a body of a known magnitude; fuppofe of a cylinder of a homogenous metal, the folidity of that cylinder being moft accurately calculated; then will the abfolute weight of an equal mafs of water be known; and confequently the weight of a cubic foot of water may be accurately obtained, *from whence the abfolute weight of a cubic foot of any other body whofe fpecific gravity is known, may be found by multiplying the fpecific gravity of that body by the weight of a cubic foot of water.*

### SOME USES OF THE TABLE.

The weights of bodies anfwering to a given folidity are of a twofold ufe.

Firft, *To find the weight of a body of a given dimenfions, or folidity.*

Secondly, *To find the folidity of a body by knowing its weight.*

EXAM I. *What is the weight of a block of marble 7 feet long, 3 feet broad, and 2 feet thick?*

Now $7 \times 3 \times 2 = 42$ feet for the folidity.

A cubic foot of marble weighs 168,8757 pounds.

Then $168,8757 \times 42$ gives 7092,7794 pounds.

  C qrs. lb.

Or, 63 .. 1 .. $8\frac{3}{4}$ is the weight of that marble.

EXAM II. *What is the weight of a 13 inch iron bomb fhell, the metal being two inches thick on a mean?*

Here the folidity of two fpheres muft be found, one of 13 inches diameter, and the other of 9 inches diameter; then their difference being taken will give the folidity of the fhell.

Now the cube of 13 is 2197.

And the cube of 9 is 729.

Alfo $2197 \times 0,5236$ gives 1150,3492 folidity.

And  $729 \times 0,5236$ gives 381,7044 folidity.

Their difference is 768,6448 cubic inches.

And

And 768,6448 divided by 1728 gives 0,4448 parts of a cubic foot.

Now a cubic foot of caſt iron weighs 445,9363 pounds.

Then 445,9363 × 0,4448 gives 198,363 pounds for the weight of the ſhell.

EXAM III. *How many pigs, each of 12 inches long, 6 wide and 4 thick, may be caſt out of 10 tons of melted lead?*

Now 10 ton = 10 × 20 = 200 Cwt.

And 112 × 200 = 22400 pounds in 10 ton.

By the table, 707,0458 pound makes a cubic foot of lead.

And 22400 divided by 707,0458, gives 31,681 cubic feet, which the 10 ton will make.

Now the ſolidity of each pig is $\frac{1}{6}$ of a foot.

Therefore 31,681 feet ſolid will make 190 pigs.

From ſeveral experiments it appears that middling ſized men, or thoſe between 5 feet 6 inches and 5 feet 9 inches in height, weigh about 150 pounds, and are in bulk equal to about 2 $\frac{3}{4}$ ſolid feet; and the ſmall ſized men, or thoſe between 5 feet 3 inches, and 5 feet 6 inches in height, weigh about 135 pounds, and are in bulk equal to about 2 $\frac{1}{2}$ ſolid feet: And from thoſe experiments it alſo appears, that moſt men are ſpecifically lighter than common water, and much more ſo than ſea water. Conſequently could perſons who fall into water, have preſence of mind enough to avoid the fright uſual on ſuch occaſions, many might be preſerved from drowning. And a very ſmall piece of wood, ſuch as an oar, would buoy a man above water while he had ſpirits to keep his hold.

A gentleman who had been on board of a Malteſe ſhip of war, obſerved hanging to the tafarel, a block of wood almoſt like a buoy, and ſo balanced that one end ſwam upright, carrying a little flagſtaff with a ſmall vane; the perſon who was on duty on the poop, had orders to cut the rope by which the buoy hung, upon any cry of a perſon's falling overboard; and as the block would be in the ſhip's wake by the time the perſon floated therein, he was ſure of having ſomething at hand to

ſuſtain

suftain him, till the boat could come to his affiftance; and fhould that take fo long time to do, as the diftance from the fhip to the man rendered him invifible, yet the boat would have a mark to row towards, fhewn them by the vane.

EXAM IV. *How many fpars of white fir, each of 20 feet long and a foot fquare, are to be lafhed together, till the raft is fufficient to float, in common water, 100 barrels of gunpowder conducted by four middling fized men, fo as to keep the barrels three inches clear of the water?*

A barrel of gunpowder, barrel and all, weighs about 120 lb.

So 100 barrels will weigh 12000 lb.

And 4 men, at 150 lb each, weigh 600 lb.

So that the raft muft fuftain a weight of 12600 lb.

Now the deal will of itfelf fink in the water, until the weight of the water difplaced is equal to the weight of the wood.

In each fpar there is 20 feet of timber.

A cubic foot of white deal weighs 35,5624 pounds.

So 35,5624 × 20 = 711,248 lb. the weight of one fpar.

And is alfo equal to the weight of the water difplaced.

A cubic foot of water weighs 62,5 lb.

Then 62,5 : 1 :: 711,248 : 11,38 the number of cubic feet which each fpar will have immerfed by its own weight.

As the barrels are to be 3 inches clear of the water, therefore the fpar muft be funk 9 inches; and confequently 15 feet folid of each fpar muft be immerfed:

Then 15 − 11,38 = 3,62 the additional cubic feet of water to be difplaced by each fpar, by its incumbent weight.

And 1 : 3,62 :: 62,5 : 226,25 lb. the weight which each fpar is to fuftain.

Then 226,25 : 12600 :: 1 : 55,6, &c.

Confequently 56 fuch fpars lafhed together will make a float fufficient for to fuftain the given weight in the manner propofed.

ARTICLE

## ARTICLE X.

*Of the quantity of powder ufed in firing of cannon.*

On the circular head of the callipers, on the face D is a table contained between five concentric fegments of circular rings; the inner one markt GUNS, fhews the nature of the gun, or the weight of the ball it carries: The two next rings contain the quantity of powder ufed for proof and fervice to brafs guns; and the two outermoft rings fhew the quantity for proof and fervice, ufed in iron cannon.

### THE TABLE.

| Nature of guns | Brafs | | Iron | | Salutes | Scaling |
|---|---|---|---|---|---|---|
| | Proof | Service | Proof | Service | | |
| Pounders | lb. oz. | lb. oz. | lb. oz. | lb. oz. | lb. oz. | lb. oz. |
| I | 1.0 | 0.8 | 1.0 | 0.8 | 0.8 | 0.1$\frac{1}{2}$ |
| 1$\frac{1}{2}$ | 1.8 | 0.12 | 1.8 | 0.12 | 0.12 | 0.2 |
| 2 | 2.0 | 1.0 | 2.0 | 1.0 | 1.0 | 0.3 |
| 3 | 3.0 | 1.8 | 3.0 | 1.8 | 1.8 | 0.4 |
| 4 | 4.0 | 2.0 | 4.0 | 2.0 | 2.0 | 0.6 |
| 5$\frac{1}{4}$ | 5.4 | 2.10 | 5.4 | 2.10 | 2.10 | 0.8 |
| 6 | 6.0 | 3.0 | 6.0 | 3.0 | 3.0 | 0.8 |
| 8 | 8.0 | 4.0 | 8.0 | 4.0 | 3.12 | 0.10 |
| 9 | 9.0 | 4.8 | 9.0 | 4.8 | 4.0 | 0.12 |
| 12 | 12.0 | 6.0 | 12.0 | 6.0 | 4.12 | 1.0 |
| 18 | 18.0 | 9.0 | 15.0 | 9.0 | 6.0 | 1.8 |
| 24 | 21.0 | 12.0 | 18.0 | 11.0 | 7.0 | 2.0 |
| 26 | 22.0 | 13.0 | 19.0 | 12.0 | 7.12 | 2.4 |
| 32 | 26.12 | 16.0 | 21.8 | 14.0 | 9.4 | 2.12 |
| 36 | 28.0 | 18.0 | 22.0 | 15.0 | 10.0 | 3.0 |
| 42 | 31.8 | 21.0 | 25.0 | 17.0 | 11.4 | 3.4 |

The

The numbers in this table exprefs the Englifh ufage, which for the moft part, allows the weight of the fhot for proof, half its weight for fervice, and one fourth of its weight of fhot for falutes.

The French allowance of powder, for the charge of the piece for fervice, ufed to be two thirds of the weight of the fhot; twice as much for proof; and one fourth of the weight of fhot for falutes.

Guns carrying fhot of the weight 1 lb. $1\frac{1}{2}$ lb. 2 lb. 4 lb. $5\frac{1}{4}$ lb. 8 lb. 26 lb. 36 lb. are now out of ufe in the Britifh navy.

The ufe of this table is obvious: For feek the name of the gun in the inner ring, and the weights of powder for proof and fervice will be found between the fame two ftrait lines, like radii; and in one of the other rings, according as it is tituled at the end.

Thus to a brafs 9 pounder there is allowed 9 lb. of powder for to prove, or try the goodnefs of the gun when it is firft caft; and 4 lb. 8 oz. of powder for each charge in common fervice: But an iron 9 pounder has 9 lb. for proof, and 6 lb. for fervice.

When cannon are proved they are ufually loaded with two fhot.

On fhipboard, after there are five or fix rounds fired on warm fervice the allowance of powder is to be proportionally leffened each time the gun is loaded, until the charge is reduced to one third or a fourth of the weight of the fhot: And the guns as they grow warm in firing, are not to be wetted left the gun be in danger of fplitting by checking the metal with cold water.

The ingenious Mr. *Robins*, from fome hints he gathered from a manufcript lent him by the Right Honourable Lord *Anfon*, advifes to leffen confiderably the common charges allowed to cannon in fervice: For from thofe papers it appeared that in fervice, where 24 pounders have been ufed to batter in breach, the charge was only 8 pounds of powder: Indeed the velocity of the ball could not be quite fo great with 8 pounds of powder as with 12, and confequently the fhot would not be

drove

drove fo far into the rampart, and the breach not made altogether fo foon; notwithftanding which, the advantages attending the fmaller charges, greatly overbalanced the difference of a few hours in making a fufficient breach.

In fea fervice it would perhaps be found of greater ufe to begin with one third of the weight of fhot in powder, and to diminifh that to one fourth or one fifth as the gun waxed warm; for by fome experiments it has appeared that fuch fmall charges of powder has produced greater ravage in timber, than has been found with the ufual charges: From whence it may be concluded, that if a fhot has juft force enough to go through one fide of a fhip, there will be a greater quantity of fplinters rent out of the plank, and confequently do more mifchief, than if the fhot went with a velocity fufficient to drive it through both fides of the fhip.

## ARTICLE XI.

### *Of the number of fhot or fhells in a finifhed pile.*

Iron fhot and fhells are ufually piled up by horizontal courfes into a pyramidal form, the bafe being either an equilateral triangle or a fquare, or a rectangle; in a triangle or fquare, the pile finifhes in a fingle ball; but in the rectangle, the finifhing is a fingle row of balls.

In the triangular and fquare piles, the number of horizontal rows, or the number counted on one of the angles from the bottom to the top, is always equal to the number counted on one fide, in the bottom row.

In triangular piles, each horizontal courfe is a triangular number, produced by taking the fucceffive fums of the numbers 1 and 2; 1, 2 and 3; 1, 2, 3 and 4; 1, 2, 3, 4 and 5, &c. Thus.

Numbers in order 1 . 2 . 3 . 4 . 5 . 6 . 7 . 8 . 9 . 10 . 11, &c.
Triangular numb. 1 . 3 . 6 . 10 . 15 . 21 . 28 . 36 . 45 . 55 . 66, &c.

And the number of fhot in a triangular pile is the fum of all the triangular numbers taken as far, or to as many terms, as the number in one fide of the bottom courfe.

*A rule*

*A rule to find the number of shot in a triangular pile.*

Count the number in the bottom row, and multiply that number more two by that number more one: Then the product multiplied by one sixth of the said number, the product will be the sum of all the shot in the pile.

EXAM. I. *How many shot are in a finished triangular pile, in one side of whose bottom course are 20 shot?*

Now the number more two is 22; and the number more one is 21.

And 22 × 21 gives 462.

Then $462 \times \frac{20}{6} = 1540$, the number of shot in that pile.

EXAM. II. *Required the number of shot in a finished pile; there being in one side of the triangular base 40 shot?*

Here the number more two is 42; and the number more one is 41.

And 42 × 41 gives 1722.

Then $1722 \times \frac{40}{6} = 11480$ shot in that pile.

In square piles, each horizontal course is a square number, produced by taking the square of the number in its side.

Number in the side     1.2.3. 4. 5. 6. 7. 8. 9. 10, &c.

Square, or horiz. courses   1.4.9.16.25.36.49.64.81.100, &c.

And the number of shot in a square pile is the sum of all the squares, taken from one, as far as the number in the sides of the bottom course.

*A rule to find the number of shot in a square pile.*

Count the number in one side of the bottom course; to that number add one, and to its double add one; multiply the two sums together; then their product being multiplied by one sixth of the said number, the product will give the number of shot contained in that pile.

EXAM. III. *How many shot are in a square finished pile, one side of its base containing 20 shot?*

Here

Here the number is 20.

The number more one is 21; and its double, more one is 41.

The product of thefe numbers is 861 (= 21 × 41)

Then 861 × $\frac{20}{6}$ = 2870, the number of fhot in that pile.

EXAM. IV. *Required the number of fhot in a fquare finifhed pile, one fide of the lower courfe, or tier, having 40 fhot in it?*

Here the number counted is 40.

That number more one is 41; its double, more one is 81.

And 81 × 41 gives 3321.

Then 3321 × $\frac{40}{6}$ = 22140 the number in that pile.

From thefe examples it may be obferved, that where room is wanted, 'tis moft convenient to have the fhot ftowed in triangular piles: For on the equilateral triangle, which is lefs than half the area of a fquare on one of its fides, there can be piled a greater number than half of what can be raifed on the fquare: Indeed the height of a fquare pile is fomewhat lefs than a triangular one, as a fhot will fink lower in the fpace between 4 others, than in the fpace between 3 others, all the fhot being of equal diameter; they being fo reckoned in every pile.

In a rectangular pile, each horizontal courfe is a rectangle, the upper one being one row of balls: Now every fuch oblong pile may be confidered as confifting of two parts, one a fquare pyramid, and the other a triangular prifm.

*To find the number of fhot in a rectangular pile.*

1ft. Take the difference between the number in length and breadth in the bottom courfe.

2d. Multiply the number in breadth, more one, by half the breadth; the product multiplied by the faid diftance, will give the number in the prifmatic pile.

3d. Upon the fquare of the breadth, find (by the laft rule) the number in a pyramidal pile.

4th. Then the fum of thefe two piles will fhew the number in the rectangular pile.

N. B.

N. B. The number of horizontal courſes, or rows, is equal to the number in breadth at the bottom: And the number leſs one, in the top row, is the difference between the number in length and breadth at the bottom.

EXAM. V. *How many ſhot are in a finiſhed pile of* 20 *courſes, the number in the top row being* 40 *?*

Here 39 is the difference between the length and breadth.

And 20 is the breadth.

Now $20 + 1 = 21$; and $2 \times 20 + 1 = 41$.

Then $21 \times 41 \times \frac{20}{6} = 2870$, are the ſhot in the pyramidal pile.

Again. The breadth more one is 21; and 10 is the half breadth.

And $21 \times 10 = 210$.

Then $210 \times 39 = 8190$, and the ſhot in the priſmatic pile.

Conſequently the ſum of 2870 and 8190, or 11060 ſhot will be the number contained in that rectangular pile.

If any of theſe piles are broken, by having the upper part taken off, and the remaining number of ſhot are required; it may be obtained by computing what the whole finiſhed pile would contain; and alſo what the pile wanting, or taken away contained; for then their difference will ſhew the number remaining.

The foregoing rules are thus expreſſed on the Callipers.

Number of ſhot or ſhells in a pile.

Let $n = $ Nº in an angular row $\Big\}$ of a Pile

$m = $ Nº leſs one in the top row

Then $\overline{n + 2} \times \overline{n + 1} \times \dfrac{n}{6}$ $= $ Nº in a $\triangle$

And $\overline{n + 1} \times \overline{2n + 1} \times \dfrac{n}{6}$ $= $ Nº in a $\square$ $\Big\}$ Pile.

Alſo $\overline{2n + 1 + 3m} \times \overline{n + 1} \times \dfrac{n}{6} = $ Nº in a $\square$

In Examples I & III. The letter $n$ ſtands for 20.

In Examples II & IV. The letter $n$ ſtands for 40.

In Example V. The letter $n$ ſtands for 20.

And

And the letter $m$ ſtands for 39.

Then $2n + 1 = 2 \times 20 + 1 = 41$.

And $3m \qquad\qquad = 117$.

So $\overline{2n + 1 + 3m} \qquad = 158$.

Alſo $\overline{n + 1} \qquad\qquad = 21$.

And $\dfrac{n}{6} \qquad\qquad\quad = \dfrac{20}{6}$

Then $\overline{2n + 1 + 3m} \times \overline{n + 1} \times \dfrac{n}{6} = 158 \times 21 \times \dfrac{20}{6} = 11060$.

# ARTICLE XII.

### *Concerning the fall of heavy bodies.*

When heavy bodies are ſuffered to fall, it is well known they fall in lines perpendicular to the ſurface of the earth.

The force with which any body in motion ſtrikes an obſtacle, depends on the weight of that body, and on the velocity or ſwiftneſs with which it moves.

Thus a man by throwing, with the ſame ſtrength, a pound of iron and a pound of cork, will hit a much harder ſtroke with the iron than with the cork.

Alſo a man and a boy each throwing a pound of iron againſt the ſame objeƈt, the ſtroke given by the man will be ſtronger than that given by the boy, on account of the man's weight flying the ſwifteſt.

The ſame heavy body by falling from different heights, will ſtrike blows of different ſtrength, that being the ſtrongeſt where the height is greateſt. Conſequently heavy bodies by falling acquire velocities greater and greater according to the length of their fall.

The three following propoſitions in falling bodies have been proved many ways.

1ſt. *That the velocities acquired, are direƈtly proportional to the times.*

2d. *That the ſpaces fallen through, are as the ſquares of the times,*

*times, or as the squares of the velocities.*

3d. *That a body moving uniformly with the velocity obtained by falling through any height, will fall twice as far in the same time it was passing through that height.*

Experiments shew that heavy bodies fall about 16 feet in one second of time: Confequently at the end of the first second of time, a falling body has acquired a velocity that would carry it down 32 feet in the next second of time.

Then from the foregoing three proportions may be derived the following rules.

1*ſt*. That the square root of the feet in the space fallen through, will ever be equal to one eighth of the velocity acquired at the end of the fall.

2*d*. That the square root of the feet in the space fallen through, will ever be equal to four times the number of seconds of time the body has been falling.

3*d*. And that four times the number of seconds of time in which the body has been falling, is equal to one eight the velocity in feet per second, acquired at the end of the fall.

From these three rules most of the questions relative to the fall of bodies may be readily solved.

As these rules cannot, for want of room, be put in words at length on the callipers, they are, on the face A of one of the legs, expressed in an algebraic manner. Thus,

### FALL OF BODIES.

Let s = space run in feet.

T = time in seconds.

v = velocity in feet per second.

Then $\sqrt{s} = 4\text{T} = \frac{1}{8}\text{v}$.

Bodies fall 16 feet in the 1ſt sec.

*Note.* The character $\sqrt{}$, signifies the square root of the letter joined to it.

SOME

### SOME USES.

EXAM. I. *How many feet will a bullet fall in 5 seconds of time ?*
Here the time $T = 5$;
Then $4T$, makes $4 \times 5 = 20$.
Now $\sqrt{S} (= 4T) = 20$.
And $S = (20 \times 20 =) 400$.

EXAM. II. *From what height must a bullet fall to acquire a velocity of 160 feet per second ?*
The rule is $\sqrt{S} = \frac{1}{8} V$.
Here $V$ is 160 feet.
And $\frac{1}{8} V = (\frac{160}{8} =) 20$.
Then $S = (20 \times 20 =) 400$.

EXAM. III. *How long must a bullet be in falling to acquire a velocity of 160 feet per second ?*
The rule is $4T = \frac{1}{8} V$.
Here $V = 160$ feet.
And $\frac{1}{8} V = (\frac{160}{8} =) 20$.
So $4T = 20$.
Then $T = (\frac{20}{4} =) 5$ seconds of time.

EXAM. IV. *How many seconds will it require for a heavy body to fall through a space equal to 3375 yards ?*
The rule is $4T = \sqrt{S}$.
Therefore $T = \frac{1}{4} \sqrt{S}$.
Here $S = 3375$ yards, or 10125 feet.
And the square root of 10125 is 100,6.
Then 100,6 divided by 4 gives 25,15.
So that it will require $25''. \ 9'''$ of time for the body to fall through 3375 yards.

ARTICLE

# A R T I C L E  XIII.

*Rules for the raising of water.*

Experiments have shewn, that taking horses and men of a moderate strength, one horse will do as much work in raising of water, and such like labour, as five men can.

It has also been found, that one man in a minute, can raise a hogshead of water 12 feet high upon a mean: For a stout man, well plied with strong liquor, will raise a hogshead of water 15 feet high in a minute: Now as the quantity of liquor equal to a hogshead was raised to these heights only by way of experiment for a few minutes, such numbers ought not to be esteemed as the common labour of a man who is to work 4 or 5 hours on a stretch: But it may be reckoned, that of common labouring men, taken one with another, one of them will raise a hogshead of water 8 feet in height in one minute, and work at that rate for some hours.

It is quite indifferent in what manner the man is supposed to apply his force; whether by carrying the water in manageable parcels up a stair-case, or raising it by means of some machine: For the advantage gained by using of engines arises chiefly from the ease with which the power can be applied.

On the face A of the callipers, are the rules, thus denoted.

To raise water.

The power $=$ P men.
Or to $\frac{1}{5}$ P horses
Can raise to 8P feet high $=$ F.
The quantity H, hhds. in T min.
Or G, gallons in 60 T seconds.
Or, $H \times F = P \times 8 \times T$ minutes.
*N. B.* Cubic feet $\times$ 6,1277 gives gall.

Here hogsheads are reckoned at 60 gallons, this estimate being nice enough for any computations on water engines.

SOME

### SOME USES.

EXAMP. I. *How many hogsheads can six horses raise, by an engine, to 25 feet high in 3 hours?*

Now 6 horses, at 5 men to a horse, is equal to 30 men.

And the time 3 hours is equal to 180 minutes.

The height to be raised is 25 feet.

The general rule is $H \times F = P \times 8 \times T$.

Here $F = 25$; $P = 30$; $T = 180$.

And H is required.

Then $H = \dfrac{\overline{P \times 8 \times T}}{F}$

Or $H = \left( \dfrac{30 \times 8 \times 180}{25} = \right)$ 1728 hogsheads.

*Hence this rule.* Multiply eight times the power by the time, the product divided by the height gives the hogsheads.

EXAMP. II. *It is proposed to throw out of a pond, by an engine, 432 tuns of water in 3 hours by six horses; to what height can the water be raised?*

As 4 Hhds make one tun; so 432 tuns make 1728 Hhds.

And 3 hours, or 180 minutes is the time.

Also the power of six horses, is equal to that of 30 men.

The general rule is $H \times F = P \times 8 \times T$.

Here $H = 1728$; $P = 30$; $T = 180$.

And F is required.

Then $F = \dfrac{P \times 8 \times T}{H}$

Or $F = \left( \dfrac{30 \times 8 \times 180}{1728} = \right)$ 25 feet high.

*Hence this rule.* Multiply eight times the power by the time; the product divided by the hogsheads, gives the height in feet.

EXAMP. III. *How long will it require six horses to raise with an engine 1728 hogsheads of water to the height of 25 feet?*

Now

Now the power of 6 horfes, is equal to that of 30 men.

The hogfheads to be raifed are 1728.

The height raifed to is 25 feet.

The general rule is $H \times F = P \times 8 \times T$.

Here $H = 1728$; $F = 25$; $P = 30$.

And $T$ is required.

Then $T = \dfrac{H \times F}{P \times 8}$

Or $T = \left( \dfrac{1728 \times 25}{30 \times 8} = \right)$ 180 minutes, or 3 hours.

*Hence this rule.* Multiply the hogfheads, by the height in feet; the product divided by eight times, the power will give the time in minutes.

EXAMP. IV. *How many horfes will it require to work an engine, to raife 1728 hogfheads to the height of 25 feet, in 3 hours?*

Now the hogfheads to be raifed are 1728.

The height to be raifed is 25 feet.

The time to be done in is 3 hours, or 180 minutes.

The general rule is $H \times F = P \times 8 \times T$.

Here $H = 1728$; $F = 25$; $T = 180$.

And $P$ is required.

Then $P = \dfrac{H \times F}{8 \times T}$

Or $P = \left( \dfrac{1728 \times 25}{8 \times 180} = \right)$ 30 men, or 6 horfes.

*Hence this rule.* Multiply the hogfheads, by the height in feet; the product divided by eight times the number of minutes, gives the number of men.

# ARTICLE XIV.

### *Of the fhooting in cannon and mortars.*

It has been proved by many writers, that the flight of fhot, or the track they defcribe in the air, is a curve line called a Parabola: But then they fuppofe that the refiftance made by the air is fo inconfiderable as fcarcely to affect the motion of heavy
bodies.

bodies.

Upon this fuppofition then, which is very far from being true; there have been collected the following obfervations and rules.

I. All bodies projected by any force, are urged with two motions, viz. one in the direction of the power exerted by the engine, and the other in a perpendicular direction to the earth, by the force of gravity; and the track or path defcribed by the body with thefe two forces is a curve called the parabola.

II. The axis of the curve will be at right angles to the horizon; and the part in which the body defcends will be alike to that in which it afcends.

III. If the point to which a body arrives in its defcent, be on the fame level with the point from which it was projected, thofe points are equally diftance from the vertex, or higheft point of the curve.

IV. If a body be projected oblique to the horizon, it will fall there again in the fame obliquity, and with the fame velocity it was projected withal.

V. The horizontal ranges of equal bodies, when projected with the fame velocity, at different elevations, will be in proportion to one another; as the right fines of twice the angles of elevation.

VI. Among equal bodies, projected with equal velocities, the heights to which they will rife in the air, are in the fame proportion to one another as the verfed fines of twice the angles of elevation.

VII. When equal bodies are projected with equal velocities, the times of the continuance in the air will be in proportion to one another as the right fines of the angles of elevation.

VIII. In the fame piece, different charges of equally good gunpowder will produce velocities, nearly the fame in proportion as the fquare roots of the weights of the charges.

IX. If equal bodies be projected at the fame elevation, but with
different

different velocities, the horizontal ranges will be in proportion to one another, as the ſquares of the velocities given to the ſhot, or as the weights of the charges of powder nearly.

X. The greateſt horizontal range is double to the height from which the body ſhould fall to acquire that force or velocity which would projećt it to that horizontal range.

XI. The greateſt horizontal range, or diſtance to which a body can be thrown, will be obtained when it is projećted at an angle of 45 degrees of elevation.

XII. The greateſt height to which a projećted body can riſe, at an elevation of 45 degrees, is equal to one fourth part of its horizontal range.

XIII. To hit an objećt that lies above or below the horizon of the piece, the beſt elevation, is equal to the complement of half the angular diſtance between the objećt and the zenith.

XIV. At elevations equally diſtant from 45 degrees, both above and below it, the horizontal ranges will be equal.

XV. The time which a heavy body, projećted at an elevation of 45 degrees, will continue in the air, before it arrives at the horizon, will be equal to the time that the body would take to deſcend, by the force of gravity, through a ſpace equal to the horizontal range.

It has been found that a 24 pounder at an elevation of 45 degrees, and charged with 16 pounds of powder, has ranged its ſhot upon the horizontal plane about 6750 yards.

Therefore 3375 is the impetus, or perpendicular ſpace which a 24 pounder muſt fall through to acquire ſuch a velocity, as, at an elevation of 45 degrees, would projećt or throw that ſhot on the horizon to the diſtance of 6750 yards.

Now a heavy body falling by the force of gravity through a ſpace equal to 3375 yards or 10125 feet, will, at the end of the fall, acquire a velocity of 804,8 or about 805 feet per ſecond (as ſhewn in Art. XII.)

And

And to fall through a fpace of 805 feet, it would require 25″. 9‴ of time.

The chief of the above principals are fhortly expreffed on the face B of the callipers in the following manner.

### RULES FOR SHOOTING.

Hor. ranges, as right $\Big\}$ fines of twice $\Big\{$ angles of
Heights, are as verfed $\quad$ elevation
Time in air, as right fines of ——— $\Big\}$

Impetus $= \frac{1}{2}$ $\Big\}$ Hor. range, at 45 deg. of elevation.
Height $\ = \frac{1}{4}$

In afcents or defcents, for the beft elevation.

Take the complement of $\frac{1}{2}$ the angular diftance from object to zenith.

To apply thefe rules to the practice of fhooting, it is to be underftood that the gunner fhould make an experiment with every gun he has the care of at fome elevation, fuppofe at 45 degrees, and with the ufual charge of powder, and then knowing how far the piece has ranged the fhot on the horizontal plane; he may apply the refult of thofe experiments to other elevations and quantities of powder.

EXAMP. I. *Suppofe the greateft horizontal range to be* 6750 *yards: How far will the fame piece, and with an equal charge of powder, range a fhot at an elevation of* 25 *degrees?*

With equal charges the horizontal ranges are as the right fines of twice the angles of elevation.

Then, As radius, or the fine of twice 45°
    Is to the fine of 50°, or the fine of twice 25°,
    So is the greateft horizontal range 6750 yds
    To the horizontal range required, 5170 yds.

That is, The extent on the line of fines from 90° to 50°
    Will on the line of numbers reach from 6750 to 5170.

EXAMP. II. *The greateft horizontal range of a* 24 *pounder being* 6750 *yards. To what height will the fhot rife at an elevation of* 25 *degrees?*

At

At an elevation of 45°, the ſhot will riſe 1687½ yards, = ¼ of 6750.

And the heights are as the verſed ſines of twice the angles of elevation.

Then, As the verſed ſine of 90 degrees, or of twice 45°,
    Is to the verſed ſine of 50 degrees, or of twice 25°;
    So is the height of an elevation of 45°, viz. 1687½,
    To the height at an elevation of 25°. 602,8 yards.

The logarithm verſed ſines on the callipers are the ſupplements of the real verſed ſines; therefore in the uſing of this line the ſupplements of the doubles angles are to be uſed.

Then the extent from the verſed ſine of 90° to the verſed ſine of 130° (the ſupplement of 50°) will on the line of numbers reach from 1687½ to 603.

Or thus. Take 1292½ = ¼ of 5170, the horizontal range on an elevation of 25°.

Then, The extent on the log. tangents from radius to 25°, will on the line of numbers reach from 1292½ to about 603 yards.

EXAMP. III. *At an elevation of 25 degrees, how many ſeconds will a 24 pounder continue in the air before it arrives at the horizon?*

At 45° elevation the ſhot takes 35½ ſeconds in the air *.

And the times in air are as the right ſines of the elevations.

Then As the ſine of the elevation, 45 degrees,
    Is to the ſine of the elevation, 25 degrees;
    So is the time in the air at 45°, viz. 35½ ſeconds,
    To the time in the air at 25°, viz. 21 ſeconds.

On the line of log. ſines take the extent from 45 degrees to 25 degrees; then will this extent, applied to the ſcale of log. numbers, reach from 35½ to 21 ſeconds.

And hence may be eſtimated the lengths of fuſes proper for
ſhells

* This time of 35½ seconds is derived from Rule XV. Then working by the rules belonging to article XII. it will be found that a heavy body will require 35½ seconds to fall through the space of 6750 yards.

fhells to be fired at given elevations and ranges.


EXAMP. IV. *Required the elevation neceffary to ftrike an object on the horizon at 5170 yards diftance, the greateft random of that piece being 6750 yards ?*

Say. As the greateft random, 6750 yards,

To a propofed random, 5170 yards;

So is radius, or twice the fine of 45 degrees,

To double the elevation required, viz. 50 deg.

The half of which, or 25 degrees, is the elevation neceffary to be given to the piece.

This elevation is called the lower one.

And the upper elevation, is at 65 degrees.

For 25 degrees and 65 degrees are equally diftant from 45 degrees.


EXAMP. V. *At an elevation of 45 degrees, 16 lb. of powder will throw a 24 pounder 6750 yards: How much powder will throw the fame fhot 5170 yards at the fame elevation ?*

By rule IX. The charges of powder are nearly as the horizontal ranges.

Then As the horizontal range   6750

To the horizontal range 5170,

So is the given charge      16 lb.

To the required charge      12,25 lb.

The proportion may be accurately enough worked by the line of numbers.

For the extent from 6750 to 5170, will reach from 16 to 12 $\frac{1}{4}$.


EXAMP. VI. *At an elevation of 25 degrees, a 24 pounder was ranged on the horizon 5170 yards: Required the impetus that would given an equal velocity to that fhot ?*

With an equal charge of powder ufed at 45 degrees elevation, as was ufed at 25 degrees, the fhot would have the greateft horizontal range.

And with equal charges in the fame piece, the impetus is the fame at any elevation.

Confequently

Confequently, to folve this queftion nothing more is required than to find the greateft horizontal range, which is double to the impetus.

Then from rule V, by inverfion

As the fine of 50 deg. twice the given elevation,

Is to radius, or the fine of twice 45°;

So is the given horizontal range 5170

To the greateft horizontal range 6750,

The half, or 3375 is the impetus required.

That is, the extent on the line of fines from 50° to 90°

Will on the line of numbers reach from 5170 to 6750.

EXAMP. VII. *Suppofe the horizontal range of a piece to be 6750 yards: Required the angle of elevation proper to ftrike an object 12° above the level of the piece, the horizontal diftance of that object being 4680 yards ?*

Say, As the greateft horizontal range   6750

Is to the given horizontal diftance   4680;

So is the cofine of the object's elevation 78° 00′

To another fine   ——   ——   ——   42° 42′.

Thus, the extent on the line of numbers from 6750 to 4680

Will on the line of log. fines reach from 78° to about 42 ¾.

Now on the natural fines, take the extent of 42 ¾ deg.

Then this extent applied from the natural fine of the elevation 12°

Will give the natural fine of about 62 ½ degrees, whofe cofine is about 27° ½.

Or rather 27°. 37′. its half is 13°. 48′.

The fum of 90° and the given elevation 12° is 102; the half is 51°.

Then the fum of thefe halves (51° + 13°. 48′ =) 64° 48′. is the greater elevation.

And the difference of thefe halves (51° − 13°. 48′ =) 37°. 12′. is the leffer elevation.

So that the piece pointed at either of thefe elevations, with the charge of powder that gave the horizontal range, the object will be ftruck.

But

But in fhooting on afcents or defcents, it is beft to take the angle between the object and zenith, and get the complement of the half of that angle; then the piece being elevated to that complement, find by trials what charge will reach the object: For on this elevation, a lefs charge of powder will do the bufinefs than on any other elevation.

So in the foregoing example the diftance of the object from the zenith is 78°,

The half of 78 is 39, and the complement of 39 is 51°, for the beft elevation.

## ARTICLE XV.

### *Of the line of inches.*

This line, the ufe of which is well known, is placed on the edge of the callipers, or on the ftrait borders of the faces C, D.

## ARTICLE XVI.

### *Of the logarithmic fcales of numbers, fines, verfed fines, and tangents.*

Thefe fcales are placed along the faces C, D of the callipers, near the ftrait edges, and are marked and numbered as fhewn in fection X; fome of the ufes of thefe fcales are alfo fhewn in the XV and following fections.

## ARTICLE XVII.

### *Of the line of lines.*

The line of lines is placed on the callipers on the faces C, D, in an angular pofition, tending towards the center of the inftrument; its conftruction and ufes are the fame as defcribed in treating of the fector; the reader will find fufficient inftructions in the fections XI. and XII.

ARTICLE

## ARTICLE XVIII.

### *Of the line of plans or superficies.*

These lines lie on the faces C, D, of the callipers, and like the line of lines tend toward the center of the instrument: They are marked near the ends of the callipers with the word *Plan*, and have the figures, 10, 9, 8, 7, 6, 5, 4, 3, 2, 1, 1, running towards the center: Each of these primary divisions is subdivided into ten parts; and each of the subdivisions is also divided into two, or more parts, according to the length of the callipers.

These divisions reckoned from the center along either leg, are as the square roots of all the whole numbers under 100; and also, of the half numbers: That is, the distance from the center to the first one, is as the square root of 1: From the center to the next divisions is as the square root of 1 ½: To the next as 2, the next as 2 ½, the next as 3, &c.

And the distance from the center to the second 1, is as the square root of 10; from the center to the next division is as the square root of 10 ½; to the next as 11; to the next as 11 ½, &c. So that the distances from the center to 2, to 3, to 4, and so on to 10, are as the square roots of 20, 30, 40, and so on to 100; and the intermediate divisions and subdivisions are estimated as before shewn between 1 and 10.

This line is easily constructed from a table of the square roots of all the units and half units under 100; together with a scale of the intended length of the line of plans, divided into 500 or 1000 equal parts; and such a scale is the line of lines.

In the following solutions, the length of lines are supposed to be taken between the points of a pair of compasses: And when the callipers are said to be opened to any line; it means, to the distance of the points of the compasses between which that line was taken; the points being applied transversely to the legs of the callipers, as shewn for the sector at section XII.

SOME

### SOME USES OF THE SCALES OF PLANS.

EXAMP. I. *To find the square root of a given number.*

1*st.* On the line of plans feek the divifions reprefenting the given number: Obferving, that numbers of an odd number of places are beft found between the divifions 1 and 1; and thofe of an even number of places, between the 2d 1 and the 10 at the end.

2*d.* Take, with the compaffes, the diftance between that divifion and the center of the callipers; and this extent being applied, from the center laterally along the *line of lines*, will give the fquare root of the number propofed.

Thus the fquare root   of 9       is 3

                    of 900      is 30

                    of 90000   is 300

                    &c.         &c.

The given numbers being reckoned between the two divifions marked 1 and 1.

Again the fquare root   of 36      is 6

                    of 360     is 18,9

                    of 3600    is 60

                    of 36000   is 189,7.

If the integer places in the given number are even, the root will confift of half as many places: But if the number of integers be odd, increafe it by one, and the integer places in the root will be half that number of places.

Thus numbers of two, four, fix, eight integer places, will have roots confifting of one, two, three, four, &c. places: And numbers confifting of one, three, five, &c. places, have roots of one, two, three, &c. places.

EXAMP. II. *Between two given numbers (fuppofe 4 and 9) to find a mean proportional.*

1*st.* Take the greater of the given numbers (9) laterally from the line of lines, and make this extent a tranfverfe diftance to (9 and 9) the fame number on the line of plans.

2*d.* Take the tranfverfe diftance between (4 and 4) the leffer
given

given number of the line of plans, and this extent applied laterally on the line of lines, will give (6 for) the mean proportional fought.

For 4 : 6 :: 6 : 9.

By this example it is eafy to fee how to find the fide of a fquare equal to a fuperficies whofe length and breadth are given.

EXAMP. III. *Two fimilar, or like, fuperficies being given; to find what proportion they have to one another.*

*1ft.* Take one fide of the greater fuperficies between the points of the compaffes, and make this extent a tranfverfe diftance on the line of plans between 10 and 10; or 100 and 100; or on any other number.

*2d.* Apply a like fide of the lefs fuperficies tranfverfely to the line of plans; and the divifions it falls on will fhew the number, that to the former number (taken tranfverfely for the fide of the greater fuperficies) bears the fame proportion of the leffer fuperficies to the greater.

This proportion may be wrought laterally on either of the legs, reckoning from the center: For like fides of fimilar plans being laid from the center on either leg, will give numbers fhewing the proportion of thofe plans.

EXAMP. IV. *To find the fides, or other lines, of a fuperficies* A, *which fhall be fimilar to a given fuperficies* B, *and in a given proportion to* B, *fuppofe as 3 to 7 ?*

*1ft.* To the fcales of plans, apply tranfverfely, any given line of B to the confequent of the given ratio, as from 7 to 7.

*2d.* Take the tranfverfe diftance, on the plans, of the given antecedent, as from 3 to 3, and this extent will be a like line of the figure A.

*3d.* As many lines being thus found as is neceffary, the figure A may be conftructed.

EXAMP. V. *To find the fides, or other lines, of a fuperficies* D, *which fhall be like to either of two given plane figures* A *and* B; *and also*

*alſo be equal to the ſum or difference of* A *and* B.

1ſt. Find (by Ex. 3.) two numbers expreſſing the proportion of the given figures A and B; and take the ſum and difference of thoſe numbers.

Suppoſe the proportion of A to B, to be as 3 to 7.

Their ſum is 10, and their difference is 4.

Then if D is to be like A.

For the ſum, it will be  3 : 10 :: A : D.

For the diff. it will be  3 :  4 :: A : D.

But if D is to be like B.

Then, for the ſum, it will be  7 : 10 :: B : D.

And for the diff. it will be    7 :  4 :: B : D.

2d. Find (by Ex. 4.) the ſides of a ſuperficies D, ſimilar to A, ſo that A may be to D as 3 to 10 for the ſum, or as 3 to 4 for the difference; or if like to B, ſo that B may be to D, as 7 to 10 for the ſum, or as 7 to 4 for the difference.

And thus, a ſufficient number of lines being found, the figure D may be conſtructed.

EXAMP. VI. *Three numbers being given to find a fourth in a duplicate proportion: Or, the like ſides,* a, b, *or two ſimilar figures* A, B, *being known, and alſo the area* A, *of one, to find the area* B, *of the other.*

On the ſcale of plans, take the given ſuperficies A laterally; and on the ſcale of lines, apply this difference tranſverſely to the given ſide *a* of that ſuperficies: Take the tranſverſe diſtance of the given ſide *b* of the other ſuperficies, from the ſcale of lines; then this diſtance applied laterally on the ſcale of plans, will ſhew the area of B.

Thus. *If* 40 *poles be the ſide of a ſquare whoſe area is* 10 *acres; what is the area of that ſquare whoſe ſide is* 60 *poles ?*

Take the lateral diſtance 10 on the ſcale of plans; apply this diſtance tranſverſely to 40 and 40 on the line of lines: Then the tranſverſe diſtance of 60 and 60 on the lines, applied laterally to the ſcale of plans, will give 22 ½ acres the area required.

Again.

Again. *How many acres of woodland measure, of 18 feet to the pole, is that field which contains 288 acres, at 16½ feet to the pole ?*

Apply the lateral distance of 288, taken from the scale of plans, to the line of lines, transversely from 18 to 18; then the transverse distance of 16½ and 16½ on the lines, will, on the scale of plans, give 242 the area in woodland acres.

EXAMP. VII. *To open the callipers, so that the lines of plans make with one another a right angle ?*

On the line of plans take the lateral extent of any number theron.

Then set the callipers so, that this extent shall be a transverse distance to the halves of the former number, and the lines of plans will then stand at right angles to one another.

Thus: The lateral extent of 60 on the plans, put transversely to 30 and 30 on the plans, will set those lines at right angles to one another.

# ARTICLE XIX.

### *Of the line of solids.*

These lines are laid on the faces of D, C, of callipers, like sectoral lines tending to the center, and are distinguished by the letters SOL placed at their ends.

There are twelve primary divisions on these lines, marked 1, 1, 1, 2, 3, 4, 5, 6, 7, 8, 9, 10; each of the eleven spaces or intervals is divided into ten other parts; and each of these parts is divided into two or more parts, according to the length of the instrument.

These divisions are best taken from a scale of equal parts, such as the line of lines, and thence transferred to the scales of solids, reckoning from the center; from whence the several distances of the divisions are, as the cube roots of such numbers under 100 as are intended to be introduced.

Thus the distance of the first 1 from the center is as the cube root of $\frac{1}{10}$, and the greater divisions following to the second 1, express the cube roots of $\frac{2}{10}$, $\frac{3}{10}$, $\frac{4}{10}$, &c. to the number 1, which

the

the fecond 1 ftands for; and if thefe fpaces are fubdivided, their diftances from the center are as the cube roots of $\frac{15}{100}$, $\frac{25}{100}$, $\frac{35}{100}$, $\frac{45}{100}$, &c.

The diftance from the center to the fecond 1 is as the cube root of 1, and the greater divifions between the fecond 1 and the third 1, are as the cube roots of the whole numbers 2, 3, 4, 5, 6, 7, 8, 9; the intermediate fmaller divifions are as the cube roots of the mixed numbers to which they belong: Thus if the fpace between the divifions reprefenting the roots of 1 and 2 is parted into 4; then thofe fubdivifions will be as the cube roots of 1 $\frac{25}{100}$, 1 $\frac{5}{10}$, 1 $\frac{75}{100}$; and the like for other fubdivifions.

The diftance between the center and the third 1 is as the cube root of 10; and fo the following divifions marked with 2, 3, 4, &c. to 10, are as the cube roots of 20, 30, 40, &c. to 100: each of thefe fpaces are divided into 10 parts, which are as the cube roots of the intermediate whole numbers; and if thefe fubdivifions are again divided, thefe latter divifions will be as the cube roots of the mixed numbers to which they belong.

On the French inftruments, the divifions of this line is ufually extended to 64; and confequently only the cube roots of integer numbers under 64 are thereon expreffed: Now whether the divifions proceed only to 64 or to 100, the beft way of laying them down, is from a table of cube roots ready computed; reckoning the length of the greateft root, or the length of the fcale of folids, to be equal to the length of the line of lines, taken from the center.

The cube roots of $\frac{1}{10}$, $\frac{2}{10}$, $\frac{3}{10}$, $\frac{4}{10}$, $\frac{5}{10}$, $\frac{6}{10}$, $\frac{7}{10}$, $\frac{8}{10}$, $\frac{9}{10}$, are 0,464. 0,585. 0,669. 0,737. 0,794. 0,843. 0,888. 0,928. 0,965.

The following table contains the cube roots of all the whole numbers from 1 to 100.

TABLE

TABLE *of cube numbers and their roots.*

| Cubes | Roots | Cubes | Roots | Cubes | Roots | Cubes | Roots | Cubes | Roots |
|---|---|---|---|---|---|---|---|---|---|
| 1 | 1,000 | 21 | 2,759 | 41 | 3,448 | 61 | 3,936 | 81 | 4,327 |
| 2 | 1,260 | 22 | 2,802 | 42 | 3,476 | 62 | 3,958 | 82 | 4,344 |
| 3 | 1,442 | 23 | 2,844 | 43 | 3,503 | 63 | 3,979 | 83 | 4,362 |
| 4 | 1,587 | 24 | 2,884 | 44 | 3,530 | 64 | 4,000 | 84 | 4,379 |
| 5 | 1,710 | 25 | 2,924 | 45 | 3,557 | 65 | 4,021 | 85 | 4,397 |
| 6 | 1,817 | 26 | 2,962 | 46 | 3,583 | 66 | 4,041 | 86 | 4,414 |
| 7 | 1,913 | 27 | 3,000 | 47 | 3,609 | 67 | 4,061 | 87 | 4,431 |
| 8 | 2,000 | 28 | 3,036 | 48 | 3,634 | 68 | 4,082 | 88 | 4,448 |
| 9 | 2,080 | 29 | 3,072 | 49 | 3,659 | 69 | 4,102 | 89 | 4,465 |
| 10 | 2,154 | 30 | 3,107 | 50 | 3,684 | 70 | 4,121 | 90 | 4,481 |
| 11 | 2,224 | 31 | 3,141 | 51 | 3,708 | 71 | 4,141 | 91 | 4,498 |
| 12 | 2,285 | 32 | 3,175 | 52 | 3,732 | 72 | 4,160 | 92 | 4,514 |
| 13 | 2,351 | 33 | 3,207 | 53 | 3,756 | 73 | 4,179 | 93 | 4,531 |
| 14 | 2,410 | 34 | 3,240 | 54 | 3,780 | 74 | 4,198 | 94 | 4,547 |
| 15 | 2,466 | 35 | 3,271 | 55 | 3,803 | 75 | 4,217 | 95 | 4,563 |
| 16 | 2,520 | 36 | 3,302 | 56 | 3,826 | 76 | 4,236 | 96 | 4,579 |
| 17 | 2,571 | 37 | 3,332 | 57 | 3,848 | 77 | 4,254 | 97 | 4,595 |
| 18 | 2,621 | 38 | 3,362 | 58 | 3,871 | 78 | 4,273 | 98 | 4,610 |
| 19 | 2,668 | 39 | 3,391 | 59 | 3,893 | 79 | 4,291 | 99 | 4,626 |
| 20 | 2,714 | 40 | 3,420 | 60 | 3,915 | 80 | 4,309 | 100 | 4,642 |

The numbers in the foregoing table may be laid on the line of folids in the following manner.

Make the length of the line of folids equal to the length of the line of lines, apply this extant tranfverfely to 4,642 on the line of lines; then the other numbers in the table taken tranfverfely from the line of lines, are to be laid laterally, from the center, on the line of folids.

*Some*

*Some uſes of the lines of ſolids.*

EXAMP. I. *To find the cube root of a given number.*

Seek the given number on the line of ſolids, and take its extent from the center.

Then this extent applied laterally to the line of lines will give the cube root ſought.

It ſhould be remarked, that a given number

of 1, 2 or 3 places, has a root of one place.

of 4, 5 or 6 places, has a root of two places,

of 7, 8 or 9 places, has a root of three places.

And when a given number is ſought for on the line of ſolids,

The primary diviſions from 1 to 10 may be reckoned as ſo many hundreds, or as ſo many hundred thouſands, or as ſo many hundred millions.

Thus the diviſion marked 5 may either repreſent 500, 500000, or 500000000.

And the like of the other primary diviſions and their intermediates.

And hence the diviſions between the center and the firſt of the primary ones, are to be eſtimated for numbers of one, two four, five, ſeven and eight places.

EXAMP. II. *To a number given, to find another in a triplicate ratio of two given numbers.*

Thus. Suppoſe an iron ſhot of 4 inches diameter to weigh 9 lb.; required the weight of that ſhot which is 8 inches in diameter?

Here a number is to be found, that to 9 ſhall be in the triplicate ratio of 4 to 8.

That is, as the cube of 4 is to the cube of 8, ſo is 9 to the number ſought.

Now from any ſcale of equal parts, ſuppoſe inches, take 4; and make it a tranſverſe diſtance to 9 and 9 on the line of ſolids (reckoning the 10 at the end, as 100): Then will the extent of 8 inches, applied tranſverſely to the line of ſolids, give 72 for the number ſought, which is the pounds weight of an iron ſhot of 8

inches

inches diameter.

Again. *Suppose a ship of* 2000 *tons burthen is* 144 *feet* 6 *inches on the keel, and* 51 *feet by the beam: Required the length and breadth of another similar ship that shall be of* 1415 *tons burthen ?*

From any scale of equal parts take 144 $\frac{1}{2}$, and make this extent a transverse distance to 2000 on the line of solids; then will the transverse distance of 1415 taken on the line of solids give the length of the keel, which applied to the said scale of equal parts will give about 128 $\frac{3}{4}$ feet.

Also the extent in equal parts of 51 being made a transverse distance to 2000 on the line of solids; then the transverse distance on the solids of 1415 will give in equal parts 46 $\frac{1}{3}$ feet for the breadth by the beam.

EXAMP. III. *Between two given numbers or lines to find two mean proportionals.*

1*st.* From any scale of equal parts take the measure of the greatest of the given lines or numbers, and apply this extent transversely to that number on the line of solids; then the transverse extent on the solids, of the least of the given numbers, being taken, will be the greater of the required means, whose measure will be found on the said scale of equal parts.

2*d.* Make the extent of the greater mean, a transverse distance to the greater of the given numbers, on the line of solids; then the transverse distance of the lesser of the given numbers, taken from the line of solids, will give the lesser of the required means.

*Suppose two mean proportionals were required between* 9 *and* 41 $\frac{2}{3}$.

The lateral extent of 41 $\frac{2}{3}$, taken from the line of lines, apply transversely to 41 $\frac{2}{3}$, and 41 $\frac{2}{3}$ on the line of solids; then the transverse extent of 9 and 9 taken on the solids, and applied laterally to the line of lines, will give 25 for the greater of the two means.

Apply

Apply the faid extent of 25 tranfverfely to 41 $\frac{2}{3}$ and 41 $\frac{2}{3}$ on the line of folids; then the tranfverfe extent on the folids from 9 to 9 applied laterally to the line of lines, will give 15 for the leffer mean.

For 9, 15, 25 and 41 $\frac{2}{3}$ are in continual proportion.

EXAMP. IV. *To find the fide of a cube equal to a parallelo-pipedon whofe length, breadth and depth are given.*

1*ft*. Between the breadth and depth find a mean proportional by Ex. 2. Art. 18.

2*d*. Find the meafure of the mean proportional on the line of lines, and apply it to the lines of folids tranfverfely, at the numbers expreffing that meafure: Then the tranfverfe extent of the length being taken from the line of folids and applied laterally to the line of lines, will give the fide of a cube equal to that parallelopipedon.

Thus. *Suppofe a parallelopipedon, whofe length is 72, breadth 64, and depth 24.*

The number 64 taken laterally from the line of lines and applied tranfverfely to 64 and 64 on the line of plans; then the tranfverfe diftance of 24 and 24 on the plans meafured laterally on the line of lines gives about 39,2 for the mean proportional.

Apply the extent of the mean proportional, to 39,2 tranfverfely on the line of folids; then the tranfverfe extent of 72 and 72 on the folids, being applied to the line of lines laterally, will give 48 for the fide of the cube equal in folidity to the given parallelopipedon.

For $48 \times 48 \times 48 = 24 \times 64 \times 72 = 110592$.

EXAMP. V. *Two fimilar folids* A *and* B *being given, to find their ratio.*

1*ft*. Take any fide of the folid A, and apply it tranfverfely on the line of folids from 10 to 10, or from any other number to its oppofite.

2*d*. Apply the like fide of the folid B tranfverfely to the line of folids, and obferve the number it falls on: Then will the

numbers

numbers on which thofe tranfverfe extents fall, fhew the ratio of the folids A and B.

EXAMP. VI. *A folid* A *being given to find the dimenfions of a fimilar folid* B, *that to* A *fhall have any affigned ratio.*

1*ft*. On the line of folids feek two numbers expreffing the terms of the given ratio.

2*d*. Take the extent of one fide of the given folid A, and apply it tranfverfely on the lines of folids to the antecedent of that given ratio; then the tranfverfe extent of the confequent taken on the lines of folids will be a like fide of the folid B.

Thus. *To find the fide of a cube* B, *double to a given cube* A.

Here the ratio is as 1 to 2.

Apply the fide of the cube A to the line of folids tranfverfely from 1 to 1; that is from 10 to 10; then will the tranfverfe diftance of the numbers 2 and 2 or 20 and 20 fhew the fide of the cube B.

Again. *To find the diameter of a fphere* B, *that to the fphere* A, *whofe diameter is given, fhall be in the ratio of* 3 *to* 2.

Make the diameter of the fphere A a tranfverfe diftance to 2 and 2 on the lines of folids; then will the tranfverfe diftance of 3 and 3 on the line of folids be the diameter of the fphere B.

EXAMP. VII. *Any number of unequal fimilar folids being given; to find the fide of a fimilar folid equal in magnitude to the fum of the magnitudes of the given folids.*

Take, in equal parts, a number expreffing the fide of one of the given folids, and apply this extent to the lines of folids tranfverfely, to any number (fuppofe 10 at the 3d 1).

Alfo take in the fame equal parts, the numbers fhewing fimilar fides of the other folids, and apply thefe extents to the lines of folids tranfverfely, noting the numbers they fall on.

Then will the tranfverfe extent on the line of folids of a number equal to the fum of the noted numbers, be the like fide of the fimilar folid required, which applied to the fame fcale of

equal

equal parts the others were taken from will give the meafure of that fide.

Thus. *What will be the diameter of that iron fhot caft from 3 other fhot whofe diameters were 4 inches, 4,4 inches, and 5 inches; fuppofing no wafte in melting?*

Make 4 inches a tranfverfe extent on the line of folids, to any number, fuppofe 10. Then 4,4 inches applied tranfverfely to the folids will give about 13 $\frac{1}{3}$; and 5 inches alfo applied tranfverfely to the folids will give about 19 $\frac{2}{3}$: Now the fum of the noted numbers 10 and 13 $\frac{1}{3}$ and 19 $\frac{2}{3}$ will be 43; then the tranfverfe extent of 43 on the line of folids will give 6 $\frac{1}{2}$ inches for the diameter of the new fhot.

EXAMP. VIII. *To find the dimenfions of a folid which fhall be equal to the difference of two given fimilar folids, and alfo fimilar to them.*

Apply a dimenfion of one folid tranfverfely to the line of folids at any number; and alfo note what number on the line of folids, the like dimenfion of the other folid falls tranfverfely on; take the difference of thofe noted numbers; and on the line of folids take tranfverfely the extent of the remainder, and that will be a like dimenfion of the fimilar folid required.

Thus. *With the powder out of a fhell of 10 inches concave diameter is filled a fhell of 7 inches: What fized fhell with the remaining powder fill?*

The extent of 10 inches being applied tranfverfely to the line of folids, at any number, fuppofe 100; the extent of 7 inches will fall tranfverfely on the lines of folids, about the number 34 $\frac{1}{4}$: The difference between 100 and 34 $\frac{1}{4}$ is 65 $\frac{3}{4}$: Then the tranfverfe extent at 65 $\frac{3}{4}$ on the line of folids, will give 8,7 inches for the concavity of that fhell which the remaining powder will fill.

EXAMP. IX. *How many fhells, each of 2 $\frac{1}{2}$ inches concave diameter, may be filled with the powder out of a full fhell of 9 inches concave*

*concave diameter ?*

Here the capacities being fimilar, the Example is like Ex. V.

Now make the 9 inches a tranfverfe diftance to 10 and 10, that is 100 and 100, on the line of folids.

Then the tranfverfe diftance anfwering to 2½ inches, on the line of folids, will be nearly 2,15. So that the ratio of the 9 inch concavity, to that of the 2½ inch concavity, will be nearly as 100 to 2,15.

Then as 2,15 : 100 :: 1 : 46,5 the number of the fmall fhells which may be filled; that is, 46, allowing a little wafte.

# A R T I C L E   XX.

## *Of Ship Guns and Sea Mortars.*

The author of this Treatife, foon after he was appointed, by the late Lord *Anfon*, to be the head Mafter of the Royal Academy at *Portfmouth*, obtained permiffion of the officers of the Gun Wharf there, to take sketches and meafures of fuch military machines as he defired; whereby he was furnifhed with a competent number of dimenfions of fhip guns and their carriages, alfo of fea mortars and their beds, to enable him to draw up fome papers for the inftruction of his fcholars in the names of the parts of thofe machines, and alfo to delineate their figures in nearly a juft reprefentation of thofe already in ufe: The dimenfions which were taken with great accuracy in inches and centefimal parts, being reduced to parts of the diameter of the proper fhot, it appeared that thefe numbers might be applied to every fized gun, without materially affecting the lengths at prefent eftablifhed for the navy.

Mr. *Muller*, who in his treatife of Artillery, propofed that the dimenfions of cannon, &c. fhould be proportioned to the diameter of the fhot, gave precepts for conftructing thefe machines from fuch dimenfions, founded upon a theory, which he with great ingenuity endeavored to eftablifh, and for which, the Corps of Artillery are much obliged to him: But as the Britifh eftablifhment differs confiderably from that propofed by this gentleman; the publication of the abovementioned papers

may

may probably be uſeful to perſons who wiſh to be acquainted with ſuch matters.

*A general Method of conſtructing the Figures of Iron Ship Guns, and their Carriages; and of Sea Mortars and their Beds.*

As the tables here given for this purpoſe, contain the names of the ſeveral parts noted in theſe machines; it may be proper to mention ſome particulars, which ſeem neceſſary for the better underſtanding of the tables and their uſe.

1. It has been cuſtomary for many ages paſt, to diſtinguiſh the length of a piece of ordnance, or cannon, into three parts, viz. See Plate X. Fig. 1.

Firſt. The FIRST REINFORCE, or that part of the length containing a little more than the charge or loading: This part is made the thickeſt in metal, the better to withſtand the force of the powder when firſt fired.

Second. The SECOND REINFORCE, another part of the length, joined to the firſt reinforce, but having leſs thickneſs of metal; as the force of the fired powder is ſuppoſed not to act ſo violently on this part as on the firſt reinforce.

Third. The CHACE, the remaining part of the cannon's length, which is more than its half: And herein the thickneſs of the metal is leſs than in the ſecond reinforce.

So that the external figure, excluſive of its mouldings, is formed of three diſſimilar *Conic Fruſtrums*.

2. Beſides theſe parts there is another, which apparently makes a part of the length, though not reckoned ſo, lying behind the firſt reinforce, and called the CASCABLE; which is a maſs of metal joining to the hinder part of the firſt reinforce, and thence gradually diminiſhing in diameter to a proper thickneſs, called the NECK; and finally terminating at the hindmoſt extremity in a knob, called the BUTTON, of about the ſize of a man's fiſt.

3. Near the foremoſt end of the ſecond reinforce jut out two cylindrical pieces, one on each ſide, called TRUNNIONS; which being placed near the center of gravity, ſerve as an axis

to

to bear the gun on its carriage.

4. In the abovementioned parts are others, having diſtinct names: The Caſcable conſiſts of the *Button*, and the *Neck* and the *Breech rings*; the firſt Reinforce contains the *Ventfield*, the *Firſt Zone* * and the *Reinforce rings*; the ſecond Reinforce includes in its length, the *Trunnions*, the *Second Zone* * and the *Trunnion rings*; the Chace contains in its length, the *Chace Girdle*, the *Third Zone* * and the *Muzzle* or mouth.

5. It ſeems by this kind of diviſion and ſubdiviſions, that the ancient conſtructors of cannon had in their view the diviſions of an order in architecture; eſpecially as they ornamented the guns with mouldings uſed in that art, and called by the ſame names; but theſe mouldings, on pieces of ordnance; have much ſmaller projections than the like ornaments in a column.

6. The Caſcable is ornamented with ſeveral mouldings, the chief of which are called *Breech rings*; both the Reinforces have at each end their mouldings; thoſe in the firſt, next the Breech rings, are called *Baſe rings*; and thoſe at the other end are called *Reinforced rings*: The ſecond Reinforce begins with a ſingle ring, and ends with others called *Trunnion rings*: The Chace alſo begins with a ſingle ring, and ends with ſeveral others called the *Muzzle rings*.

7. † A flat broad ring is called a *Band*, and a flat narrow ring is called a *Fillet*: Of mouldings which are nearly ſemicircularly convex, the larger ſort are called *Toro*'s; the ſmaller kind *Aſtragals*. Mouldings of a quadrantal form, or nearly ſo, if convex, are called *Ovolo*'s; if concave, are called *Cavetto*'s. Some mouldings are convexo-concave; that where the convex part projects moſt, is called an *Ogee*; and that where the concave part projects moſt is called a *Cima*. Every Band and Aſtragal hath a Fillet on each ſide. The Ventfield, Chace-Girdle

---

* By the word *Zone*, is to be underſtood that portion on the ſuperficies, in either of the three chief parts, which lies uniformly even between the mouldings on those parts.

† See pages 45 and 53, for the definitions and conſtructions of ſuch mouldings in Architecture.

Girdle and Muzzle have each their Aſtragal; that at about three calibres length behind the Muzzle, is called the *Corniſh ring*.

The rings, in general, beſides being ornamental, have their uſe in ſtrengthening the gun, and partly hiding the ſudden decreaſe in the diameters between the Reinforces and the Chace.

8. The diameter of the ſhot is called its CALIBRE; which is a name alſo given to the diameter of the Bore, or hollow cavity of the Gun. The calibre of the Gun is greater than that of the ſhot, by about a 19th or 20th part of that of the ſhot; which is a ſufficient allowance for what is called WINDAGE; that the ſhot may paſs freely in and out of the Gun.

9. The BORE, or HOLLOW CYLINDER, is that cavity along which the charge enters and returns: This *Bore* extends the length of the Gun, all but one of its calibres; the ſolid maſs between the bottom of the Bore, and the Caſcable is called the BREECH.

10. From the hinder part of the *Breech* to the *Mouth*, or front extremity of the *Bore*, is reckoned as the length of the gun; excluſive of the *Caſcable*, which has a length generally allowed to it, of about a ninth part of that of the Gun.

The Iron ſhip guns uſed, by the preſent eſtabliſhment, have neither their whole length, nor either of their chief parts, in a conſtant ratio to the calibre of their reſpective ſhots; ſome being longer, others ſhorter, than any one Gun choſen for a ſtandard: However, a general relation between the whole length and the lengths of the three chief parts, has been eſtabliſhed in Britain; which differs but little from the practice of moſt of the neighboring nations.

11. The preſent Rules obſerved in the lengths of the parts of a Cannon, are the following:

The firſt Reinforce is $\frac{2}{7}$ths of the whole length.

The ſecond Reinforce is, of the whole length, $\frac{1}{7}$th $+ 1$ calibre of the ſhot,

The Chace is, of the whole length, $\frac{4}{7}$ths $- 1$ calibre of the ſhot.

The

The center of the Trunnions is diſtant from the hinder part of the Breech $\frac{3}{7}$ths of the whole length.

But a ſmall variation in the lengths of theſe parts, will not materially affect the Gun, either in ſtrength, uſe, or pleaſing proportion.

12. In the following table, the common notion of a 9 pound iron ſhot being 4 inches in diameter (which is very near the truth) was uſed, to compute the diameters of other ſhots, from their weights being given.

Now if $w$ repreſents the weight of any ſhot, whoſe diameter is $d$.

Then $9 : w :: \overline{4}|^3 : d^3 = \dfrac{64}{9} \times w$.

And the logarithm of $d = \frac{1}{3}$ log. $w + 0,84194$.

The length of the Gun in inches, divided by $d$, gives the length in calibres of the ſhot.

TABLE *of the Britiſh Eſtabliſhment of the weights of Shot; and of the lengths of Cannon and their chief parts; with their reduction to calibres of the ſhot.*

| Weight of the Shot, in pounds. | Calibre of the Shot, in inches. | Length of the Gun, in inches. | Length of the Gun, in calibres. | Length of the 1ſt. Reinforce in calibres | Length of the 2d. Reinforce in calibres. | Length of the Chace in calibres. | Length from the breech to the cent. of the Trun. |
|---|---|---|---|---|---|---|---|
| 4 lb. | 3,0526 | 72, inch | 23,587 | 6,739 | 4,369 | 12,478 | 10,108 |
| 6 lb. | 3,4944 | 84, inch | 24,039 | 6,868 | 4,434 | 12,736 | 10,302 |
| 9 lb. | 4,0000 | 84, inch | 21,000 | 6,000 | 4,000 | 11,000 | 9,000 |
| 12 lb. | 4,4026 | 108, inch | 24,531 | 7,009 | 4,504 | 13,018 | 10,513 |
| 18 lb. | 5,0397 | 108, inch | 21,430 | 6,123 | 4,061 | 11,246 | 9,184 |
| 24 lb. | 5,5469 | 108, inch | 19,470 | 5,563 | 3,781 | 10,126 | 8,343 |
| 32 lb. | 6,1051 | 114, inch | 18,673 | 5,335 | 3,668 | 9,670 | 8,002 |
| 42 lb. | 6,6844 | 120, inch | 17,953 | 5,129 | 3,565 | 9,259 | 7,693 |

*A* TABLE

*A* TABLE *shewing the dimensions of the several parts of an Iron 24 pounder, whose length was 9 feet.*

| Great Parts. | Lesser Parts. | Members. | Lengths on Axis. | Diameters. |
|---|---|---|---|---|
| Cascable Length 2,217. | Button | ½ Sphere — — — — | 0,595 | 1,280 |
| | | Fillet — — — — — | 0,054 | 1,334 |
| | | Zone — — — — — | 0,406 | |
| | | Neck — — — — — | 0,370 | 1,100 |
| | Breech rings 0,792 | Fillet — — — — — | 0,054 | 1,568 |
| | | Ovolo — — — — | 0,126 | 1,929 |
| | | Fillet — — — — — | 0,054 | 2,109 |
| | | Cima — — — — — | 0,378 | |
| | | Fillet — — — — — | 0,054 | 3,299 |
| | | Ovolo — — — — | 0,126 | 3,569 |
| Length Diam. { 3,425 { 3,209  First Reinforce 5,562 | Base rings 0,612 | Fillet — — — — — | 0,054 | 3,641 |
| | | Band — — — — — | 0,216 | 3,695 |
| | | Fillet — — — — — | 0,054 | 3,641 |
| | | Ogee — — — — — | 0,288 | { 3,605 3,461 |
| | | Ventage — — — — | 0,847 | |
| | Astragal | Fillet — — — — — | 0,054 | |
| | | Astragal — — — — | 0,126 | |
| | | Fillet — — — — — | 0,054 | |
| | | Clear, or Zone — — | 3,563 | |
| | Reinforce Rings | Fillet — — — — — | 0,054 | 3,245 |
| | | Band — — — — — | 0.198 | 3,299 |
| | | Fillet — — — — — | 0,054 | 3,245 |
| Length Diam. { 3,065 { 2,902  Second Reinforce { 3,836 { 2,902 | | Ogee — — — — — | 0,180 | { 3,173 3,101 |
| | | Clear, or Zone — — | 2,062 | |
| | | Trunnions — — — | 1,054 | |
| | | Clear, or Zone — — | 0,234 | |
| | Trunnion Rings | Fillet — — — — — | 0,054 | 2,938 |
| | | Band — — — — — | 0,198 | 2,992 |
| | | Fillet — — — — — | 0,054 | 2,938 |
| Length Diameters { 2,776 { 2,253  Chace 10,071 | | Ogee — — — — — | 0,180 | { 2,884 2,812 |
| | | Girdle — — — — — | 0,847 | |
| | Chace Girdle Length | Fillet — — — — — | 0,054 | |
| | | Astragal — — — — | 0,126 | |
| | | Fillet — — — — — | 0,054 | |
| | | Clear, or Zone — — | 5,656 | |
| | Cornice Rings 0,234 | Fillet — — — — — | 0,054 | |
| | | Astragal — — — — | 0,126 | |
| | | Fillet — — — — — | 0,054 | |
| | | Collar — — — — — | 2,380 | |
| | | Ovolo — — — — | 0,198 | 3,010 |
| | Muzzle Rings Length 0,540 | Fillet — — — — — | 0,054 | 2,812 |
| | | Ogee — — — — — | 0,234 | { 2,722 2,397 |
| | | Fillet — — — — — | 0,054 | 2,289 |

13. A very neat twenty-four pounder was chofen as a ftandard for the meafures of its members; thefe were reduced to parts of the calibres of the fhot; and are contained in the foregoing table: where the bore of the Gun is 1,054 diameters of the fhot; the thicknefs of the metal at the vent, is 1,185; and the Trunnions projeĉt 1,100 calibres clear of the Gun, having its middle line, or Axis, a tangent to the lower part of the bore.

In the preceding difpofition, the length of the fecond Reinforce is increafed by the breadth of the laft Fillet, and the Chance is as much diminifhed from the general proportions in the table, Article XII.

Each Aftragal projeĉts 0,063 above its Fillet; and the Fillet projeĉts 0,018 above the furface of the Gun.

14. In the delineation of Cannon by the table, Art. 13. in order to preferve the eftablifhed lengths, thofe under 24 pounder, where the length of each part contains more calibres of its fhot, than the correfponding parts of the 24 pounder does of its own fhot; the Zone in each of the three great parts of the 24 pounder, is to be increafed by the difference between the length of thofe parts in the two Tables: But the Zones in the 24 pounder is to be diminifhed by the faid difference, in Cannon carrying a greater weight of fhot.

15. *To delineate a Piece of Cannon.* Plate X. Fig. 1.

In a line AF drawn to reprefent the axis, or middle of the Gun; beginning at A, apply the lengths, fucceffively in order from one to the other, as fhewn in the table, Art. 13. and taken from a conveniently fized fcale; as of the Cafcable, from A to B; of the firft Reinforce, from B to C; of the fecond Reinforce, from C to D; of the Chace, from D to F; and to the center of the Trunnions from B to E; through the points B, C, E, D, F, draw lines at right angles to AF: On thefe normal lines, apply the refpeĉtive diameters, at the end of the firft and fecond Reinforces, and alfo at thofe of the Chace; then the refpeĉtive parts being joined by ftraight lines, will reprefent the feĉtions of the three diffimilar Conic fruftrums of which the Gun is compofed.

Add

Add alfo, taken from the fame fcale, the Breech, Bore, Vent and Trunnions; alfo the feveral members of the Cafcable, reinforces and Chace, are to be applied to the line AF, in the manner as directed for a column in pages 61, 62; and the diameter of each member applied to the normal through the divifion for that member, will give the difpofition of the feveral rings; whofe extremities are to be formed according to the kind of moulding to be reprefented: Obferving that a graceful curvature is preferved in that part of the chace within about half of the length of the muzzle from the front, where that curvature begins, and finally falls in with the large fwelling moulding or ovolo.

16. The lengths of cannon for many ages, after their firft invention, were much longer, nearly double, than what are now ufed: It is apprehended that this practice arofe from the notion that a large quantity of powder, viz. about $\frac{2}{3}$ of the weight of the fhot, produced a greater force in the fhot than a lefs quantity; and therefore it was neceffary to have long Cannon, that all the powder taking fire before the fhot parted from the piece; the expected force might be obtained: Accidents and experience have long fince fhewn thefe notions to be fallacious; and that a charge of a third, or even lefs than a third, of the weight of the fhot is fufficient for battery in Breach; whereby the Gun is lefs heated, and the carriage lefs ftrained. And with regard to Ship Guns, even a lefs charge is fufficient to force the fhot through the neareft fide of the fhip, from whence the mifchief chiefly proceeds: Efpecially as our Naval Officers are not now afraid to engage an enemy at a diftance, *where they can fee the whites of their eyes*, as was gallantly faid and executed by a brave Captain in the laft war. Now if equal fervice is produced by a lefs quantity of powder, the fhortening of Cannon may, perhaps, be attended with advantage; and were they all to be conftructed of lengths equimultiples of the calibre of the fhot, fuppofe in the ratio of 1 to 18, or 19, the four pounder would be little fhort of five feet; And then one table of the parts for one Gun, would ferve for every other, without alterations in the parts, here called Zones: But thefe things

fhould

ſhould be determined by careful experience.

## OF THE PARTS OF A SHIP GUN CARRIAGE.

Gun Carriages are Machines, generally running on wheels, whereby the Cannon are ſupported, and more readily moved from one place to another; and for ſhipping are compoſed of Wood and Iron.

The parts of Wood, are the two Sides, Cheeks or Brackets, the two Axtrees, the four Trucks, the Tranſom, the Stool-bed and the Coins.

The parts of Iron, are the two Cap-ſquares, the 16 Bolts with four Burrs; the ſix Loops; the 12 Plates: the 4 Axtree hoops, and two Stays; the 4 Linch, and 4 Dowel pins; Rings and Keys 10; with two Staples, Chains and Keys.

BRACKETS, are the two ſide planks of the Carriage; of a thickneſs equal to the calibre of the ſhot; the hinder half length and breadth is faſhioned into four equal gradations called STEPS, ſo as to make the breadth of the cheeks behind only half the breadth before; and to diminiſh their weight, without leſſening their ſtrength, the bottom of the bracket is uſually hollowed away, a quantity of about a third the length and ſixth of the breadth, and bounded by a circular curve.

In 12 pounders, and all above, the bracket conſiſts of two planks faſtened edge to edge by two *Dowel pins*.

AXTREES, are the two timbers croſſing the brackets before and behind, which ſupport them, and on which run the four wheels, called TRUCKS.

TRANSOM is that piece of wood joining the brackets over the fore Axtree, or that next the mouth of the Gun, and is of the ſame thickneſs as the brackets; and ſerves to preſerve the brackets in their proper vertical poſition.

STOOL-BED is a board, having a croſs piece or *bolſter* at one end, which reſts on the hind Axtree; and, with the COINS, or wedge-like pieces of wood, ſerve to raiſe of lower the breech of the Gun.

TRUNNION-HOLES, are thoſe ſemicircular cavities ſunk in

the

the upper fides of the brackets over the fore Axtrees, which receives the Trunnions of the Gun.

CAP-SQUARE is a thick iron plate, bent circularly in the middle to go over the trunnions and retain them in their places; with a flat part on each fide of the circular part; one end of the hinder flat part moves in a joint, and in the fore flat is a hole to receive the Eye bolt, by which the cap-fquare is held down with a key faftened to a chain hanging to a ftaple fixed on the fide of the bracket.

The EYE BOLT paffes quite through the plane of the bracket and the middle of the fore Axtree, its upper end going through the hole in the fore flat of the Cap-fquare.

The JOINT BOLT paffes alfo through the plane of the bracket, a little behind the trunnion hole and fore axtree; in the upper end of this bolt is a circular hole to receive one end of the Cap-fquare, which moves in that hole like the joint of a hinge: The lower ends of thefe two bolts are connected by the AXTREE STAY, which is an iron plate bent like an $\bigwedge$, with holes in its extremities to receive the ends of the bolts.

HIND AXTREE BOLTS and BRACKET BOLT, all pafs through the plane of the bracket; the former two, through the two lower fteps and the hind Axtree; and the latter through the upper ftep, and terminates in the circular hollow in the lower part of the bracket. In the lower end of each of the above-mentioned bolts, are holes, called *Eyes*, over which flips a circular iron plate, called a *Ring*, and a flat piece, called a *Key*, paffes through the eye, which being then fomewhat twifted prevents their being jolted out of the eyes.

TRANSOM BOLT and BED BOLT, both pafs acrofs the Carriage and through both brackets; each end of thefe bolts are rivetted with a round head, on circular plates, called BURRS. The tranfom bolt paffes through the tranfom, under the Trunnion hole, about the middle of the breadth of the bracket; and the bed bolt lies below the middle of the upper ftep, about two thirds of the breadth of the bracket in this part.

BREECHING BOLTS are two, placed one in each bracket about the middle of the length, a little before the bed-bolt; the inner

end

end lies flush with the inner fide of the bracket; the outer end is finished in a circular eye, which holds the *Breeching ring*; by which the carriage is lashed to the ship's fide.

LOOPS are bolts, like the breeching bolt, having a large round eye at one end; two are placed in each bracket, one over the bed bolt, about mid-height of the third step; another over the fore part of the hind truck, about mid-height of the bracket in this part: the inner ends of thefe four loops, and the two breeching bolts, are rivetted flat, on fquare plates, which lie flush with the inner fide of the brackets. Thefe loops ferve alfo to stay the carriage in its place.

There are two other loops, one in the middle of the front of the Tranfom, and the other in the middle of the rear of the hind Axtree; ferving to haul the Carriage forwards or backwards.

TRAVERSING PLATES, one in the bottom of each bracket, between the tail and the hind trucks. Thefe plates lapping from under the brackets a fmall way up the fides, preferve the wood from being fretted by the *handfpikes* in frequent traverfing of the Carriage.

AXTREE HOOPS, one on the end of each *arm* to keep them from fplitting: Between thefe hoops and the trucks, are cut fquare holes, one through each arm, to receive the *Linch-pins*.

STOOL-BED BOLTS, are two, fixing the plank of the *Stool-bed*, to its crofs piece or *bolfter*.

In the Stool-bed is another excavation, called the hind notch; its ufe is alfo to receive the Bed bolt, when the Stool-bed is pufhed fo much forward as to let the bolfter drop off the hind axtree; for then the breech of the Gun defcends between the brackets.

TABLE

TABLE *of general Dimenſions of the Parts of a Ship Gun Carriage,*
*in Calibres of the reſpeƈtive Shot.*

### Of the Brackets

| | Calib. | | Calib. |
|---|---|---|---|
| Length – – – – – – | 12,522 | Thickneſs – – – – – | 1,000 |
| Breadth, before – – – | 4,686 | Breadth behind – – – | 2,343 |
| Diſtance, at the Trunnions – | 2,992 | Diſtance at mid. of hind Axtree | 3,695 |
| Diſtance of the center of the trunnion hole from the front – – – – | | | 1,983 |
| Diameter of trunnion hole – 1,082. Center ſunk in the ſide – – | | | 0,045 |
| Radius of the Ovolo next the upper ſtep – – – – – – – – – | | | 0,500 |
| Excavation in the bottom { length of its chord – – – – – – – | | | 5,000 |
| diſt. from the front – – – – – – – | | | 3,500 |

### The Axtrees.

| | | | Calib. |
|---|---|---|---|
| Whole length – – – – 9,735, The Arms { length – – – | | | 1,767 |
| diameter – – – | | | 1,118 |
| Breadth, between the brackets, at the { fore – – – – – – – – | | | 1,226 |
| hind – – – – – – – – | | | 2,163 |
| Breadth between the bracket and Arms – – – – – – – – – | | | 1,226 |
| Depth in the mid. of fore – – 1,659 Depth in mid. of hind – – – | | | 1,226 |
| Diſtance between the middle of the Axtrees – – – – – – – | | | 8,684 |
| Diſt. of middles from the bracket ends, { fore – – – – – – – | | | 1,622 |
| hind – – – – – – – | | | 2,215 |
| Depths of the Axtrees let into the brackets – – – – – – – | | | 0,432 |
| Trucks, their thickneſs – – 1,000; their diameter { fore – – – – | | | 3,245 |
| hind – – – – | | | 2,884 |

| Cap-ſquare | Calib. | | | |
|---|---|---|---|---|
| | | Breeching ring, diam. { inner | | 0,800 |
| | | outer | | 1,300 |
| Whole length 2,974. Breadth | 0,721 | Stool-bed. | | |
| Thickneſs – 0,125. Bend | 1,082 | Whole length 5,822. Thickneſs | | 0,721 |
| Fore flat – – 1,171. Hind flat | 0,721 | Breadth before 1,082. Behind | | 1,803 |
| Head of Joint bolt { length – | 0,631 | Bolſter, length 2,974. Breadth | | 1,000 |
| breadth – | 0,216 | Depth – – 1,250. let in – | | 0,090 |
| Head of Eye bolt { length – | 0,415 | { breadth – – – | | 0,342 |
| breadth – | 0,216 | Fore notch { depth – – – | | 0,234 |
| Rounding at ends of Cap-ſquare | 0,216 | { diſt. from front | | 0,613 |
| Joint bolt projeƈts out of Capſq | 0,207 | The Tranſom { length – – | | 3,000 |
| Thickneſs of the key – – – | 0,054 | thickneſs – | | 1,000 |
| Bolts, their diameter – – – | 0,270 | | | |
| Diam. of Burrs, and heads – | 0,360 | | | |
| Diam. of Burr rings – – – | 0,486 | | | |
| Loops { inner diam. – – – | 0,300 | | | |
| outer diam. – – – | 0,721 | | | |

*To*

*To conſtruct the elevation and Plan of a Ship Gun-Carriage.*

### For the Elevation. Plate X. Fig. 2.

In the ground line AB, take the diſtance of the points A,B, equal to 8,693 * calibres of the ſhot; and in perpendiculars through thoſe points, take BD, AC for the radius's of the fore and hind trucks; and deſcribe the Trucks, and the Arms of the Axtrees.

From the centers D,C, deſcribe arcs with the radius's of the heights of the brackets above the centers of the arms †; then a tangent drawn to theſe Arcs will repreſent the bottom line of the bracket; to which, Normals from the centers D,C, give E,F, for the middles of the Axtrees.

In the line EF, take the diſtances EG, FH, of the brackets ends from the middles of the Axtrees; compleat the parallelogram of the brackets, with the ſteps and ovolo; put in the Trunnion hole, and mark its loweſt point I.

### To repreſent the ſections of the Axtrees and Tranſom.

By the depths, breadths, and parts let into the brackets, the ſections of the Axtrees may be expreſſed.

From K, the middle of the upper part of the fore Axtree, deſcribe an arc L, at the diſtance of the thickneſs of the tranſom; draw a tangent from I to L, and compleat the ſection of the tranſom LM.

Let the length of the excavation at the bottom of the bracket be the baſe of an equilateral Triangle, whoſe vertex is the center of the curve.

### For the Plan. Plate X. Fig. 3.

Let the line AB repreſent the middle line and length of the carriage.

* $\overline{AB}^2 = \overline{CD}^2 - \overline{BD-AC}\,|^2 = \overline{FE}^2 + \overline{DF-CE}\,|^2 - \overline{BD-AC}\,|^2$.

† The ſum of the depth in the bracket and radius of the Arm, taken from the depth of the Axtree, leaves the height of the bracket above the center of the Arm.

carriage.

Take BG, AC, the diftance from the bracket ends of the middles of the fore and hind Axtrees, and BD the diftance of the center of the trunnion holes from the front; through G,C,D,B,A, draw normals to AB.

Make DE, CF, the half diftance of the Brackets, at the middle of the Trunnion holes and hind Axtree; a line through E,F, fhews the inner line of the bracket, and a parallel to it, at the diftance of the thicknefs, fhews the outfide line of the bracket, terminating in the normals through A,B, and on thefe mark the fteps, quarter round, and trunnion hole.

In the Normals, through G,C, take the lengths of the Axtrees, and of the Arms; to the Arms, apply the thicknefs of the trucks, and their diameters; alfo apply the breadths of the fore and hind Axtrees, as well between the brackets as without them, and alfo the diameters of the Arms; and compleat the plan of the Axtrees and Trucks.

Put in the Cap-fquare and its bolts; the bolts in the upper, and the two lower fteps, with the Bed and Tranfom bolts, and the loops in their places, alfo the ferrels or rings on the ends of the Axtree Arms, with the holes for the linch-pins.

The plan and fection of the Stool-bed may be eafily formed from its dimenfions. See Fig. 4 and 5.

From the mid-line of the fore Axtree, a calibre applied on both fides of it, will give nearly the limits of the fore and hind lines of the tranfom, which thereby fhelters the fore Axtree from the rain.

## Of Sea Mortars.

BOMBS are hollow balls of Iron, called SHELLS, whofe cavities being filled with gunpowder, and fired by a flow burning fufe, breaks the fhell with great violence into a multitude of pieces.

MORTARS are a fort of Guns, fhorter than cannon, but with larger bores, for the paffage of the *Shells*; thofe ufed at fea, are called thirteen inch and ten inch mortars, thefe meafures being

about

about the diameters of their bores.

The BORE *bbcc* is cylindrical, having its lower end terminating in a hemifpherical hollow *caac*, to receive the convexity of the *Shell*.

The CHAMBER *aafdf* is a cavity beyond the bore, and is to receive the charge of powder: Its figure *aaff* is ufually that of a truncated cone, the greater end *aa* opening out of the fpherical part *caac* of the bore, but much lefs in diameter; and the leffer end *ff*, terminating in a hemifphere *fdf* of equal diameter to it: The communication *g* with the chamber, by which the charge is fired, is called the VENT.

The BREECH IEI is that hemifpherical mafs furrounding the lower part of the chamber: The Mortar has alfo its parts, called *reinforce* and *Chace*, with their refpective mouldings or rings.

The TRUNNION HFFH is that great cylindrical part joining croffwife on to the Breech; and the Arms FG are the two cylindrical parts at the ends of the Trunnion.

The EARS IH, IH, are thofe wedge-like parts which join to the Breech and Trunnion; propofed to ftrengthen thofe parts againft the great ftrain in firing.

The DOLPHINS K, K, are thofe kind of handles in the form of Fifh on the upper fide of the Reinforce, by which the Mortar is flung when lifted on, or off, its Bed or Carriage.

The CHOCK is a wedge-like piece joining on the lower fide of the Reinforce rings; which by entering into a cavity in the Coin, (a part belonging to the Bed) contributes to keep the Mortar fteady.

TABLE

TABLE *of general Dimenſions for deſcribing Sea Mortars, in Diameters of the Shell.*

| | | | Length. | Diameter. |
|---|---|---|---|---|
| The length of the | Whole Mortar – – | | 4,976 | —— |
| | Breech, including the Trunnion | | 1,858 | 2,141 |
| | Reinforce – – – | | 1,488 | 2,255 |
| | Chace – – – – | | 1,630 | 1,752 |
| The Bore – – – – – – | | | 1,900 | 1,031 |
| The Chamber – – – – – | | | 1,654 | 0,669 / 0,551 |
| From the Muzzle to the Breech incluſive | | | 4,598 | —— |
| The Trunnions. | Greateſt part – – | | 2,661 | 0,937 |
| | the Arms – – – | | 0,488 | 0,779 |
| Muzzle rings IL 0,394 | Fillet – – – – | | 0,032 | 1,909 |
| | Band – – – – | | 0,172 | 1,940 |
| | Fillet – – – – | | 0,032 | 1,909 |
| | Ogee – – – – | | 0,126 | 1,877 / 1,752 |
| | Fillet – – – – | | 0,032 | 1,783 |
| Girdle LM 0,598 – – – – – | | | 0,598 | 1,752 |
| Reinforce rings MD 0,785 | Ogee – – – – | | 0,172 | 1,783 / 1,929 |
| | Band – – – – | | 0,126 | 1,949 |
| | Ogee – – – – | | 0,338 | 1,978 / 2,236 |
| | Fillet – – – – | | 0,039 | 2,255 |
| | Band – – – – | | 0,110 | 2,283 |
| Reinforce 1,181 – – – – | | | 1,181 | 2,255 |
| Breech rings cg 0,158 | Band – – – – | | 0,126 | 2,264 |
| | Fillet – – – – | | 0,032 | 2,255 |
| The Vent, before the Breech-band 0,110 | | | | |
| Side pieces, or Ears, length 0,677 | breadth | 0,807 | —— | 2,378 |
| | | 0,748 | —— | 2,264 |

*To*

## To delineate the reprefentation of a Sea Mortar.

In a line AB drawn for the axis or middle line, apply from the fcale chofen for the Calibre of the fhell, the lengths AC, CD, DB, for the Breech, Reinforce and Chafe; and then put on the Axis the feveral lengths fhewing the breadths of the Rings.

In lines drawn perpendicular to AB, apply the refpective diameters of the Rings; and let the extremities of thefe diameters be joined with the proper lines and curves to reprefent the feveral Mouldings.

Take the length from the Muzzle to the Breech, which apply from B to E, from which fet on the axis, the femidiameter of the breech, and it gives the center, from whence the curvature of the breech is to be defcribed.

Let the length of the Bore and Chamber together, be fet from B to *d*, and the length of the Chamber be fet from *d* towards B; then may the reprefentation of the Chamber *afdfa*, of the Bore *bcaacb*, and Vent *g*, be defcribed from their refpective meafures: And fo the Trunnion FF, its Arms FG, and the Ears HI. See Pl. XI. Fig. 1.

## Of a Sea Mortar Bed. See Fig. 2.

A SEA MORTAR BED, or *Carriage*, is a Machine compofed of Wood and Iron, ferving to bear the Mortar fo, that it may be traverfed to throw its Shell, or Bomb, in any propofed direction. This *Bed* is ufually compofed of two courfes, or tiers, of Oak timbers, ftrongly dowelled and bolted together; three timbers in the lower tier, each of the whole length; and four in the upper tier; the two outfide ones, called CHEEKS, are of the whole length; and the two middle pieces are partly of the whole length, and partly lefs than half the length.

The TRUNNION BED, is that cylindrical cavity XX, fcored out of the timbers in the upper tier, and which receives the greater part of the Trunnion: And the TRUNNION HOLES LK, are thofe cylindrical cavities cut in the *Cheeks* to receive the

Arms

Arms of the Trunnions.

The BREECH BED, YY, is that fpherical cavity interfecting the Trunnion Bed, fitted to receive the breech of the Mortar: And the BREECHES, YYZZ, is that part left of the two middle timbers in the upper tier, wrought into two hollow cavities, called LEGS, Z,Z, lying lengthwife parallel to the Cheeks; the fore ends reach the front of the carriage BB, and the other ends terminate in the fpherical cavity of the Breech Bed.

The DOWN-BED is the lower tier of timbers; but is the name ufually given to the whole excavation, including the *Splays*, VV, or infexions of the cheeks, againft the *Breech-Bed*, to receive the *Ears* of the Mortar.

The COIN is a fhiftable piece of elm timber, which is placed over the *Breeches*, and tenons into the Cheeks, at a diftance from the front, of about a quarter of the length of the carriage: Its ufe is to bear up the mouth of the Mortar at its defignated elevation when fired; and that the Reinforce of the Mortar may lie eafy and fteady againft the Coin, its upper, and under edges, next the *piece*, are fcooped out, to receive the fwelling roundnefs of the Mortar, and the figure of its *chock*. When the Coin is taken off, the Mortar falls in between the Cheeks and the *Legs* of the Breeches, the *Chock* reaching the *Down bed*; whereby the Mortar is ftowed compactly when out of ufe.

The dotted rectangle *c,c,c,c*, fhews the place of the Coin.

The MOULDINGS are the Ovolo, Cavetto and Fillet made in the upper edges of the timbers at the tail EDE, and at the front of the Cheeks SB.

The BOTTOM BED, or TRAVERSING WHEEL, is a folid timber cylinder placed horizontally under the bed, bearing it up and revolving with it when traverfed; which is reprefented by the large circle marked *x,x,x,x*.

The PINTLE is a large iron fpindle, or vertical axis, of about half a Calibre in diameter, its upper end having a broad flat head: It paffes through the *Down* and *Bottom* beds, and has its lower end fixed into fome ftrong timber work, called the *Bed* by the Shipwrights who conftruct and fix it to the Veffel called a BOMB-KETCH: Round this *Pintle* the Carriage with its Mortar is traverfed,

traverfed, or turned, into any pofition.

The WASHER is an iron ring, inclofing the Pintle-hole, whofe center is C; it is let into the wood, and lies flufh with the top of the *Down-bed*, and the head of the *Pintle* refts on this ring, whofe breadth is reprefented by *ab*. The BED-PLATE is a circular iron plate, including the Pintle-hole at the under furface of the *Bottom Bed*, with which it lies flufh: From this plate fpread three Arms equally diftant from one another; through thefe Arms pafs three bolts Z,Z,Z, called Down Bed Bolts, which go quite through the Down and Bottom Beds; one in the middle line of the Bed; and the other two fall in the Trunnion Bed, touching the Breech Bed.

The CAP-SQUARES are two iron plates *m,m*, the middle parts whereof, about one third the length, are circularly bent to go over the Trunnion Arms: In the middle of each flat end is a rectangular hole *n*, to receive the head of an Eye-bolt, whereby the Cap-fquare is ftrongly fixed to the Cheek, to prevent the ftarting of the Mortar when fired. Thefe heavy plates are attached to the upper furface of the Bed by a ftrong chain to each; having one end fixed to a ftaple on the top of the Bed, and the other end to a ftaple on the Cap-fquare near its hinder end.

The RIVETTING-PLATE is an iron plate near the tail mouldings, to which it is concentric; it lies flufh with the upper furface of the timbers, to fuftain the head of four bolts, called RIVETTING-PLATE BOLTS, paffing through both the tiers of timbers: The outfide two, in the middle line of the Cheeks, have Loops; the other two are fo placed as to leave nearly equal fpaces between the four bolts.

The REVERSE-PLATE goes acrofs the Bed, juft behind the Trunnion; it lies level with the upper furface of the timbers, and ferves to fuftain the head of fix bolts, called REVERSE-PLATE BOLTS; thefe paffing through both tiers of the timbers and the *Bottom bed*, contribute to hold all thefe parts ftrongly together: The two outfide ones are *Eye-bolts*, for the hindmoft holes in the Cap-fquare; the other four are fo placed as to leave nearly equal fpaces between the fix bolts.

The

The REVERSE-BAR is an iron bar, out of fight, lying dowelwife in its breadth, between the two tiers of timbers.

LOOPS there are four, two on the middle line of each *Cheek*; one at each end of the *Rivetting-plate*, and one near the front of each *Cheek*, the extremity of the *Loop* reaching the *Ovolo*; thefe two Loops are parts of bolts which pafs through both the tiers of timbers.

EYE-BOLTS there are fix; three in each *cheek*, lying in the fame ftraight line, a little within the middle line of the *Cheeks*: the Eyes of the two foremoft ferve to fix down the Coin; and the eye of the four *n,n,n,n*, ferve for retaining the two Capfquares over the Trunnion Arms: Thefe fix bolts go through both tiers of timbers and the bottom bed.

JAGG'D BOLTS twelve; in each *leg* of the *Breeches* there are fix, in two rows, three in a row; dividing the breadth into two equal fpaces, and the length, taken from the front of the carriage to the foremoft *Down-bed bolt*, into nearly equal intervals: Thefe bolts are only a kind of jagg'd nails to fix this part of the *down-bed* to the lower timbers.

TRAVERSING BOLTS, four; fixed to the lower tier of timbers; two in the front nearly oppofite to the middle of the *Cheeks*; and two in the tail, nearly oppofite to thofe in the front, thefe bolts ferve to traverfe the Carriage round its center.

CROSS-BED BOLTS, are in number feven; two, *m,m* Fig. 3. which bind together the timbers in the upper tier, lie one above the other a little before the tail *Loops*: Of the other five, connecting the timbers, in the lower tier, one pair *q,q*, lying one above the other, pafs a little behind the front loops; another pair *o,o*, lie a little behind the tail loops, one above the other, oppofite the other two *n,n*; and the fifth *p*, lies againft the interval of the laft pair *o,o*, in the midway, nearly, between the hindmoft Eye-bolts and tail loops. The ends of all the *crofs-bed bolts* pafs through *fquare rivetting plates*, which lie flufh with the furface of the timbers: The ends of thefe bolts finifh in a male fcrew, to receive on them *hexagonal fcrew nuts*; which by a proper winch are turned down clofe to the fquare plates, and fo draw the timbers into as clofe contact as they can be forced.

Of

Of the fixteen bolts which pafs vertically through the *Bed*, ten of them, namely, the four *Loops*, and the fix *Eye-bolts*, enter at the upper furface, and are faftened at the lower ends by *circular fcrew nuts*, which are turned by a forked key, and enter into the wood until they are flufh with its furface: The other fix, viz. two *rivetting plate*, and four *reverfe plate bolts*, enter at the bottom, and are ftayed there by their fquare flat heads, which are counter-funk in the wood fo as to be flufh with its furface; the upper ends are, by the fcrews on them, fixed by *hexagonal fcrew nuts*, which are turned by the winch clofe down upon the *rivetting* and *reverfe plates*.

To the bottom of the *Coin*, are fixed two iron plates, called STAY-PLATES, each having in the part projecting behind, a rectangular hole to receive an Eye-bolt, whereby the Coin is fixed in its place.

On the fides of the Carriage, againft the fix *Eye-bolts*, hang, by fmall chains, as many iron pieces, called KEYS; which being paffed through the Eyes in the bolts, faften down the *Cap-fquares*, and the *Coin*.

*General*

## *General Dimensions of a Sea Mortar Bed, in parts of the Calibre of the Shell.*

| | | Calibr. | | | Calibr. |
|---|---|---|---|---|---|
| Breadth of the Bed  – – – | | 4,252 | Rivetting Plate | Distance from the mouldings – – | 0,159 |
| Middle length  – – – – | | 7,559 | | Breadth  – – – | 0,317 |
| Side length  – – – – | | 6,929 | | Chord of its length | 3,543 |
| Depth of { both tiers  – – | | 2,205 | | Ends spreading | 0,472 |
| { upper tier  – – | | 1,181 | Reverse plate | Fore edge, distance from the front | 4,608 |
| Pintle's center from front – | | 3,288 | | Middle breadth  – – | 0,317 |
| Washer { Inner diameter  – | | 0,511 | | Length, behind – – | 3,742 |
| { Outer diameter  – | | 0,747 | | Breadth, at ends  – | 0,394 |
| { Thickness  – | | 0,039 | Cap-square | Length –  – – – | 2,008 |
| Bed-plate { Outer diameter – | | 1,024 | | Breadth  – – – | 0,472 |
| | Arms { Breadth  – | 0,236 | | Thickness  – – – | 0,118 |
| | { Longest  – | 1,024 | | Breadth of the End, rounding  – – | 0,157 |
| | { Shorter  – | 0,709 | | Bolt hole { from end | 0,197 |
| Bottom-bed { Diameter  – | | 4,646 | | { Length – | 0,257 |
| { Bottom depth | | 0,433 | | { Breadth – | 0,118 |
| { Side depth  – | | 0,630 | | Radius of the bend  – | 0,326 |
| Mouldings { Ovolo  – | | 0,236 | Coin | Distance of the middle from the front | 1,575 |
| { Fillet  – | | 0,079 | | Length –  – – – | 4,173 |
| { Cavetto  – | | 0,236 | | Breadth  – – – | 1,062 |
| Trunnion { Middle line, from the front  – – | | 4,094 | | Depth –  – – – | 1,299 |
| { Breadth of the Bed  – | | 0,946 | | Lets in between the Cheeks  – – | 0,354 |
| { Arms, their { Distance  – | | 2,677 | | The Tenon in the middle, is { long | 0,570 |
| { { Length  – | | 0,531 | | { broad | 0,118 |
| { { Breadth  – | | 0,787 | | { deep | 0,315 |
| { { Depth –  – | | 0,457 | | Height of the head  – | 0,354 |
| Down-Bed { Bottom Breadth  – | | 0,709 | Heads of Eye-bolts | Thickness  – – – | 0,110 |
| { Lower step { Breadth | | 0,157 | | Bottom breadth  – – | 0,270 |
| { { Height | | 0,058 | | { Length  – – | 0,138 |
| { Legs { breadth of the concavity | | 0,551 | | Eyes { Breadth  – – | 0,039 |
| { { breadth of the upper step | | 0,118 | | { Distance from the upper end | 0,098 |
| { Extent from the front | | 4,252 | Bolts | their diameter  – – | 0,118 |
| Splay for the Ear { Begins, from the front | | 2,834 | | their square heads  – | 0,117 |
| { Where the Cheeks are distant  – – | | 2,362 | | Side of the hexagonal screw nuts  – | 0,159 |
| { Length of Splay  – | | 0,787 | | Diameter of the circular screw nuts | 0,334 |
| { Here the Cheeks are distant  – – | | 2,480 | | Side of sq.-rivet-plate | 0,315 |
| Cheeks { Breadth  – – – | | 0,945 | | Loop { Outside diam. | 0,394 |
| { Depth  – – – | | 0,551 | | { Inside diam. | 0,197 |

*To*

*To delineate the reprefentation of the Plan of a Sea Mortar Bed.*
Pl. XI. Fig. 2.

In a line BB drawn equal to the breadth of the front of the
Bed, let the point A be the middle; through the points A,B,B,
draw lines at right angles to the front: In the middle line, or
axis, apply the whole length AD, and the diftance to the center
of the Pintle C, and on the lines through B,B, apply the fide
lengths BE,BE.

From C defcribe the arc EDE, reprefenting the rear, or tail,
of the Bed; and concentric to EDE, defcribe the mouldings
between D and F, and the Rivetting-plate GH; alfo the Pintle-
hole, with its radius C*a*, and the Collar, or Wafher, with its
radius C*b*.

In AD take AI for the diftance of the center of the Trunnion
from the front; through I draw KK at right angles to AI; in
which take LL, for the diftance of the Trunnion holes, and LK
for their length; NM for the breadth of the Trunnion bed, and
OO for the breadth of the Trunnion holes.

On each fide of A, make PP equal to the bottom breadth of
the Down-bed; PQ, for the lower ftep; QR for the Legs; RS, for
the upper ftep; and SB for the breadth of the Cheeks; through
P,Q,R,S, draw lines parallel to AC; thofe through P meeting the
Wafher in *p*. From C, with the radius C*r* = AR, defcribe an arc
*rt*, meeting the line NN in *t*: Make AT equal to the extent of the
Down-bed from the front; and through *t*,T,*t*, defcribe the
elliptic curve *t*T*t*, which may be done fufficiently exact by the
hand: Alfo reform the inner fide of the Cheeks into the Splay
V*v*, to receive the Ears of the Mortar.

The middle line of the Cap-fquare *mm* paffes through the
middle of LK, the breadth of the Trunnion holes.

*To draw the Elevation of a Sea Mortar Bed.* Plate XI. Fig. 3.

Form rectangles with the lengths and depths of the Bed; as
AABB; and with the lengths and depths of each courfe of
timbers

timbers AACC, and BBCC; alfo fet off the mouldings *bb*. And the bottom Bed with the diameter DD and depth DE.

Put in F the center of the Trunnion hole, and form the Hole, Cap-fquare and Eye-bolts *n,n*; the Loops *r,r*, and the Eye-bolt *t*, for the Coin: Alfo put in the Crofs-bed bolds *m,m*, *n,n, o,o, p*; and the Chains and Keys againft the Eye-bolts.

*For the Section.* Plate XI. Fig. 4.

With the breadth AA, height AB, and depth BC of the upper tier of timbers, form the Rectangles AABB, BBCC; and draw the middle line DE.

Take the breadth BF and depth FG of the cheeks: And take *ee* for the bottom breadth of the Down-bed; *ed* for the height, and *db* the breadth of the firft ftep; alfo make G*g* the breadth of the upper ftep: On D, with the radius D*g* defcribe the concavity *ga* of the *Down-bed legs*, meeting *ba* drawn at right angles to *bd*.

The Traverfing bolt T is in the mid height of the lower tier, and about the fame diftance from the outfide.

# F I N I S.

BOOKS printed for *J. Nourſe*, in the Strand,
Bookſeller to His MAJESTY.

1. THE Elements of Navigation: Containing the Theory and Practice, with all neceſſary Tables. By *J. Robertſon*, Librarian to the Royal Society. The third Edition, with Additions and Compendiums for finding the Latitude and Longitude at Sea. 2 vols. large Octavo. 18 *s.*

2 A general Treatiſe of Menſuration. By Mr. *Robertſon*. The third Edition. Duodecimo. 3 *s.*

3 The Elements of Aſtronomy, deduced from Obſervations, and demonſtrated upon the Mathematical Principals of the Newtonian Philoſophy. Tranſlated from the French of M. *De la Caille*. By *J. Robertſon*. Octavo. 6 *s.*

3 * Mathematical Tracts of the late *Benjamin Robins*, Eſq. F. R. S. with a ſhort account of the Author by *James Wilſon*, M. D. 2 vols. Octavo. 10 *s.* 6 *d.*

4 The Elements of Euclid, *viz.* The firſt ſix Books, together with the eleventh and the twelfth. The Errors, by which Theon and others have long ago viſited theſe Books, are corrected; and ſome of Euclid's Demonſtrations are reſtored: alſo the Book of Euclid's Data, in like Manner corrected. By *Robert Simſon*, M. D. Emeritus Profeſſor of Mathematics in the Univerſity of Glaſgow. The fourth Edition. To which are added, the Elements of Plane and Spherical Trigonometry. Octavo. 6 *s.*

5 Cyclomatheſis: or an eaſy Introduction to the ſeveral Branches of the Mathematics; being principally deſigned for the Inſtruction of young Students, before they enter upon the more abſtruſe and difficult Parts thereof. By *William Emerſon*. In 10 Volumes Octavo. 3 *l.* 5 *s.*

 N. B. *Any of the Volumes may be had ſeparate, to accommodate ſuch Perſons that do not chuſe to purchaſe the whole.*

6 Miſcellanies: or a miſcellaneous Treatiſe, containing ſeveral mathematical Subjects. By Mr. *Emerſon*. Octavo.

7 The Method of Increments, wherein the Principals are demonſtrated, and the Practice thereof ſhewn in the Solution of Problems. By Mr. *Emerſon*. Quarto. 7 *s.* 6 *d.*

8 A ſhort Comment on Sit Iſaac Newton's Principia, containing Notes upon ſome difficult Places of that excellent Book. To which is added, a Defence of Sir Iſaac againſt the Objections that have been made to ſeveral Parts of the Principia, and Optics, by Leibnitz, Bernoulli, Euler, *&c.* and a Confutation of the Objections made by Dr. Rutherford and Bedford againſt his Chronology. By Mr. *Emerſon*. Octavo. 3 *s.*

9 Navigation; or the Art of Sailing upon the Sea, with all the neceſſary Tables. By Mr. *Emerſon*. The ſecond Edition enlarged. Duodecimo. 4 *s.*

10 The

10 The Mathematical Repofitory. Containing Solutions of feven hundred Queftions, moftly felected from fcarce and valuable Authors; defigned to conduct Beginners to the moft difficult Properties of Numbers. By *James Dodfon*, F. R. S. 3 vols. Duodecimo. 12 s.

Mr. *Thomas Simpfon*'s Works; Containing,

11 The Elements of Geometry, the third Edition, carefully revifed. Octavo. 5 s.

12 Trigonometry Plain and Spherical, with the Conftruction and Application of Logarithms. The fecond Edition, corrected. Octavo. 1 s. 6 d.

13 A Treatife of Algebra. The fourth Edition, revifed. Octavo. 6 s.

14 The Doctrine and Application of Fluxions. Octavio.

15 Select Exercifes for young Proficients in Mathematics. Octavo. 5 s. 6 d.

16 The Doctrine of Annuities and Reverfions, with ufeful Tables. Octavo. 3 s.

17 An Appendix to ditto, containing fome Remarks upon Mr. Demoivre's Book on the fame Subject. Octavo. 6 d.

18 Effays on feveral curious and ufeful Subjects, in fpeculative and mixed Mathematics. Quarto. 6 s.

19 Mathematical Differtations on a Variety of Phyfical and Analytical Subjects. Quarto. 7 s.

20 Mifcellaneous Tracts on fome curious and interefting Subjects in the Mathematics. Quarto. 7 s.

---

21 An eafy Introduction to the Theory and practice of Mechanics. By *S. Clark*. Quarto.

22 Mathematical Lucubrations, containing new Improvements in various Branches of Mathematics. By *John Landen*, F. R. S. Quarto. 6 s.

23 A Difcourfe concerning Refidual Analyfis. By Mr. *Landen*. Quarto. 2 s. 6 d.

24 The Refidual Analyfis: A new Branch of the Algebraic Art, of very extenfive Ufe, both in pure Mathematics and Natural Philofophy, Book I. By Mr. *Landen*. Quarto. 6 s.

25 Animadverfions on Dr. Stewart's Computations of the Sun's Diftance from the Earth. By Mr. *Landen*. Quarto. 1 s.

26 A Geometrical Treatife of the Conic Sections, in which the Properties of the Sections are derived from the Nature of the Cone, in an eafy Manner, and by a new Method. Tranflated from the Latin Original, of *H. Hamilton*, D. D. F. R. S. and of Trinity College, Dublin. Quarto. 12 s.

27 The fame Book in Latin. Quarto. 12 s.

28 Philofophical Effays on the following Subjects: I. On the Afcent of Vapours, the Formation of Clouds, Rain, and Dew, and of

feveral

feveral other Phœnomena of Air and Water. II. Obfervations and Conjectures on the Nature of the Aurora Borealis, and the Tails of Comets. III. On the Principals of Mechanics. By *Hugh Hamilton*, D. D. F. R. S. The third Edition, corrected. 2 *s*. 6 *d*.

29 Four introductory Lectures in Natural Philofophy. I. Of the Rules of Philofophifing, the effential Properties of Matter, and Laws of Motion. II. Of the feveral Kinds of Attraction, and particularly of Cohefion. III. Of Gravity, or the Attraction of Gravitation. IV. The Laws of Motion explained, and confirmed by Experiments. By *Hugh Hamilton*, D. D. F. R. S. Profeffor of Philofophy in the Univerfity of Dublin. Dueodecimo. 2 *s*.

30 Hydroftatical and Pneumatical Lectures. By *Roger Cotes*, A. M. late Profeffor of Aftronomy and experimental Philofophy at Cambridge. Publifhed from the Author's original Manufcript, by *Roger Smith*, D. D. late Mafter of Trinity College, Cambridge. The third Edition. Printed from a Copy corrected by the Editor. Octavo. 5 *s*.

31 A Voyage towards the North Pole, undertaken in the Year 1773, by His Majefty's Command, for making Difcoveries and Nautical and Philofophical Obfervations in the Northern Seas. By the Honourable Captain *Phipps*. In One Volume Quarto, printed upon fine Royal Paper, and illuftrated with Fifteen elegant Prints and Charts. 12 *s*. 6 *d*. *in Boards*.

32 An elementary and methodical Atlas, on Thirty-two Copper-plates. Originally intended for the Ufe of his Serene Highnefs the Prince of Orange and Naffau, &c. By Mr. *John Palairet*. The fecond Edition, greatly improved, with all of the late Difcoveries, and carefully coloured under the Infpection of the Author. Folio. 2 *l*. 12 *s*. 6 *d*.

33 An Account of Sir Ifaac Newton's Philofophical Difcoveries, in Four Books. By *C. Maclaurin*, M. A. F. R. S. with an Account of the Author by Dr. *Murdoch*. The third Edition. Octavo. 6 *s*.

34 A Treatife of Algebra, in three Parts. To which is added, an Appendix, concerning the general Properties of Geometrical Lines. By *C. Maclaurin*. The third Edition. Octavo. 6 *s*.

35 A Courfe of Lectures in Natural Philofophy, by the late Dr. *Richard Helfham*. Publifhed by *Bryan Robinfon*, M. D. The fourth Edition. Octavo. 5 *s*.

# NOTES
ON A
# TREATISE
OF
## Mathematical Inſtruments

By DAVID MANTHEY

---

## THE CONTENTS

## S ECT. I.

### *Preface to the Notes.*

A LTHOUGH there have been many books written on *mathematical inſtruments*, this treatiſe touches on many points that are otherwiſe neglected or treated only briefly. More than any other work, it has thorough details on the *sector*, an inſtrument which ſerved as a calculator for three centuries, only to be gradually eclipſed by the ſlide rule, and later by the electronic calculator.

Of the inſtruments that are detailed, ſome have fallen from uſe whilſt others are ſtill readily available. For inſtance, it is very difficult today to find a drawing pen that adjuſts in width; it is more likely that one will have a half dozen pens to do the ſame job. Similarly, it is rare to find a ſet of compaſſes that have the neceſſary joints and attachments to draw circles and arcs with the ſame exactneſs and with the variety evinced in this work. However, protractors and parallel rules are ſtill available, eſſentially unchanged aſide from the materials from which they are made.

The reader is encouraged to ſeek out the inſtruments and to uſe them. For many tasks, the inſtruments will ſoon become indiſpenſable. For inſtance, the sector can be uſed as a univerſal ſcale, which makes protracting a map ſwifter and more facile than manually calculating the diſtances and lengths required.

#### *Acknowledgements*
The editor thanks R.R.M. for her extenſive help and C.D.P. for his encouragement in producing this reprint.

S ECT.

## SECT. II.

## *Biographical Note on John Robertson.*

JOHN Robertfon was born in 1712. He was initially apprenticed to a trade. At fome point he quit this, and by 1739 had become a teacher of mathematics.

Robertfon was elected a Fellow of the Royal Society on 17 December 1741. The citation on his election certificate is as follows:

> *John Robertfon*
> *An able Mathematician in London, known to many worthy Members for his skill in Mechanicks, Experimental Philofophy and other Branches of ufefull knowledge, and one who is defirous of becoming a Member of this Honorable Society, is recommended by us as worthy of your favourable acceptance.*

In 1748, he was appointed Mafter of the royal mathematical fchool in Chrift's Hofpital. In 1755 he was appointed by the Admiralty to be Firft Mafter of the Royal Naval Academy at Portfmouth.

In 1761, Robertfon was given the task of calibrating the famous H.4 chronometer made by John Harrifon prior to fea trials. This involved comparing the rate of the chronometer againft meafurements of local time obtained by aftronomical obfervations.

Robertfon was one of feveral learned men who ferved as advifors to the Penn family during the Pennfylvania-Maryland border difpute. The difpute was refolved with the furvey of the Mafon-Dixon line.

Robertfon held the poft of Firft Mafter at the Royal Naval Academy until the year 1766. In that year, as a refult of the petty cabals of the Second Mafter, the firft lord of the Admiralty difmiffed both men.

Sometime before the end of 1767, Robertfon was appointed Clerk of the Royal Society. On becoming Clerk, he had to refign

refign his Fellowfhip in the Society. On 24 December 1767, Robertfon applied for the poft of Librarian of the Royal Society. He withdrew his application on 4 January 1768, believing that the Council had already decided on another candidate. However, he was appointed Librarian on 7 January 1768. He ferved as Clerk and Librarian until his death.

He was an exemplary, hard-working fervant of the Society. He worked to improve the conditions in which the Royal Society's books and papers were kept and to acquire new material for the library fuch as the Boyle Papers. Robertfon was alfo charged to make meteorological obfervations and received a fmall gratuity for his extra work. The ufe of the Library increafed under his care fo much that on 9 February 1775 he was inftructed to be regular in his attendance, to look after any Fellow wifhing to read, to provide a fire "when the weather requires it", to attend to no other bufinefs during thofe hours, and to keep the reading room quiet.

Robertfon was a perfon of very honorable character and conduct, being greatly refpected by the more learned and beft characters among the members of the Royal Society. He had the honor to ferve on the committee chofen to infpect and report on the government's powder magazine at Purfleet, concerning its damage and fecurity from lightning.

In his mode of teaching and arranging the matter in his publications, Robertfon was remarkably neat and methodical; a habit which he likely acquired from his good friend and mafter, William Jones, Efq.

He is faid to have been the firft to difcover the theorem that, in ftereographic projection, the angle between two circles on the fphere equals the angle between the two circles on the projection.

Robertfon died fuddenly in December 1776 leaving a widow and a family of moftly young children. The Royal Society elected his widow, Mrs. Mary Robertfon, to the pofition of Houfekeeper. His eldeft fon John fucceeded him as Librarian, Keeper of the Repofitory and fubfequently as Clerk. After Robertfon's death, many of his papers were auctioned off and

purchafed

purchafed by Charles Hutton.

Robertfon was the author of feveral books. Thefe were:

*A General Treatife of Menfuration.* Firft edition in 1739, with a fecond edition in 1748. The title page explains the intent of the work: "Compofed for the Benefit of artificers, builders, meafurers, furveyors, gaugers, farmers, gentlemen, young ftudents, &c. The Whole being intended as an eafy Introduction to feveral Parts of the Mathematics."

*Treatife on Mathematical Inftruments.* Firft edition in 1747, fecond edition in 1757, third edition in 1775, and a fourth edition in 1778. The laft edition was edited by W. Mountaine.

*A Tranflation of De La Caille's Elements of Aftronomy.* 1750. This book contains many ufeful afpects on the mathematics of aftronomy, moft notably methods for determining longitude.

*Elements of Navigation.* Firft publifhed 1754, and going through feven editions over a courfe of fifty years. This was Robertfon's mafter work; more details are given in Sect. IX. of thefe Notes.

Robertfon was alfo the author of numerous articles, including the following:

"A Letter from Mr. John Robertfon to the Prefident, Containing an Explanation of the Late Dr. Halley's Demonftration of the Analogy of the Logarithmic Tangents to the Meridian Line, or Sum of the Secants." *Philofophical Tranfactions*, Vol. 46. (1749 – 1750), pp. 559-569.

"The Conftruction of the Logarithmic Lines on the Gunter's Scale." *Philofophical Tranfactions*, Vol. 48. (1753 – 1754), pp. 96-103. Here Robertfon explains how to conftruct the logarithmic lines of fines, tangents, and verfed fines.

"An Extraordinary and Surprifing Agitation of the Waters, though without Any Perceptible Motion of the Earth, Having Been Obferved in Various Parts of This Ifland, Both Maritime and Inland, on the Same Day, and Chiefly about the Time, That the More Violent Commotions of Both Earth and Waters fo Extenfively Affected Many Very Diftant Parts of the Globe;
The

The Following Accounts, Relating to the Former, Have Been Tranfmitted to the Society; In Which are Specified the Times and Places When and Where They Happened." *Philofophical Tranfactions*, Vol. 49. (1755 – 1756), pp. 351-398. This is a fet of reports from a fcore of different authors, all recounting how water temporarily wafhed out of ponds and canals and greatly agitated fhipping. The caufe is not identified.

"An Effay Towards Afcertaining the Specific Gravity of Living Men." *Philofophical Tranfactions*, Vol. 50. (1757 – 1758), pp. 30-35. Robertfon meafures the fpecific gravity of 10 men by immerfing them in a fpecially conftructed ciftern. His purpofe is to better determine how to make life buoys.

"An Account of an Extraordinary Operation Performed in the Dock-Yard at Portfmouth." *Philofophical Tranfactions*, Vol. 50. (1757 – 1758), pp. 288-293. Robertfon reports on ufing wedges and fcrews to lift a heavy fhip, and the forces and friction encountered in the task.

"On the Fall of Water under Bridges." *Philofophical Tranfactions*, Vol. 50. (1757 – 1758), pp. 492-498. Equations are prefented to determine how water backs up and flows around obftacles fuch as bridge piers.

"Of the Theory of Circulating Decimal Fractions." *Philofophical Tranfactions*, Vol. 58. (1768), pp. 207-213. Methods involving recurring decimal fractions are fhown to maintain accuracy while keeping calculations brief.

"A Letter Containing the Demonftration of a Law of Motion, in the Cafe of a Body Deflected by Two Forces Tending Conftantly to Two Fixed Points." *Philofophical Tranfactions*, Vol. 59. (1769), pp. 74-78.

"A Letter Containing the Inveftigations of Twenty Cafes of Compound Intereft." *Philofophical Tranfactions*, Vol. 60. (1770), pp. 508-517.

"Of Logarithms, by the Late William Jones, Efq.; F. R. S. Communicated by John Robertfon, Lib. R. S." *Philofophical Tranfactions*, Vol. 61. (1771), pp. 455-461. Logarithms of different bafes are examined.

Information

Information for this biography was compiled from Robertſon's own works and from the following:

[1] Anderſon, Clara, Aſſiſtant Archiviſt of the Royal Society. Perſonal communication, drawn from [5] and from the Royal Society library catalogue.

[2] Andrewes, William J. H., Editor. *The Queſt for Longitude: The Proceedings of the Longitude Sympoſium, Harvard Univerſity, Cambridge, Maſſachuſetts,* November 4-6, 1993. pp. 240-243. Cambridge: Harvard Univerſity, Collection of Hiſtorical Scientific Inſtruments, 1996.

[3] Cope, Thomas D., "Charles Maſon and Jeremiah Dixon", *The Scientific Monthly.* Vol. 62, June 1946.

[4] Danſon, Edwin, *Drawing the Line: How Maſon and Dixon Surveyed the Moſt Famous Border in America.* New York: John Wiley & Sons, 2000.

[5] Hall, Marie Boas. *The Library and Archives of the Royal Society* 1660–1990.

[6] Hutton, Charles. *Philoſophical and Mathematical Dictionary.* Vol. 2, p. 333. London: printed for the author, 1815.

[7] Hutton, Charles, George Shaw, and Richard Pearſon. *The Philoſophical Tranſactions of the Royal Society of London, from their commencement, in 1665, to the year* 1800; *Abridged.* Vol. 11-14. London: printed by and for C. and R. Baldwin, New Bridge-Street, Blackfriars, 1809.

[8] Lee, Sidney, Editor. *Dictionary of National Biography.* London: Smith, Elder, & Co., 1899.

## Sᴇᴄᴛ. III.

### *On the Different Editions of the Treatiſe.*

THE *Treatiſe of Mathematical Inſtruments* ran through four editions. All of theſe were printed in London.

The firſt edition was printed in 1747. It was printed and ſold by T. Hᴇᴀᴛʜ, *Mathematical Inſtrument-maker,* oppoſite *Exeter-Change,* in the *Strand*; J. Hᴏᴅɢᴇs, at the *Looking-Glaſs* on

*London-*

*London-Bridge*; and J. FULLER, at the *Bible and Dove* in *Ave-Marie-Lane.*

The fecond edition was printed in 1757. The fellers remain the fame, with a fingle addition of J. NOURSE, located in the *Strand.*

The third edition, of which this is a copy, was printed in 1775. The only lifted dealer is J. NOURSE.

The fourth edition was printed in 1778, after John Roberfon's death. It was overfeen by W. Mountaine, and was fold by J. Nourfe.

The plate fronting the title page is nearly identical in all editions. In the firft edition, there is an infcription next to the drawing of the fector reading "Made by Thos. Heath in the Strand, London." This infcription does not appear in later editions. Thomas Heath was a mafter inftrument maker in the Grocers' Guild; he and his affiftants produced high quality inftruments from 1720 onwards.

The fecond edition added feveral examples on the ufe of the fector and added the Appendix. The third edition added the fection on perfpective and the fection on delineating cannons and mortars. The fourth edition was effentially identical to the third.


S E C T.  IV.

## *About this Printing.*

THIS printing of John Robertfon's Treatife has been newly typefet bafed on an original copy of the third edition. The original book was 9 inches high by 5 inches wide, with fold-out plates interfperfed through the text. This printing has been made wider in order to fit the original plates on bound pages with a minimum of adjuftment. Additionally, the book has been repaginated to fit the new page fize. Although the fpacing on the page has been adjufted, the fpelling, punctuation, font, and type fize match the original.

In

In the original third edition, there were a few errata lifted at the end of the table of contents. Thefe errata have been corrected in this text.

The font is a variant of Caflon expreffly adjufted to match the original. Some fpecial characters were created to match thofe in the original text, fuch as the pound weight abbreviation, ℔, and the fhape of the axtree ftay, ⌒. Ligatures, fuch as the combination of f and i into a fingle character, fi, and the ufe of the long s, ſ, are the fame as in the original.

The tables have been redrawn, and the copperplates have been cleaned. Some of the original copperplates were damaged, and have been copied from other editions of the book. In thefe cafes, the plates were identical between verfions. Some details on the plates, fuch as the fector on the plate fronting the title page, have been partially redrawn to improve clarity.

## Sect. V.

## *On the Notation uſed in this Treatiſe.*

R OBERTSON explains the meaning of the radical fign, the equal fign, the degree mark, and the angle fign. To the modern reader, all of thefe are familar. However, there are fome marks and conventions which may require explanation.

In the algebraic equations, parenthefis ( ) are not ufed for grouping. Rather, parenthefis are only ufed as punctuation marks. To indicate algebraic grouping, a *vinculum*, or horizonal line, is placed above the group. For example, in Article XI. in the Appendix, the number of fhot in a rectangular pile is given as $\overline{2n + 1 + 3m} \times \overline{n + 1} \times \frac{n}{6}$. In modern notation, this would be $(2n + 1 + 3m)(n + 1)\frac{n}{6}$.

Exponents

Exponents are written as a fuperfcript in the modern manner. However, if a definite number is raifed to a power, the quantity is often feparated from the exponent by a vinculum and vertical bar. For example, $\overline{4}|^3$ means the cube of four.

The fymbol ⊙ is ufed in two diftinct manners. With regards to furveying, ⊙ indicates a furvey ftation, or a location where the inftruments were placed to make meafurements. If ⊙ is by itfelf, it refers to the current ftation. If ⊙ is followed by a number, it indicates a fpecific ftation as recorded in the field book. For inftance, ⊙ 8 is the eighth fuch ftation.

In Sect. XIX. of the Treatife, where the conftruction of fpherical triangles is detailed, the fymbol ⊙ indicates the center of the primitive circle. It is a diftinct point. As an example, ⊙ P indicates the line through the center of the circle and point P.

*Verfed fines* are defcribed in Sect. VII. of the Treatife as the part of the radius lying between one end of an arc and the arc's right fine. In modern notation, the verfed fine is alfo called the *verfine* and is abreviated as *vers*. The verfed fine is expreffed in modern notation as $\text{vers}(x) = 1 - \cos(x) = 2\sin^2(\tfrac{1}{2}x)$. If a fector does not contain a line of verfed fines, either of thefe two equivalent expreffions may be ufed as a fubftitute.

## S ECT. VI.

### *On Mathematics.*

TO the modern ftudent of mathematics, many of the explanations in the treatife appear overly detailed. To thofe familiar with algebra, the geometric conftructions and proofs are aukward and unfamiliar. However, this prefentation gives valuable infight to the ftate of mathematics and of general knowledge at the time the treatife was firft publifhed.

Over the paft feveral hundred years there has been a fignificant change in mathematics education and perception. At the time that Robertfon was writing, the principal emphafis

was

was on geometry and graphical folutions to problems. Algebra, while taught and known, was a fecondary tool. In general, people conceptualized mathematical problems in phyfical terms. Today, mathematics ftreffes algebra and only lightly treats on geometry. Almoft all problems are rendered into equations, and, when a phyfical reprefentation is defired, it is the equation that is plotted. There are advantages and drawbacks to both fyftems.

The geometrical approach often relies on precife, neat drawings made with ftraight edge and compafs. Numerical calculations are kept to a minimum, and many folutions are determined by meafuring figures. This method is limited in its precifion bafed on the ability to draw and meafure accurate figures, but has fmall chance of a grofs blunder.

The algebraic approach can have better precifion than that of geometry. An equation allows any degree of exactnefs to be obtained, provided that the equation is painftakingly evaluated. When calculations muft be performed by hand, each calculation adds a risk of error, both in the working of the problem and in tranfcribing the equations or numbers. With the advent of computing machines, the burden of calculation has been vaftly reduced, and the likelihood of making an error has been fharply diminifhed. However, even with mechanical affiftance, a fimple error can propagate and generate an erroneous anfwer. As the internal calculation fteps do not, in and of themfelves, have particular meaning, this blunder may go undetected.

For people who have been trained to ufe the geometrical approach to mathematics, the fector is a familiar, obvious tool. The Gunter's line or flide rule is much more cumberfome, as the geometrical ideas muft be converted to algebraic notions before the workings of the problem are underftood. Inverfely, people who principally ufe the algebraic approach find the logarithmic line of numbers reafonably ftraightforward, while the fector is not intuitive.

Some problems are eafier when the geometrical method is ufed, whilft other problems are eafier when performed algebraically.

algebraically. For example, when protracting a drawing at a
fpecific fcale, the geometrical method allows a length to be laid
down in a fingle ftep, whereas algebraically, the length muft
firft be multiplied by the fcale, then laid down. Alternately,
when calculating the fize of a cube with the equivalent volume
of another folid, the algebraic method is more facile.


## S E C T. VII.

### *On* Palladio *and Architecture.*

A N D R E A di Pietro della Gondola, better known by the
name Palladio, was one of the moft influential and copied
architects in the world. He was born in Padua, part of mainland
Venice, in 1508, and died in Vicenza in 1580. He was
apprenticed to Count Gian Giorgio Triffino, under whom he
ftudied the precepts of claffical architecture.

Palladio travelled to Rome multiple times to examine the
buildings and to determine their architectural principals. He
alfo ftudied writings by the claffical Roman architect,
Vitruvius, and by contemporary commentators. From this
work he developed his ftyle, which was executed in numerous
villas and other buildings.

The ftyle developed by Palladio was a reaction to the
overly ornate and afymmetric gothic Italian Renaiffance
buildings. He featured fymmetrical buildings with dramatic
exteriors, graceful lines, and balanced interior fpaces. One of
his great innovations, now copied widely, was the projecting
double-columned loggias; this is the open columned front now
fo common on grand public buildings.

Although Palladio defigned numerous buildings, his
popularity was not due folely to thefe conftructions. He
publifhed his mafterwork in 1570, *I Quattro Libri dell'*
*Architettura*, or *The Four Books of Architecture*. Thefe
incredible volumes contained his methods along with detailed
plans of many of his buildings. They have been tranflated into
innumerable

innumerable languages and are ftill in print today.

The Palladian architectural movement has been broad and far-reaching. In England, it was firft popularized by Inigo Jones in the early feventeenth century. However, Palladio's defigns were more fuited to funny Italy than cloudy England, and it took until the early eighteenth century for the work of Richard Boyle, Lord Burlington to make Palladian ideals completely at home in England. John Robertfon was influential in obtaining copies of Boyle's work for the Royal Scoiety's library.

Palladio's architectural ideas and motifs ftrongly influenced the Georgian, Greek Revival, and neoclaffical ftyles. His fenfe of elegance, grace, and formality continue to be appreciated to this day.

## S E C T.  VIII.

### *On Surveying and Land Meafurement.*

SURVEYING is an undeniably ufeful and neceffary occupation. Although the field work of a furvey does not ufe many of the inftruments found in the portable cafe, protracting the work into a map utilizes moft of them.

The cartographer needs compaffes of the beft quality, as thefe are ufed for laying off diftances and meafuring protracted lines, both of which are critical to the accuracy of the plot.

Either an accurately divided protractor or a line of chords is required to lay off angles. A protractor fhewing degrees and minutes is ufeful for large drawings. If this protractor's markings match the circumferentor or theodolite ufed in the furvey, it will greatly facilitate protracting the information in the field book.

A good plain fcale is a neceffity, as any imprecifion in the fcale will refult in errors when the furvey is caft up. The proportional compaffes can be ufed along with the plain fcale to create a fcale of any dimenfions. The fector ufed as a univerfal

fcale

ſcale works as well.

Laying off of right angles is a frequent task when protracting a ſurvey. Although this can be done with the compaſſes and a ſtraight edge or with the protractor, a ſmall ſquare of braſs does this more readily. It is a uſeful addition to the caſe of inſtruments.

In addition to theſe major inſtruments, the ſurveyor will have uſe of the drawing pen and feeder, the pencil and crayon, and the parallel-rule and ſtraight edge.

Thoſe intereſted in ſurveying are adviſed to conſult a practical book on the matter. There are ſeveral treatiſes available, all of which will provide much greater detail than preſented here.

## SECT. IX.

## *On Spherical Trigonometry and Navigation.*

THE chief practical uſe of ſpherical trigonometry is that of navigation. When failing, it is poſſible to determine one's poſition by careful obſervation of celeſtial bodies. While the proceſs is greatly facilitated by an accurate chronometer, this is not required.

John Robertſon's book, *Elements of Navigation*, covers the complete proceſs of navigation, including determining the location of a veſſel. It details 8 methods for finding latitude and 11 methods for finding longitude while at ſea. Along with each of theſe are worked examples as would be uſed in an actual ſea voyage. Only a few of the methods of determining longitude uſe ſpherical trigonometry; the other methods rely on corrections to dead reckoning, on the uſe of a perfect time keeper, or on other factors.

The explicit uſe of ſpherical trigonometry was largely eliminated when Nathaniel Bowditch publiſhed *The American Practical Navigator* in 1802. The navigator now only needs to be able to add and ſubtract and to look up numbers in the

                                        carefully

carefully prepared tables of an almanac. The modern edition of Bowditch's book is ftill unparalleled in its clearnefs, relevance, and fimplicity. The beginner is ftrongly urged to learn from Bowditch, and only then ufe the methods difcuffed by Robertfon.

During Robertfon's time, the mariner could not be expected to have accefs to an accurate chronometer. As a confequence, the principal method for determining longitude at fea was the *method of lunars*, alfo called *clearing the lunar diftance*. Since the moon traverfes the sky relatively quickly compared to the ftars and fun, the time can be determined by meafuring the angular diftance between the moon and another celeftial body with refpect to the center of the earth. The actual time is found by comparing this diftance to information publifhed in an almanac. The actual time is then ufed with the local apparent time to determine the longitude of the obferver.

However, obfervations of the moon and celeftial bodies are made from the furface of the earth, and do not directly fhow the required diftance. Rather, the obfervation is an apparent diftance. By alfo meafuring the apparent altitudes of the moon and the celeftial body, fpherical trigonometry can be ufed to compute the actual diftance. This involves two folutions of fpherical triangles, the firft where three fides are known and an angle is fought, and the fecond where an angle and two adjacent fides are known and the third fide is fought.

Specifically, the three fides of a fpherical triangle are meafured, confifting of the apparent diftances between the moon and the other body, the moon and the zenith, and the other body and the zenith. The angle at the zenith is computed. Ufing tables for parallax and refraction, the actual diftances between the moon and the zenith and between the other body and the zenith are calculated. The zenith angle of the firft triangle is ufed along with the two new diftance values for the adjacent fides. From this, the third fide is calculated, giving the actual angular diftance between the moon and the celeftial body with refpect to the center of the earth.

For thofe who are interefted in navigating by the method of lunars,

lunars, the *Elements of Navigation* provides feveral worked examples. There are alfo fome modern books which detail the procefs; thefe books can be obtained from companies that fpecialize in celeftial navigation and inftruments fuch as fextants.

PLATES

# PLATES

The following figures were originally included as fold-out plates interſperſed throughout the book. They have been reproduced at the back of this volume for convenience in locating them. Some of the details in the plates have been ſhifted to avoid ſplitting the individual figures.

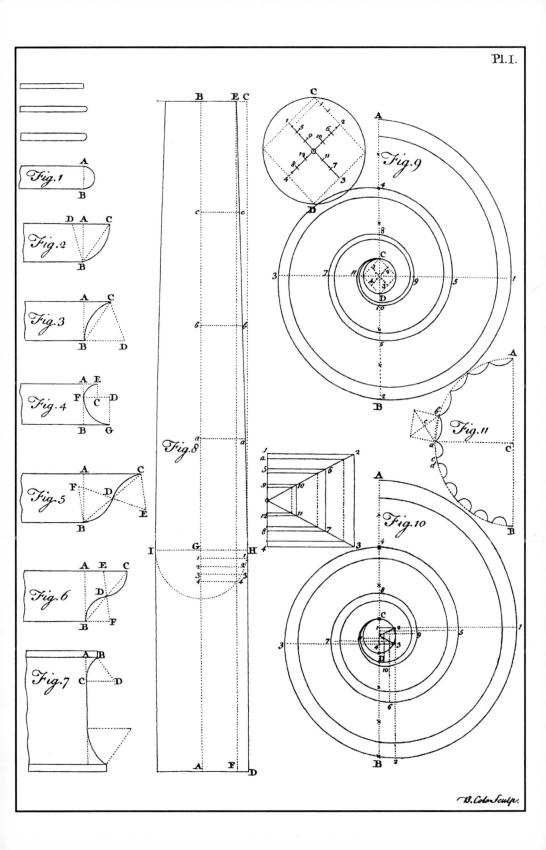

Pl. I.

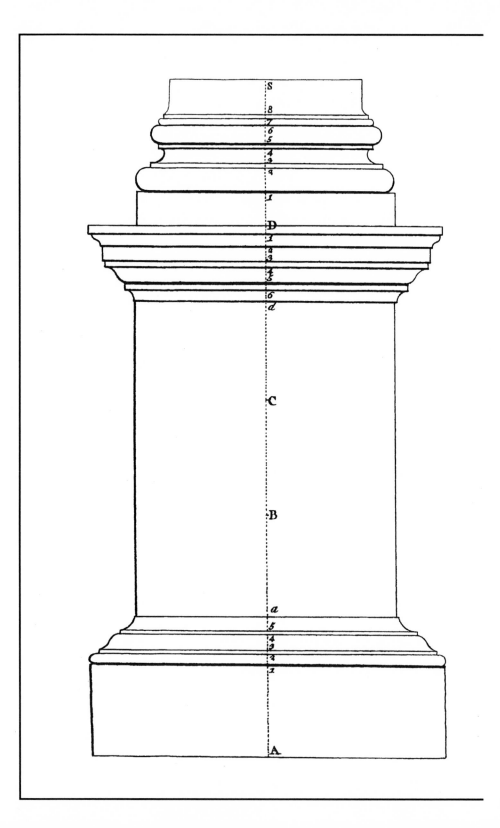

Pl. II.

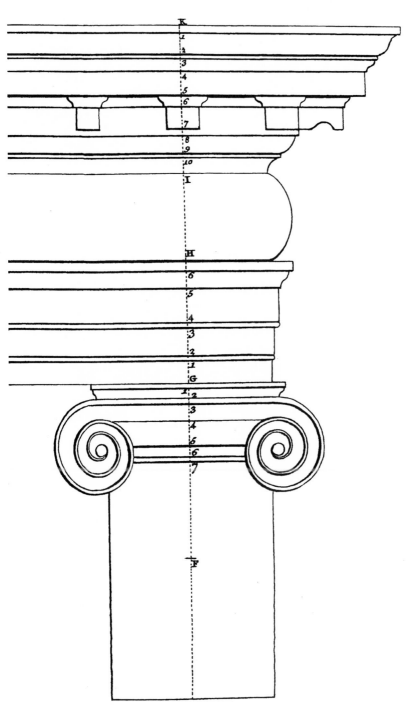

K
1
2
3
4
5
6
7
8
9
10
I

H
6
5
4
3
2
1
G
1 2
3
4
5
6
7

F

Seale Sculp.

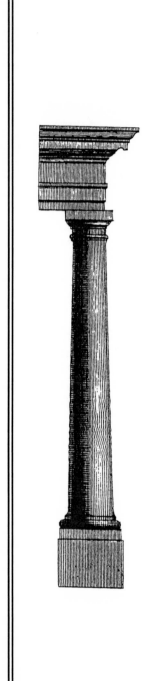
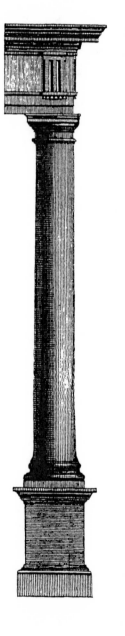

Pl. III

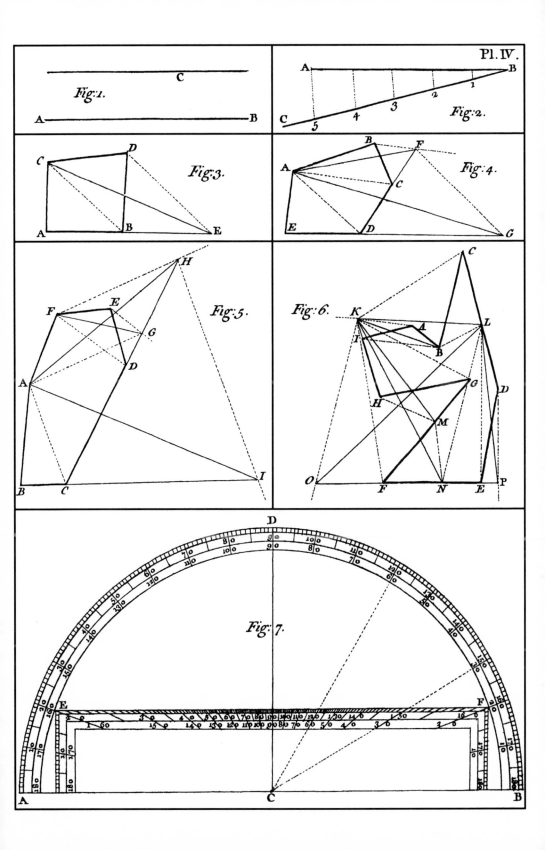

Pl. IV.

Fig: 1.

Fig: 2.

Fig: 3.

Fig: 4.

Fig: 5.

Fig: 6.

Fig: 7.

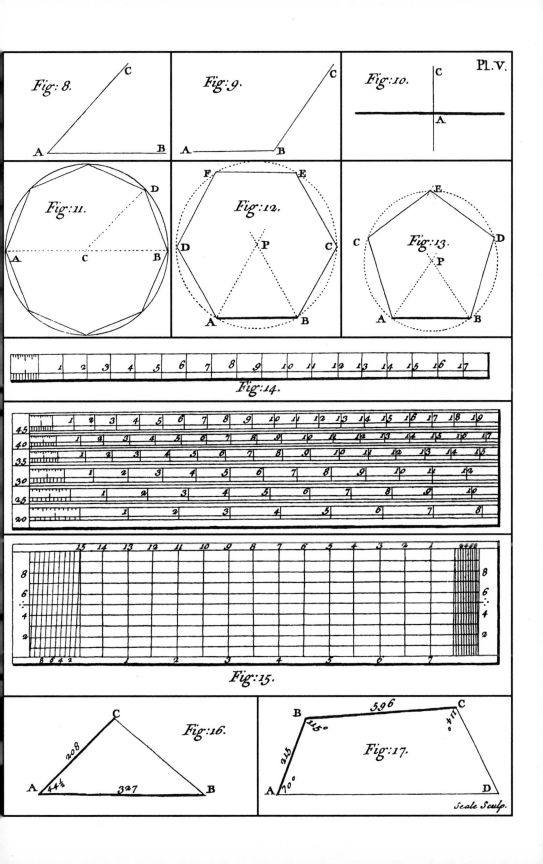

Pl. V.

Fig: 8.

Fig: 9.

Fig: 10.

Fig: 11.

Fig: 12.

Fig: 13.

Fig: 14.

Fig: 15.

Fig: 16.

Fig: 17.

Seale Sculp.

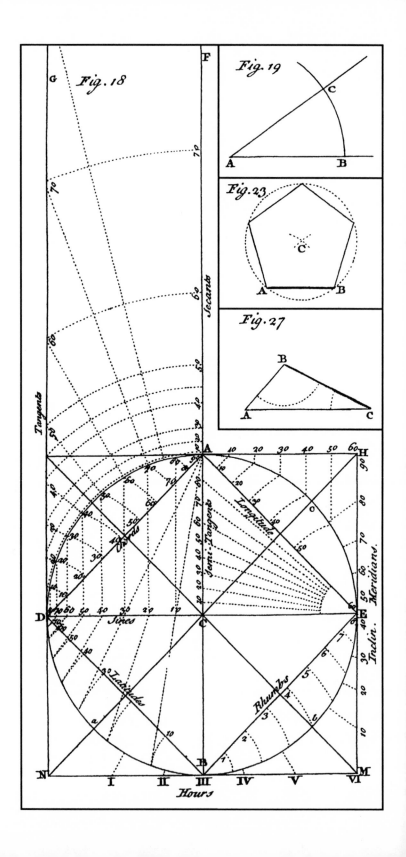

Fig. 18

Fig. 19

Fig. 23

Fig. 27

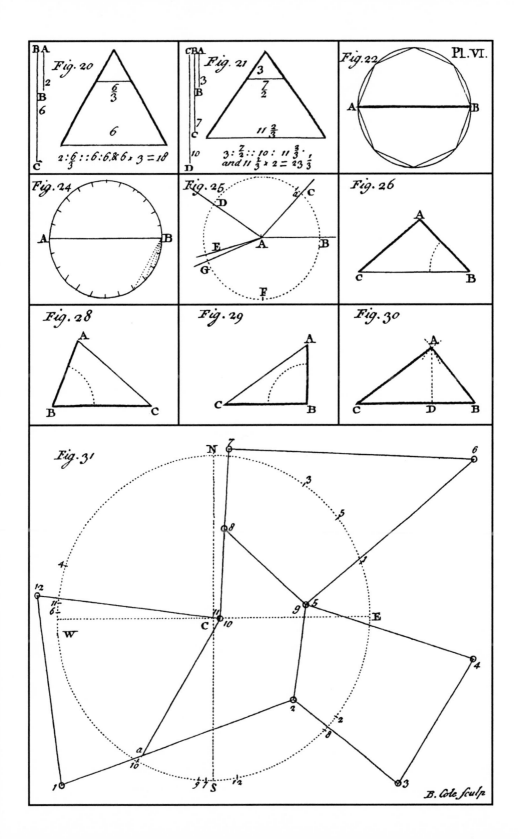

Fig. 20

Fig. 21

Fig. 22

Pl. VI.

$2 : \frac{6}{3} :: 6 : 6, \& 6 \times 3 = 18$

$3 : \frac{7}{2} :: 10 : 11\frac{3}{3} \cdot$
and $11\frac{1}{3} \times 2 = 23\frac{1}{3}$

Fig. 24

Fig. 25

Fig. 26

Fig. 28

Fig. 29

Fig. 30

Fig. 31

B. Cole sculp

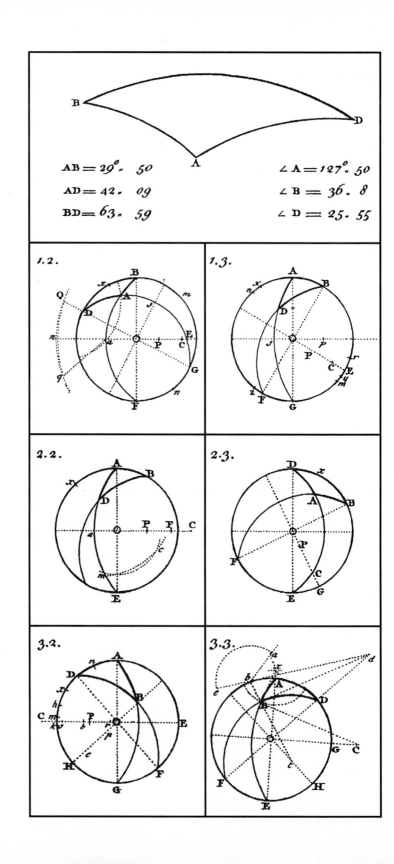

$AB = 29°„ 50$   ∠$A = 127°. 50$

$AD = 42. 09$   ∠$B = 36. 8$

$BD = 63. 59$   ∠$D = 25. 55$

1.2.

1.3.

2.2.

2.3.

3.2.

3.3.

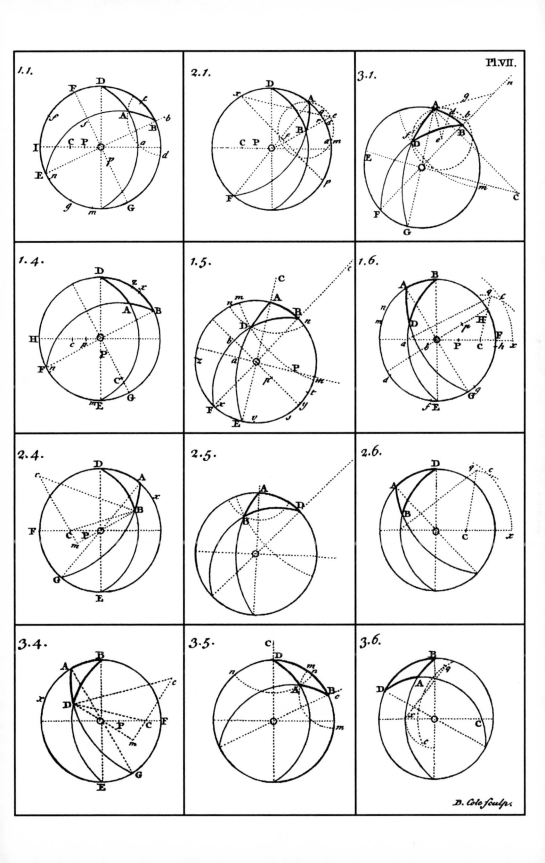

1.1.

2.1.

3.1.

1.4.

1.5.

1.6.

2.4.

2.5.

2.6.

3.4.

3.5.

3.6.

D. Cole sculp.

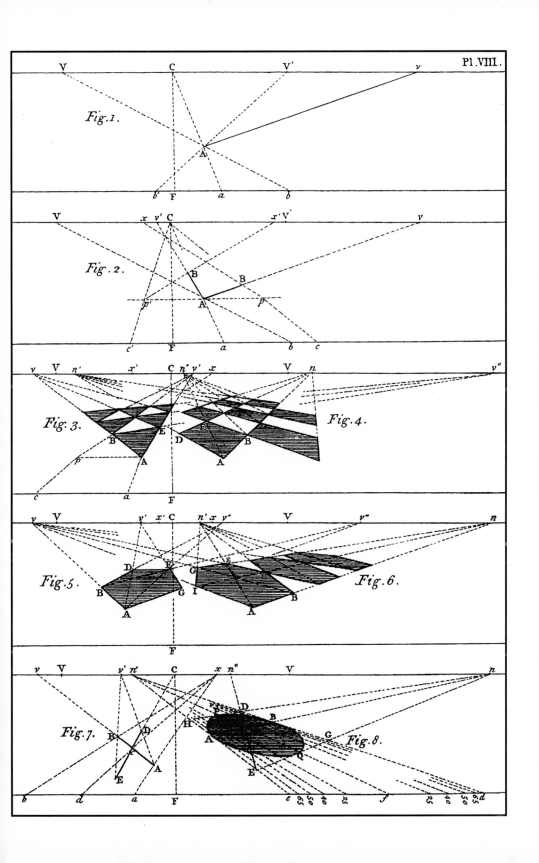

Pl.VIII.

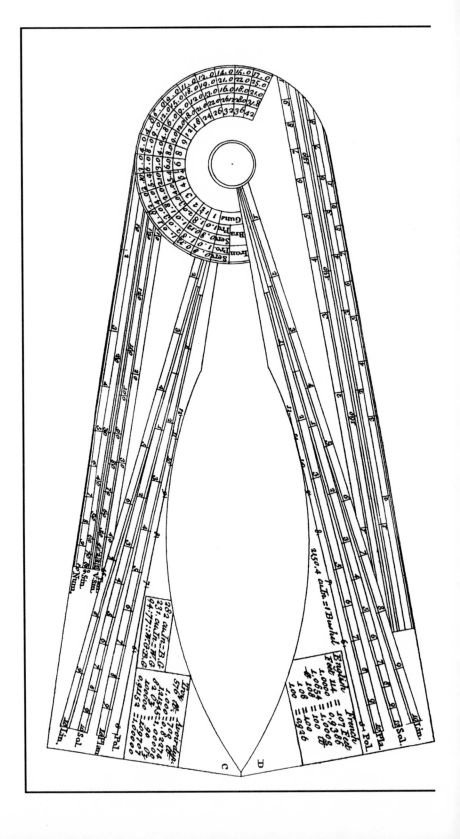

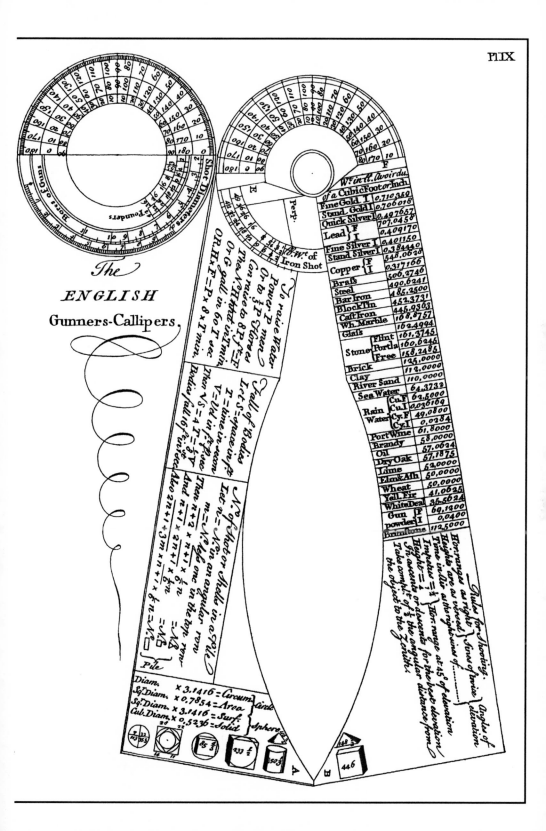

PL.IX

The

*ENGLISH*

Gunners-Callipers.

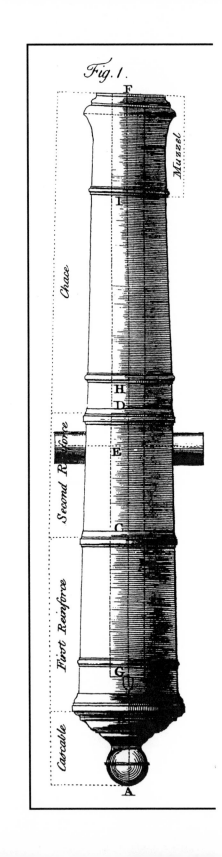

Fig. 1.

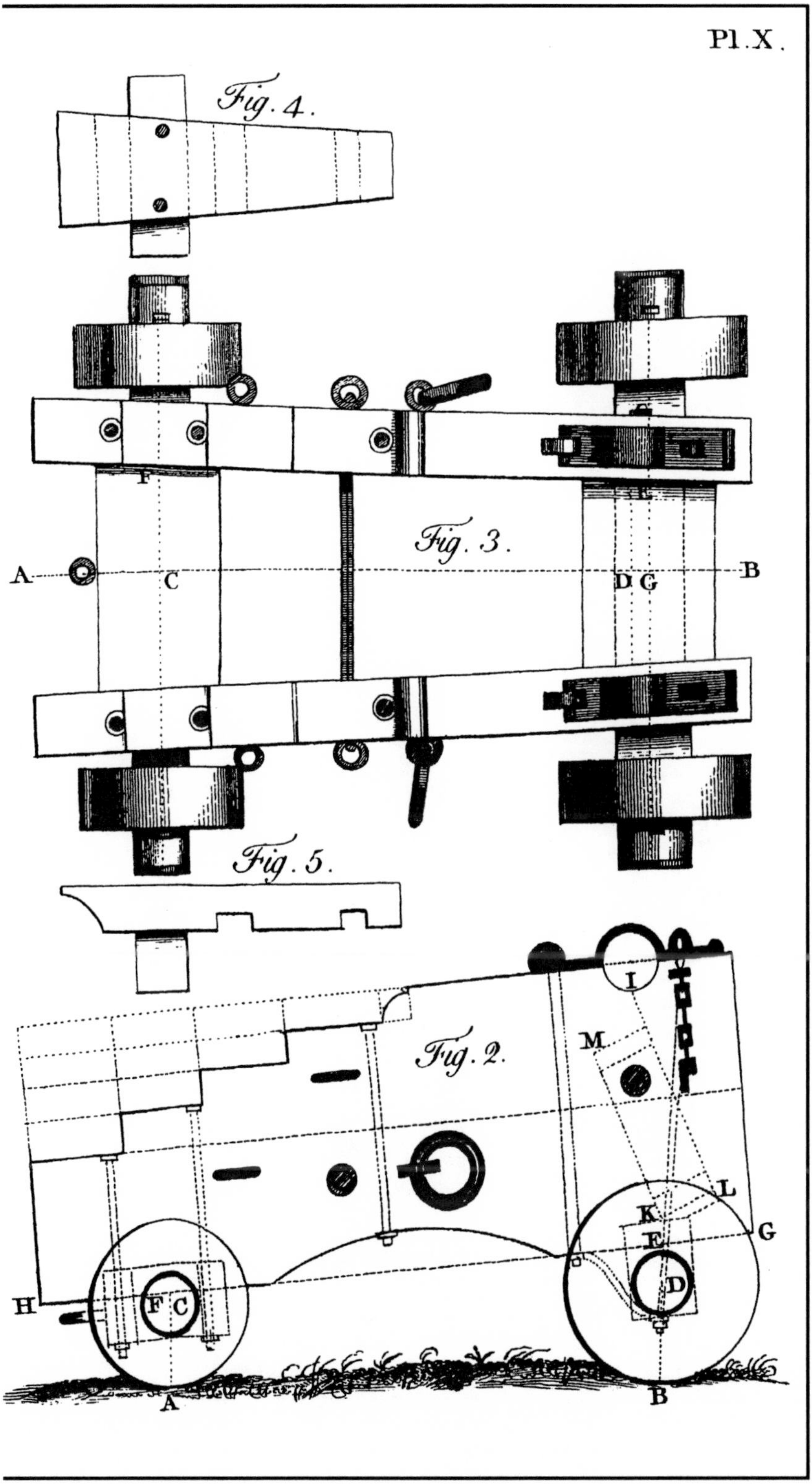
Pl. X.
Fig. 4.
Fig. 3.
A
C
F
E
D G
B
Fig. 5.
Fig. 2.
I
M
L
K
E
G
D
H
F C
A
B

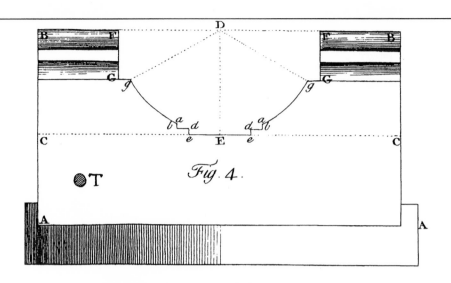

*Fig. 4.*

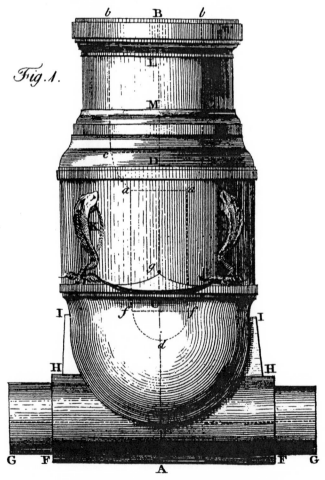

*Fig. 1.*

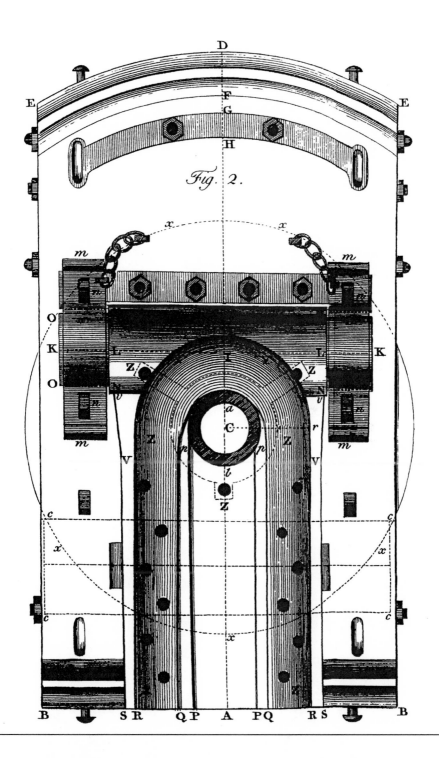

Fig. 2.

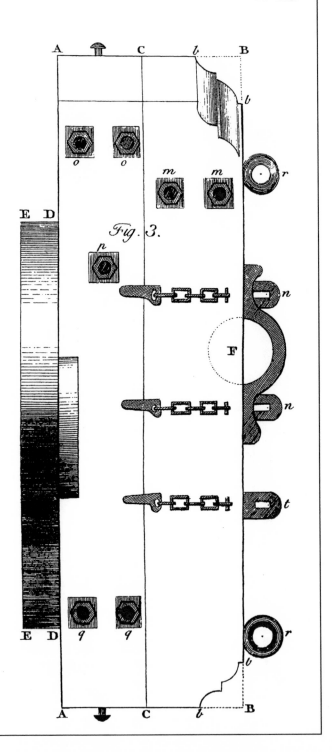

*Fig.3.*

Breinigsville, PA USA
01 September 2010
244675BV00002B/248/A